ENVIRONMENT

A CHALLENGE TO MODERN SOCIETY

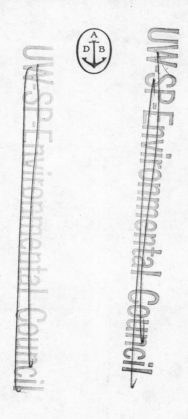

Lynton K. Caldwell is a professor of political science at Indiana University. In addition to his academic career, he has been associated with the Council of State Governments, the Agency for International Development, and the United Nations. He has also been consultant to numerous educational and research institutions and public agencies. The author of several books and numerous articles, Dr. Caldwell has devoted many years to the study and understanding of the interactions of science, technology, and public policy as they affect present-day society. He is particularly concerned with the role of government in man/environment relationships.

ENVIRONMENT

A CHALLENGE TO MODERN SOCIETY

❧ ❧

LYNTON KEITH CALDWELL

ANCHOR BOOKS

DOUBLEDAY & COMPANY, INC.

GARDEN CITY, NEW YORK

1971

ENVIRONMENT: A CHALLENGE TO MODERN SOCIETY
was originally published by
The Natural History Press in 1970.

Library of Congress Catalog Card Number 70–169939
Copyright © 1970, 1971 by Lynton Caldwell

TO

EDWIN LEE CALDWELL

AND

ELAINE LYNETTE CALDWELL

CONTENTS

IV ACTION

A NOTE TO THE READER

The relationship between modern man and his environment is a major and growing social problem. This relationship and the related problems of human population and war have become critical since mid-twentieth century. The very survival of man as a species depends upon intelligent and moral human action with respect to these problems. Unless rapid and effective action is taken to stop population growth, to reduce the threat of war and its costly burdens, and to prevent further destruction of the planetary biosphere and its living organisms, the early degradation of the human species is a certainty, and its untimely extinction is a probability.

These are not problems for which man can expect to achieve absolute and final "solutions." But even if man's aggressive and procreative behavior were to be brought under intelligent self-control, the problem of his environment relations would continue to require unremitting attention. Even with population reduced to numbers and densities consistent with personal freedom and environments of high quality, effort would still be required for environmental maintenance. Great efforts are necessary *now* to preserve and protect the natural environment threatened by overpopulation and misguided technology. There can be no doubt that men and their governments must be concerned with the wise management of their environments if their future history is to be tolerable.

In the ten chapters that follow, the challenge that man's environmental relationships present to modern society is described from several perspectives. The book is addressed to anyone willing and able to read it. It has been written for the general reader, not the environmental specialist. Its purpose is to help the reader understand why new patterns of individual behavior and social action in relation to the environment have become imperative to human welfare. Its substance is neither ecology nor political science, although it contains elements of both. It does not offer solutions to environmental problems, although it does consider the types of social attitudes and institutions that would be conducive to coping with such problems. Emphasis and illustration relate largely to the United States, where the audience for the book will largely be found and where problems of environmental policy and management are especially timely and acute. But its substance is also relevant to the entire modern world, for the biosphere has now become a political as well as a scientific concept. The space age has made the unity of the Earth environment come "real" to human perception, as it always was in physical fact.

The human environment is a matrix of elements derived by evolution through nature and contrived by man through culture. The distinction sometimes drawn between a social and a physical environment is a false dichotomy. For each individual and for all society, the environment is a complex unity, although the actual environment of no two persons is the same. There is no individual or society without an environment, and no environment exists except as something is environed. This book is therefore concerned with a set of relationships rather than with human behavior in the abstract or with physical objects in space.

Stated summarily, the message of the book is that if modern man and his civilization are to survive, administration of man's environmental relationships must become a major task of government. The term "environmental administration" has been used to designate this task, and because the meanings of both "environment" and "administration" are not readily apparent to most people, the following commentary on their usage in this book is offered by way of clarification.

Environmental administration can be given either of two interpretations. This book is concerned with both of them:

The first and more apparent meaning is the *purposive shaping of the human environment by man himself*. This interpretation concerns what man does to his environment in the familiar processes of hunting and fishing, farming, grazing, mining, lumbering, damming, draining, irrigating, building, urbanizing, and disposing of wastes or of things unwanted. Almost every activity of man has an impact upon his environment, and the foregoing list of specifics could be indefinitely extended. The impact of these activities has both direct and indirect consequences. Not all consequences are intended, and many that are inadvertent prove harmful. The world is ever in a process of change, and so long as the second law of thermodynamics holds true, there is nothing that man can do to arrest it. But human ingenuity has discovered how to accelerate and retard change. Conditions can be maintained in a state of relative stability for long periods of time. But it is now possible for human action to alter the environment almost instantly through atomic fission, or more slowly, but with equal irreversibility, through chemical or mechanical action. These possibilities and their inherent mixture of advantages and dangers lead us to the second interpretation of our subject.

The second and (today) more important meaning of the term environmental administration is *the control of human action in relation to the environment*. Here the direct concern is not with physical nature in the conventional sense, but with people. It is not that the environment is "administered"; it is that the actions of people as they impinge upon the environment become the direct focus of attention. It is not the environment that is managed, but rather people. Environmental change or protection is the primary object (but the secondary effect) of this action. We change or protect the environment through directing or constraining the behavior of people. Principal among the formal social arrangements and processes through which human behavior is controlled are those called *government* and *public administration*. But the processes through which decisions are made as to *what* is done are called *politics*. All these terms, however, are interrelating aspects of a total system of social decision making and control. Politics may be described as the art of implementing values through the actions of people; and it is with value implementation in relation to the human environment that this book is primarily concerned.

There is a third use of the term that embraces both the foregoing meanings. It refers to the study of man's management of his environment in its several aspects—technical, legal, economic, political, and philosophical. The study of environmental policy and administration is emerging as a multidisciplinary synthesis in many colleges and universities. It appears under several different names and in association with a number of leading disciplines or professional fields. Among these are urban and regional planning, civil engineering, environmental health, human ecology, and natural-resources management. It is also being treated as a field for special emphasis in the study of public policy for science and technology. The focus of this book, however, is not upon the *study* of environmental administration, but upon the *process* itself.

Yet the book has more to say about political philosophy than about management or engineering in their operational meanings. It is a book about a major area of public responsibility that is only now coming to be perceived. The emergence of the environment as a focus for public policy is a consequence of historical developments that have converged in our time. This convergence of expanding knowledge, human populations, and technological capabilities is posing for modern society a challenge without precedence in human experience. The Earth has suddenly become very small in relation to the demands that men make upon it. All terrestrial horizons are now limited, and the impediments to the freedom of men are less and less those of nature *per se* and more and more the incompatible objectives of other men. And ironically, as technoscientific man overcomes the traditional constraints of nature, he comes closer to confronting its less tractable and ultimately its inexorable limitations upon his ambitions.

The politics of environmental policy intensify as the demands of men upon the environment crowd one against another and press upon the parameters of the life-support systems of land, water, air, and living organisms. From this pressure, two circumstances arise that necessitate environmental administration. *First,* social conflict forces government to allocate or mediate the uses of the environment; *second,* the cumulative stress upon the environment forces public intervention to protect the life-support capabilities of the environment from impairment or destruction. These two factors in environmental policy do not necessarily work to mutually consistent conclusions. They are, in fact, often in conflict. The resolution of conflict over policies for the environment may simultaneously be politically "right" and substantively "wrong," or conversely, an ecologically "right" solution may be politically unfeasible—a "wrong" solution for the politically responsible decision makers. Criteria for choice and the tests of truth are therefore of major importance to any effort to understand or improve public decisions affecting the environment. Considerations of truth or value imply (or lead to) considerations of ethics. And so this book concludes with an examination of the ethical bases of environmental administration.

The book has been designed to examine man/environment relationships from several different perspectives. These have been grouped into four major divisions, or parts, identified by the key words: I Policy, II Tasks, III Management, and (new) IV Action. Inevitably the views from these vantage points include much of the same substance, yet in each case, the configuration of elements is seen in a differing set of relationships. This approach is necessitated by the many-faceted character of environmental administration. Its problems and processes are unlikely to be understood from a single perspective, and egregious errors of policy have resulted from looking at them in this way. To avoid this mistake, and because all aspects of an environmental policy issue cannot be approached simultaneously, problems and principles will reappear at various points throughout the book. Taken out of context, their recurrence might appear redundant. In fact, they are inherent in a thorough and comprehensive treatment of the subject.

Although there is a logical and progressive development from the beginning to the end of the book, an effort has been made to present each chapter as an intelligible unit—understandable without reference to the others. Hopefully, the message of the book as a whole will be stronger and clearer than that contained in any of its parts. But the separability and internal coherence of the chapters should maximize the usefulness of the book to the greatest variety of possible readers.

When a paperback edition was contemplated for late 1971, it seemed desirable to add a chapter taking account of the events that occurred during the nearly two-year interval since the original printing went into production. This was a period of major activity in the development of environmental policy and administration and accordingly a new concluding section, entitled "Action," has been added. The book ends with a plea for personal commitment to the tasks of environmental protection and of human survival in a livable world.

ACKNOWLEDGMENTS

The foregoing remarks should make clear what the book is about. It remains to acknowledge the assistance of those that have influenced its preparation and contents. The individuals whose contributions and criticisms have helped to shape this book are too numerous to list in full. Some of them would be surprised to discover that they had made contributions, for sometimes the most unsympathetic and uncomprehending critics are most helpful. They force one to re-examine premises and explanations; they cause one to try to discover the reasons for this lack of sympathy or comprehension, and to consider how these attitudes may be overcome. There is a larger value in this seemingly negative criticism that should not be discounted. If the thesis of this book is valid, it is in the interest of human welfare to overcome the skepticism of those who would treat the environment as unimportant or neutral or devoid of other than subjective meaning. In the coming era of Spaceship Earth, misinterpretation of man's relationship to his environment becomes socially dangerous. Humanity cannot afford to hazard the environmental basis of its welfare and survival in deference to sophistries of technology, economics, or political ideology. In the world of the spaceship, those who prefer to be guided by the easiness of dogma or convention rather than by the hardness of reality ought, at least, to be prevented from allocating the ship's supplies and manipulating the ship's controls.

Among the many sources of positive assistance, there are, however, several acknowledgments that it would be unjust to omit. These include the help provided by the Research

Committee of the Graduate School and the staff of the University Libraries at Indiana University, and by the Conservation Foundation and many individual members of its staff. A special debt of gratitude is owed to Wallace Bowman, now of the Library of Congress, who was associated with the Conservation Foundation at the time that the preparation of the book was begun with Foundation assistance. His interest and assistance have continued throughout the preparation of the volume. For information, suggestions, and encouragement, appreciation should also be expressed to Adele N. Wilson, William Van Ness, Richard Carpenter, and Robert Lamson, all on the Washington scene.

Although no chapter of this book has heretofore appeared in its present form, several of them had their inception in previous articles or addresses. All were heavily revised before use in this volume. Parts of Chapter 1 first appeared in *Public Administration Review*, XXIII (September 1963) as "Environment: A New Focus on Public Policy?" The antecedent to Chapter 6 was a talk given at Vassar College on April 9, 1968, and subsequently revised for publication for the University of Washington Press. Chapter 6 differs substantially from its literary parents, since it was extensively rewritten to meet the particular needs of this volume. Parts of Chapter 8 were based upon a paper prepared for the University of Oregon and published in *Oregon's Dilemmas—Report of the Second Annual Conference, The School of Community Service and Public Affairs, 1968*. Other parts of this chapter and some parts of Chapter 2 were based upon a presentation prepared for the 20th Alaska Science Conference, 1969.

This paperback edition has been updated not only by addition of a new chapter ("Meeting the Challenge"), but also by slight revisions in the body of the original text. Two appendices have been added: A. The National Environmental Policy Act of 1969, and B. Resolution 2398 [XXIII] of the United Nations General Assembly on December 3, 1969, to convene in 1972 a Conference on the Human Environment.

❧ I ❧
POLICY

Public policies are prevailing decisions regarding those activities that societies will undertake, permit, or prohibit. These policies are characteristically made explicit in declarations, laws, regulations, and judicial decisions; but they are also, and perhaps more significantly, implicit in what people do. The process through which the public activities of people are guided is "public administration"—which thus becomes a tangible expression of public policy. This complex guiding process not only includes the acts of government, but, in a functional sense, extends to the public-purpose activities of non-governmental organizations, often undertaken in association with government and sometimes in opposition to it. For any matter of social concern to become a focus for public policy and administration, there must be some minimal degree of social consensus, not only with respect to the problematic conditions, but also with respect to social goals. The first section of this book describes the difficulties of formulating public policies in relation to the human environment. It develops the theses (1) that a positive public policy to protect the quality of the human environment has now become a practical necessity, (2) that a maturing science of ecology can provide the informational basis for public environmental policy, and (3) that the spaceship provides a simplified, dramatic, and persuasive symbol of man's environmental con-

dition. The impact of man upon his environment began before history. Governments have selectively administered aspects of the environment since antiquity. Yet environment has now become a new factor in public policy, because man's practical relationship to the Earth has been changed fundamentally by his use of science and technology.

1

ENVIRONMENT:

A NEW FACTOR IN PUBLIC POLICY

A new aspect of public policy is emerging in the United States and in the more-advanced industrial countries generally. Public responsibility for the state of the human environment is becoming implicit in popular movements for environmental quality and in the actions of governments and of some industries. But until the late nineteen sixties, there had been no clear or explicit formulation of a public responsibility for the state of the environment. Popular perceptions of the environment have been fragmented and particularized. Fragmented public policies have followed, and deterioration of the environment has been a consequence. If the quality of human life is to be maintained at present levels or is to be improved, public responsibility for the quality of the total environment must become explicit and be made effective. The major task of environmental policy making in the nineteen sixties was to make explicit the general nature and extent of public responsibility. By late 1969, this task was on the way to accomplishment in the United States. To make this responsibility an effective reality is a task for the nineteen seventies.

To look at familiar things from an unfamiliar point of view is always a difficult and troublesome experience. The familiarity of the material tends to obscure the novelty of its arrangement. It is a little like looking at a picture consisting of a mass of apparently unrelated dots. If you look intently and from some distance away, the individual dots suddenly resolve themselves into a sharply defined image—a geometric figure or perhaps the profile of an animal. One may wonder why the artist didn't help the viewer by drawing the image in the first place. But perhaps the profile was created in this curious manner to illustrate an idea rather than to suggest an image. By creating the profile out of a mass of separate dots, the artist is able to show how significant relationships may be discovered among apparently unrelated things. The profile in the picture was there all the time, even though the viewer saw it only when time and distance lent the right perspective.

So it is with the complexities of the human environment and the concept of public policy that this book proposes. Most of us read no special meaning into familiar surroundings. But some, by training or experience, have come to see certain relationships that do not reveal themselves readily to the untrained glance. One sees a picture of traffic congestion on a Los Angeles freeway. This may be all that some see. Others, depending on the specialized character of their interests and perception, may see problems of transportation, public health, or engineering; or perhaps problems of urban design, metropolitan government, or public finance. But to one who sees the congested freeway as a problem of man/environment relationships, all these things and many others come into focus simultaneously, forming a profile of one aspect of our society.

A difficult way to look at things? True—but perhaps a more faithful perception of whatever reality we can know than is the more selective version of reality that appears to serve us adequately for the everyday business of life. And just as many apparently insoluble problems have eluded solution until someone discovered the "right" way to view them, so it may be that our failure to cope adequately with certain large and complex problems of our time is a consequence of failure to see the unifying elements in the complexity. In our characteristic concentration on intensive, specialized analysis of our public problems, we may omit so many data from our normal field of vision that the integrating profile does not appear.

The purpose of this chapter is to consider the extent to which "environment" as a generic concept enables us to see more clearly an integrating profile of our society in its relationship to the physical world. Would the perspective gained by looking at the way in which our society shapes its surroundings give us insight into relationships among other social, economic, or political problems—into interrelations between the parts and the whole of our public life? It is not argued that environment affords the only, or even the best, integrative approach toward understanding man's social behavior. It is now clear, however, that the development of modern society and the persistence of man's preindustrial behavior patterns in a technoscientific age have brought about circumstances in which the environment has perforce become a factor in public policy. Man is now being compelled, often unwillingly, to perceive the environment as a complex ecological unity. It is becoming too costly and too dangerous for him to perceive it in any other way.[1]

MEANING OF ENVIRONMENT

A standard dictionary describes environment as "the aggregate of surrounding things, conditions, or influences." This is environment in the generic sense, as distinguished from specific environments. The concept of environment assumes not only "surrounding things" but something that is surrounded—in our purview, man. Environment thus suggests an analogy to the concept "sound." In both concepts, the physical presence and actions of the transmitting and receiving bodies are distinguishable from the interaction between them that we call "sound." Practically speaking, sound exists only when there are ears to hear. Environment is not only the complex, interrelating reality surrounding us; it includes us. But our environment is not the same as our perception of it. The "real" environment includes much more than we sense in our ordinary, day-to-day surroundings. Yet we are in continuing interaction with this total environment in varying degrees of directness and intensity. And so "environment," in the sense in which it will be considered throughout this book, may best be understood as shorthand for *man/environment relationships*.

Obviously, the human environment in its complex totality extends far beyond our present comprehension and technology. In its grand phases, the environment is changing, beyond our power to influence or even to understand. It is subject to the natural tendencies described by the second law of thermodynamics; and man's effort to protect his terrestrial biosphere is an expression of the unending struggle of life against entropy (which may be described as a universal tendency toward disorder). But we can and do influence our terrestrial environment. We have learned to create artificial environments that increase our health and comfort, and extend the range of our activities. But when we "condition" our surroundings, we find that we must live within the regimen imposed by the artificial environment and the system that maintains it. Man has often altered his immediate natural environment, in order to overcome its limitations, only to discover that he must then conform to new conditions imposed by the circumstances or consequences of environmental change. Equipped with spaceships and space suits, he can live beyond the earthly biosphere by means of one of the most exacting administrative and technical operations that human ingenuity has devised. To leave the Earth and to return to it again, he must remain within a continuously administered environment. In outer space, absolute environmental control is the obvious price of survival.

In all this there is nothing new. Man has been adapting environments to his purposes and adapting his behavior to changing environments ever since he learned to use fire, to clothe his body, and to construct shelter. Environments have been altered on a large scale by deliberate choice as well as by inadvertence. Forests have been felled, grasslands burned, marshes drained, and wild land brought under cultivation. But in shaping their environments, men have seldom foreseen the full consequences of their action. The more remote and complex results of environmental change could not be perceived without the aid of a scientific knowledge and technology that men are only now in the process of creating. With amazing consistency, men have misread many of the most conspicuous consequences of their impact upon the environment. The reason cannot solely be want of knowledge; historians and geographers as long ago as Herodotus have noted reciprocal influences between man and environments, and in the more recent past, science has indicated many cause/effect relationships in environmental change. The explanation is more complicated, and will be clarified in subsequent portions of this volume.

One need not accept every argument advanced to support a theory of environmental influence in order to believe that in shaping their environments men shape their own societies.[2] Environments manage men even as men manage environments. Although this lesson has been written large in the landscape as well as in human history, few persons appear to have read it and fewer still to have read it with understanding.[3] Winston Churchill was one who most clearly perceived subtleties of man/environment relationships, and at the opening of his famous address on the rebuilding of the House of Commons, he declared, "We shape our buildings, and afterward our buildings shape us."[4]

Since the establishment of national independence, Americans have been using government to "develop" selected aspects of their environments; but they have seldom seen environment, as such, as an expression of anything other than opportunity to gratify personal needs and desires. They have seldom thought of it as a general object of public policy. Their readiness to control environments for particular purposes has not been accompanied by recognition of a need for comprehensive environmental policies.[5] Yet, in this lack of comprehension, they have hardly been more derelict than men in other lands. Damage to the American environment has been great, in part because the opportunities to bend nature to human purposes have been great, and also because of deep and often uncritical popular commitment to economic development and to personal freedom. In some respects, environmental degradation has been a defect of national virtues. Yet it has also been in America that the conservation and environmental-quality movements have developed out of the awakened perception and aroused conscience of public-minded men and women.

DILEMMA FOR DECISION MAKERS

In the evolution of American political institutions prior to the nineteen sixties, there appears to have been no clear concept of a public responsibility for the environment as such. It therefore follows that concern for the quality of the total environment has been the business of *almost* no one in our public life. The qualification "almost" is necessary, because urban and regional planners have increasingly thought of "total environment" as the end product of their efforts. But their responsibilities have been usually limited to a restricted group of environmental problems and situations—urban design, for example. In the professional field of public health, environment has also been a focus of concern. But rarely, aside from these policy areas, is broad environmental planning firmly joined to administrative action. At the higher levels of political decision, environment seldom has been recognized in other than the vague and generalized sense of "good living conditions," wise use of our natural resources, or "safeguarding our national heritage." Since 1960, however, a new formulation of public responsibility has been taking shape in American society. By the end of the decade, it was evident that the condition of the environment was in the process of becoming a national public responsibility. A series of bills introduced into the Ninetieth and Ninety-first Congresses, and the action of President Nixon in signing, on January 1, 1970, the National Environmental Policy Act of 1969, signaled the acceptance of environment as a legitimate focus for public policy in the United States. It was clear that an influential segment of public opinion expected public action to remedy the rapidly deteriorating environmental situation. But as late as 1969, there was available no adequate information regarding the extent of popular consensus as to the form or methods that this public action might take.[6] There was abundant room for discord over how public responsibility for the environment should be implemented, and how specific aspects of the general responsibility, and their attendant costs, should be allocated throughout the economy.

Does the absence of consensus regarding public responsibility for the environment account for widespread human failure to develop stable, self-renewing, and generally desirable communities? Certainly an absence of belief that the environment, comprehensively conceived, is a public responsibility could account for the lack of consideration for ecological or environmental factors in technological societies, which have lost most of the intuitive ecological wisdom found in some traditional cultures but have not yet acquired the ecological understanding derived from science. This transitional state of ignorance would explain the inability of most public officials to think (or thinking, to act) in ecological terms, mindful of the broad range of human needs in the *total* environment.

In brief, the modern tendency has been to deal with environmental problems segmentally, through specialists whose frequently conflicting judgments require compromise or arbitration. For example, the history of United States interagency relations in river-basin development illustrates a deeply ingrained exclusiveness in technical thinking on environmental questions and the difficulty of relating the technical competence of specialized experts to comprehensive public policy. In the absence of an adequate integrating and focusing purpose, it is difficult to mobilize and direct specialized knowledge and technique into comprehensive, well-conceived, and generally beneficial public action. Where the ultimate task is clear—as to put an astronaut on the moon—the technical task finds guidance toward its proper definition. Where no larger, integrative purpose is evident, administrators and technicians conceive policy in terms of their own immediate responsibilities, which, under the circumstances, is perhaps the only thing they can do.

The public decision makers (legislative, administrative, or judicial) have perforce dealt with environmental questions without the help of a general body of environmental policy for authoritative guidance. And so the administrator of environmental problems has been compelled to seek some calculus of objectivity that would pass as rationally defensible and would simultaneously afford room to maneuver among the fixed or conflicting political forces—the "pressures" of public life. In order to make politically feasible decisions among specialized interests (decisions that could be defended as "in the public interest"), a variety of evaluative criteria have been evoked.[7] Some have been treated almost as if they were formulas for scientific decision making.

For example, the criterion of *highest priority* has been asserted in support of military as against civilian pre-emption of resources and on behalf of industrial over aesthetic considerations. This approach assumes a hierarchy of values in the use of the environment, but provides no objective or demonstrably rational basis for determining priorities among values or their relevance to any given situation. Another criterion, that of *multiple use,* has seemed a logical avenue toward determining how varied interests in an environment might be served. But this proposition, like the "highest priority" test, runs into a problem of priorities among values—of how discrimination among values should be made in any given instance. A third criterion, that of weighing environment-affecting decisions on the basis of *costs and benefits,* is limited in conventional usage to circumstances in which measurement can be expressed in monetary or other tangible terms. A calculus of costs and benefits is obviously no more valid than the validity of the costs and benefits that are specified. The obvious utility of comparing costs and benefits should be distinguished from the process of comparison itself. Analytic techniques are inevitably subject to intentional or inadvertent misuse. The stipulation of costs and benefits involves judgments upon values, and it is doubtful that the techniques can ever be employed with complete objectivity, or that it would be sensible to suppose that they might be.[8]

Assuming a set of values to which nearly everyone subscribes, conflict in environmental management might lead to compromises among interests that would be generally acceptable within the structure of public values. These decisions would be largely of a technical or operational character, for which some objective criteria of suitability could be identified. Unfortunately for the public official, decisions are usually made in an atmosphere charged with conflicting values and with no universally accepted guidepost pointing the way toward the "public interest."

Two intellectual tendencies or viewpoints are involved in public decision making regarding natural resources and the environment. Although not necessarily opposites, their assumptions are distinctly dissimilar. First of these is the *market* view. It sees the relatively free play of economic and political forces as the most feasible determinant of environmental policy. It tends to rely for control upon the automatic expression of constraints of competition among popular preferences. The second viewpoint is *ecological,* and sees the natural world, including man and his works, as dependent for well-being and ultimate survival upon the maintenance of a "moving equilibrium," or dynamic balance, among the elements of the environment. From this viewpoint, administration appears to be the principal mechanism of control.

Each viewpoint has its mystique; each has practical strengths and weaknesses. The *ecological* viewpoint derives strength from the natural sciences. It is a viewpoint congenial to the scientist/administrator, who prefers decisions based upon verifiable facts to those based upon political fiat. It tends toward an idealist concept of "good" for people; it would not be based upon an estimate of popular preference or understanding. The market, or competitive, view has the practical advantage of appealing to men of means and action. It does not search for objectively "right" answers, but looks rather for practical solutions among the issues as people see them. The *market* is, of course, not only one of money; it includes the market in which political influence is negotiated, and it may thrive at political levels in a socialist economy as readily as in an atmosphere of free enterprise.[9]

The *market* view is not therefore synonymous with an economic approach to environmental problems. The most thoughtful economic analyses of environmental policy include market mechanisms among the full range of means for popular choice. But many economists recognize the significance of ecological considerations and employ them in their analyses. As ways of understanding natural processes, economics and ecology have much in common.[10]

In politics and business, however, the polarities of ecology and the market are conflict inducing. These two viewpoints embody strongly contrasting sets of values and assumptions regarding man and nature. They lead to equally contrasting conclusions regarding the role of government in relation to the environment. But, between the extremities of viewpoint, there are intermediate stages, in which these and other attitudes are mixed. Yet science and politics need not, as often as they do, lead to opposing conclusions regarding environmental policy. A politics better informed by science, and a science applied in the service of well-considered values, would provide a firmer and broader basis for public environmental decision making than is provided under present circumstances. A coherent political philosophy, in which the scientific attitude is emulated and scientific evidence respected in relation to human needs and capabilities, would greatly strengthen the conceptual base upon which sound environmental policy could be built.

The administrative dilemma in environmental decisions (and it is also a legislative dilemma) is that public decisions must be taken as if there were a generally accepted guiding concept of the public interest by which the "rightness" of the decision could be measured. But neither our law, our political tradition, nor the predominant elements of our cultural heritage have hitherto provided such a guiding concept. And so, on environmental issues affecting lands (urban and rural), waters, forests, wildlife, and air space, conflicting interests clash headlong in what is usually a test of sheer political strength. For want of a common denominator of differing interests, public policy makers have had to make do with rationalizations of decisions in which *the public interest* has, in fact, become synonymous with effective political power. The search for common denominators of environmental policy that are both ecologically valid and politically feasible has become a major task of environmental administration today, and will be for a long time to come.

EMERGING ENVIRONMENTAL CONCEPTS

No massive research is required to document the inadequacy of our environmental decision making. The evidence surrounds us. Clearly, a substantial percentage of our public problems, conspicuous at the local level, are the consequences of unfortunate environmental decisions. Local communities throughout the United States struggle with problems of housing, schools, water supply, sewage, transportation, parks, industrial location, and urban renewal—problems made far more difficult than necessary by failure of the community or its decision makers to think in environmental terms. The contrast between the almost indecent superfluity of its "things"-ridden material affluence and the relatively run-down, neglected, and impoverished character of its civic facilities is a mute commentary on the state of values in contemporary American society. It is also a commentary on the inadequacy both of institutions and of the allocation of public resources.

Segmental thinking, segmental decision making—the "practical" approach to practical problems—has again and again produced some very impractical results. Familiar examples are found in cities that conduct vigorous drives for safety on the streets and simultaneously permit built-in safety hazards in street layout, building construction, and outdoor advertising. Examples of "practical" nonsense can be found in the application of tax laws that, in effect, penalize the improvement or rehabilitation of run-down property—linking government with landowner as partners in slum making. And there is a monotonous, colorless, culture-free, mass housing—particularly in urban-renewal areas—that has substituted a new set of environmental problems for those presumed to have been solved.

American policies affecting the environment have been essentially segmental—largely because most people, both in government and out, taking the environment for granted, have dealt with its various elements without regard to their interrelated totality.[11] In keeping with their pioneer tradition, most Americans have been too busy cutting trees to think about consequences to the environmental forest. Consequently, American government is continually trying to solve the problems and to salvage the wreckage caused by misguided, heedless, or inadvertent environmental change. While significant public environmental needs go unmet, public funds and energies are pre-empted to remedy the waste and error of technical and economic innovations, which proceed without adequate guidance or control, destroying values and creating unforeseen situations harmful and costly to the public welfare.

There are indications, however, that the tempo and magnitude of change are forcing a reshaping of traditional American attitudes toward the environment. Increasing problems and increasing knowledge regarding the distribution of people and their activities in physical space seem certain to stimulate systematic new theories of environmental planning and administration.[12] The transformation of living conditions in

mid-twentieth century has been an almost universal phenomenon endemic to neither urban nor rural areas, and exclusively in neither developed nor underdeveloped countries.
The phenomenon has been induced by technology and is
peculiar to the times.

The basic problems are seldom new, but their magnitude
and urgency have no precedent. Governance of the megalopolis presents a host of problems nowhere adequately solved
and in many cases not yet adequately defined. Urban planning, for example, cannot now proceed realistically without
regard to the larger, surrounding region, which in the United
States, for example, lacks political or administrative coherence.[13] Meanwhile, the urgency of urban problems has
tended to divert attention from portentous transformations in
the less-urbanized areas. The mechanization, collectivization,
and industrialization of agriculture and other aspects of
natural-resources management is changing rural life as radically as Tokyo and New York were changed from the traditional cities out of which they evolved. Large-scale efforts
toward environmental change, as in river-basin development
and water-distribution systems, create numerous and continuing political and intergovernmental complications that are
consequences of the social, economic, ethnic, and ecological
changes that these developments induce.[14] Thus environmental change—its causes, problems, and consequences—
emerges as one of the practical and compelling areas for public debate, for policy focus, and for research.

The first effort toward a formulation of comprehensive
environmental policy has been through the medium of public
planning. But planning as a technical process has seldom suc-
ceeded in achieving the vital expression of policy that is evidenced through action. Planning is not necessarily self-
executory; to be realized, plans must reach a point of action—
and this is the conspicuous point of failure in the history of
formal planning.

Even urban reconstruction, which has been previously
noted as a partial exception, has been largely restricted to the
remedy of very specific environmental situations, and seldom
goes beyond the immediate renewal area to shape the future
of the larger, surrounding community. At present, town and

country planning, as understood in Great Britain, comes as close as any public effort to uniting planning and action in the control of environmental change. And yet, observation of British experience has suggested that even where the idea of environmental planning has been publicly accepted, conventional public administration may tend to compromise public objectives.[15] Could it be that objectives have been sought through planning that are realizable only through a new concept of administrative responsibility?[16]

Administration implies action, and action, leading to the ultimate test of policy, gives administration a practical advantage over segregated planning, for achieving public purposes. There may be heuristic or cautionary value in theoretical planning that does not lead to action, but its practical utility is difficult to estimate. To separate practical planning from administration is like separating cart from horse. Yet, although obvious to the point of being expressible only in clichés, this truism continues to be widely ignored in practice. Perhaps the explanation lies in the pluralistic and contradictory character of social values in American society.[17] Enough planning is provided to satisfy a public commitment "in principle" to environmental quality, but not enough to interfere with what politically significant people really want to do. In the long run, the objectives sought through urban or regional planning may more likely be realized through the emerging concept of environmental administration.

Environmental administration is a convenient word/symbol representing at least two distinguishable but related meanings. First, the term represents the policies, methods, and processes by which man shapes his environments; second, it refers to the control of human action in relation to the environment. The expression "environmental administration" suggests an attempt to deal with environments comprehensively, as environments, in contrast to focusing upon their component parts. In the first sense, we have always had environmental administration. In the second sense, we have a concept that carries profound social and political implications. There is, in addition, a third meaning: it is the study of man's efforts to influence his environment—a multidisciplinary synthesis that is now emerging in several contexts in higher education.[18]

As with most concepts, environmental administration in any of its meanings can be pushed to the point of absurdity. Dealing with environments comprehensively need not imply endlessly detailed analysis and hopelessly complex synthesis of all environmental factors before policies can be formulated. There is a common-sense balance between the two often uninformed, expedient, piecemeal methods now generally pursued and a perfectionist effort to take into account absolutely everything relevant to a contemplated environmental change. The concept of environment as a factor in public policy is only now emerging. There will no doubt be many theories of environmental administration developed before the best one, if indeed there can be any best one, is discovered.

There are currently in use several systematic concepts or approaches to environmental analysis and control. They are not analogous to the evaluative techniques described earlier in this chapter. They may be (but need not be) treated as alternative ways of approaching environmental issues. They are not necessarily incompatible with one another, and many of them could be complementary. Three of these approaches will be briefly described here. In ascending order of comprehensiveness, they are: (1) the "problem shed," (2) the settlement system, illustrated by the Doxiadis theory of Ekistics, or the science of human settlements, and (3) the ecosystem and its most dramatic paradigm: Spaceship Earth.

The "problem shed" approach employs economics as its primary organizing concept, but incorporates physical science, engineering, and all other data relevant to the analysis of particular environmental problems for which specific boundaries can be identified. The problem may be relatively simple (e.g., a specific form of water pollution in a specific geographical area) or it may be as complex and extensive as the increase of carbon dioxide in the atmosphere of the Earth. The identification of the "problem" and its ramifications points, in the words of Allen V. Kneese ". . . to inferences about desirable institutional arrangements for environmental management."[19] The principal application of "problem shed" analysis has been to water-quality management. Kneese observes, ". . . it is now being carried over to other problems of managing environmental contamination, air pollution, pesticides, solid wastes, etc.," but the approach ". . . may be much harder to implement with respect to some of these problems."

The settlement-system approach is an unconventional way to understanding cities. It is characteristically a result of efforts to apply science and technology to the structuring of human settlements without being bound by traditional patterns, practices, or techniques. The approach is illustrated by the Experimental City project (an effort to construct a wholly new city—new in concept and in technology)[20] and by the theory of Ekistics, developed by the environmental and urban planner C. A. Doxiadis.[21]

Ekistics, "the science of human settlements," is both a general approach to environmental development and a body of specific doctrine. Its distinguishing feature is a method of urban and regional design to permit the orderly and rational growth of cities and to accommodate at all stages of growth the total needs of their human populations. Doxiadis sees Ekistics as a science to be developed. "We are," he declares, "only starting to grasp the need for it. . . ." Derived from the Greek word *ekos,* meaning habitat, and from the verb *eko,* meaning to settle down, Ekistics has a conceptual affinity to economics and ecology. It is in purpose a practical discipline, drawing upon the substance and methodology of the physical, biological, and social sciences for much of its basic content and directed to the problem "How to make a settlement so as to fill the two basic requirements laid down by Aristotle: security and happiness." The genius of Doxiadis has been to combine a theoretical concept and an operational method with a systematic exposition, and to give the combination an appropriate name. The novelty of Ekistics lies in its formulation rather than in its elements. It is no mean accomplishment to discover a name that will crystallize a concept so as to make clear what, for many people, is obscure—to spark imagination and thus persuade to action those whom a conventional analysis of environmental factors would fail to move. Ekistics is therefore more than a theory of planning; it is also a theory of action, and its realization assumes an ongoing administration of the total environment in accordance with verified ecological understanding.

The ecosystem is scientifically the most fundamental concept for environmental analysis and control.[22] To approach environments as ecosystems means that the totality of the interacting entities and systems, physical and social, that comprise every environment must be taken into account in any decision regarding the environment. The ecosystem approach is also the most complex, and is the least easily translated into public policy and action. Men have found it easier to "think down" to the assumed limits of their ability to handle complexity rather than to "think up" to the complex realities of the natural world. The advent of the computer and of systems science is extending human capability, and the feasibility of ecological approaches to environmental problems is to this extent being enlarged. There is also a great deal that may be done through formal education and training to facilitate ecosystems thinking. It is not merely the uncertainty and complexity of the data that have retarded the use of the ecosystems concept; the heretofore non-ecological method and content of pedagogical practice in the United States has ill prepared the people to think in ecological terms. Efforts are being made on many fronts to remedy this situation, but time and money are required, and the supply of neither appears to be adequate for the task. There is need for an obvious and persuasive symbol of the ecosystems concept that will help to achieve "instant awareness" even though it cannot instill instant understanding. Fortunately such a symbol has become available.

This is the paradigm, or model, of Spaceship Earth.[23] It is an ecological concept, described in detail in Chapter 3, in which the planetary life-support system—ecosphere or biosphere—is perceived as an essentially closed system in which the indefinite expansion or exploitation of any of its elements would ultimately be self-defeating and disastrous to human welfare. Implicit in the concept are some fundamental assumptions regarding the ultimate structure and dynamics of society. Spaceship Earth implies a steady-state society, in which dynamism is largely internalized and controlled by the authority of knowledge. This may be the model of future industrial societies, but it has no analogue among present sociopolitical systems.

A NEW FACTOR IN PUBLIC POLICY

Examination of the literature of human ecology, public health, natural-resources management, engineering, urbanism, and development planning (economic, social, and political) suggests a growing tendency to see man/environment relationships as a policy framework within which many specific problems can best be solved.[24] A readily apparent and probable explanation for this tendency is that, over a wide range of issues, our society is now confronting the limits of the capacity of the finite environment to absorb an infinite number of human demands, many of which are mutually incompatible. Environmental awareness is being stimulated by frustration and disappointment.

The intellectual foundations for an environmental-policy focus are being laid. The social and material pressures toward a formalization of environmental policy are already present. The need for a generalizing concept of environmental development that will provide a common denominator among differing values and interests is becoming clearer. And the concept of "good" environment, however one defines it, is certainly no less concrete, tangible, and specific than the concepts of freedom, prosperity, security, and welfare, which have on various occasions served to focus public policy. "Environmental quality" has been rapidly gaining acceptance as an organizing concept, and succeeding chapters in this book will document the extent to which it has already been incorporated into legal doctrines and administrative procedures.

Ecological thinking has resulted both from an examination of past environmental errors and from a growing awareness of the probable consequences of present environmental decisions. It is doubtful whether circumstances henceforth will allow human society as wide a margin for environmental miscalculation as that enjoyed in the past. An accelerating demand on all resources is resulting from a burgeoning technology throughout the world and from increasing populations with their needs, expectations, and changing ways of life. We have both the occasion and the means to make bigger, more-disastrous, and more-irremediable environmental

mistakes than ever in the past. But how would a policy focus
on the environment help peoples and governments to follow
a wiser course now and in the future?

It can be demonstrated that many of the worst environmental errors have been consequences of segmental, or single-
purpose, public decision making, or failure to perceive specific environmental situations in comprehensive ecological
terms. A policy focus on the environment in its fullest practicable sense would make more likely the consideration of all
the major elements relevant to an environment-affecting decision. Whatever content is ascribed to the adjective "good,"
it becomes daily more evident that public administration of
the environment will not be "good" if it fails to deal with
environmental problems in comprehensive terms.[25] This
task would not of necessity be hopelessly involved and time-
consuming. In contrast to some of our more primitive current
methods of environmental decision making, it would indeed
be complex. But methods oversimplified in relation to the
problems are not likely to produce satisfactory results.

Consideration of environmental problems in comprehensive terms may lead to fewer errors and hence to better environmental decisions. But here an important reservation must
be added: the approach is not a panacea. Ecological considerations may facilitate, but cannot eliminate, the political
task of reconciling a great diversity of interests and values.
The scientific base and content of environment-related decisions would no doubt be increased beyond those employed in
the segmental, or linear, type of thinking that most people
find convenient. But value judgments, particularly with respect to ends, ethics, and accountability in public action,
would also gain significance. For through these decisions, the
future of communities would be shaped not by accident or
inadvertency, but by responsible, deliberate, purposeful design. Scientists may one day tell us what kinds of environment are best for our physical and mental health, but it seems
doubtful if scientists alone will be able to determine the environmental conditions that people will seek. There will still
remain an element of personal preference, which cannot be
relegated to the computer.[26]

A major advantage of the comprehensive approach is that

it tends to force consideration of basic value questions, as for example: What in a given instance is a "good" environment? What kind of environment under prevailing circumstances should be sought? What objective data can be found that are valid indicators of the interacting effects of environmental factors and people? Until we find answers to these questions better than those we now have, our environmental policies, although capable of effecting improvement, will still leave much to be desired.

Environment as a factor for public policy has thus grown out of past experience, but its major development extends into the future. In the United States, Canada, and Western Europe, public responsibility for the state of the environment is in the process of receiving explicit public recognition. The principal operational objectives and guidelines are beginning to be identified (and will be described in subsequent chapters in this volume). Even in its relatively new and undeveloped state, the concept of public responsibility for the environment may provide a new and better focus for many public policy decisions. The growth of environmental policy can take place, however, only as two other developments evolve: First, the public generally must have begun to see the comprehensive environment as a legitimate and necessary field for public action. Second, means must be found for more effectively interrelating or integrating the tasks of the public agencies as they bear upon the environment. In both these developments, research is needed to guide the course of action.[27] It seems unlikely that we will find the legislative, organizational, and administrative answers to environmental development and control before we have developed the policy concepts and goals toward which our political efforts can intelligently be directed.[28]

Public policy in the shaping of the environment thus emerges as a vast, multidisciplinary field of inquiry in which significant work has been started but with most of it as yet restricted to specific environmental factors, as for example, water resources, air pollution, or radioactivity. Investigation of specific environmental problems is essential to any larger or more-generalized concept of environmental policy. But ultimately the accumulating special studies must be related to a larger order of generalization if comprehensive environmental administration is to become a reality. For it does not follow that, if the lesser jobs are pursued with diligence, the greater ones will take care of themselves.

A CONCLUDING OBSERVATION

The history of this chapter illustrates the change that has occurred in public concern for the environment during the decade of the nineteen sixties. The chapter is based upon an article first published in *Public Administration Review*, XXII, September 1963. In the six years separating that publication from the writing of this chapter, changes have occurred in American society that have made the original manuscript unsuitable for further use without major editorial revision. But the original article carried the message that Chapter 1 was to bring—and so the article was heavily edited and updated with new material. In 1963, the title of the article ended with a question mark: "Environment: A New Focus for Public Policy?" In late 1969, a question mark was no longer appropriate. As this chapter was being rewritten, the United States Senate, Ninety-first Congress, passed a bill "declaring a national policy on the environment" (S.1075). Environment had indeed become a focus for policy; it had also become a factor in policy—as even the federal agencies traditionally most resistant to ecological values were beginning to discover. On May 29, 1969, the President of the United States established a cabinet-level Environmental Quality Council with himself as Chairman. Universities, research institutes, and industrial firms that six years earlier had generally evidenced indifference or supercilious skepticism regarding the importance of the environment as an object of study were now committing themselves to major efforts in research and education on environmental issues. And at least four new journals generally concerned with man/environment relationships had come into existence (*Environmental Science and Technology* and *Environmental Research*, 1967, and *Environment* and *Environment and Behavior*, 1969). In addition to these, more than a dozen new journals or periodicals were established or reorganized to deal with specific aspects of environmental policy (e.g., *Journal of Applied Ecology,* 1964; *Water Control News,* 1966; *Clean Air News,* 1967; *Air and Water News,* 1967; *Atmospheric Environment,* 1967; and *Natural Resources Lawyer,* 1968; and *Biological Conservation,* 1968). Deeply committed to the thesis developed in "Environment: A New Focus for Public Policy?" the author was gratified that, although its principal argument remained valid, much of its substance in detail had been "dated" by the changing climate of opinion and course of political events. It was a rarely experienced pleasure to be compelled to make heavy revisions, not because what had been said earlier had been wrong, but because in retrospect it had been so right.

With the adoption of the National Environmental Policy Act of 1969 the United States entered the decade of the nineteen seventies committed for the first time as a nation to responsibility for the quality of its environment. As *The Washington Post* editorialized, "environment is now a 'big issue'."[29] The environment had become a focus for public policy not only in the United States, but throughout the major industrial nations of the world. The international scope of environmental policy is illustrated by the United Nations Conference on the Human Environment scheduled for 1972; by the Economic Commission for Europe Meeting of Governmental Experts on Problems Relating to the Environment to be held in 1971; and the activities on the environment sponsored by the Council of Europe, as well as the International Declaration of Environmental Rights proposed by the United Nations Associations of the Nordic Countries in 1970. The environment as a policy focus emerged during the nineteen sixties; the nineteen seventies mark the beginning of efforts toward implementation of policy on a world-wide scale.

2

QUALITY OF THE ENVIRONMENT
AS A SOCIAL ISSUE

The condition and tendency of the environment has recently begun to assume the character of a comprehensive social issue. In the United States, it has emerged under the general rubric "environmental quality." But the issue is still inchoate. Public responsibility for the state of the environment is presently the product of a number of separate environment-related social movements in the process of fusion. Among these are the conservation of natural resources, environmental health, human ecology, the protection of natural beauty, and urban and regional planning. Diversity of viewpoint within these movements, compounded by numerous specialized environmental concerns (such as those involving economic, aesthetic, political, military, or scientific considerations), have complicated environmental quality as a social issue. An adequate conceptual basis for public environmental policy formulated in ecologically valid operational terms has yet to obtain popular comprehension. Nevertheless, a national environmental policy has been adopted in the United States (Public Law 91–190) and, through international action, a comprehensive policy for the world environment, or biosphere, may be in the making.

A social issue is a question or problem that has aroused concern within society and that requires a social or public decision for its resolution. Such issues are social because they require collective action and cannot be resolved solely by individual choice. They inevitably become political and governmental, because politics in the broad sense is the principal process of social decision, and the principal instrument of politics is government.

In its earlier stages, an incipient social issue may have little political significance. It acquires political importance as proponents of a particular solution attempt, with some prospect of success, to invoke the support of government. For example, air pollution becomes a social issue when the numbers of people perceiving it to be a problem are sufficient to lift it from mere subjective concern to a matter of general public discussion. The social issue becomes a political issue when widespread conviction arises that "there ought to be a law," and when public control is sought over activities that are believed to be its causes.[1]

The state or condition of the human environment presents a peculiar issue for social or political action. The peculiarity derives from the circumstance that man, like all other living creatures, is both part and product of his own environment. His very existence is absolutely dependent upon certain minimal environmental conditions such as oxygen and food, temperature and humidity. As an animal, he tends to accept his environment as a fish accepts its aqueous medium: he takes it for granted. As a man, however, he is capable of objectifying his environment; he can conceptualize it as separate from himself and can imagine himself as separable from it.[2]

This capacity of human thought and perception leads to several significant consequences. It has characterized Western religion, philosophy, and technology, which set man apart from nature.[3] It has facilitated the deification and idealization of nature, while paradoxically enabling man to overcome an inhibiting reverence for nature and to manipulate the natural environment (often shortsightedly) to serve human ends. It seems plausible that loss of identity with nature has facilitated abuse of the environment both consciously and inadvertently. But this capacity to objectify the environment also makes possible its scientific study. And many of the very capabilities that have enabled man to degrade and destroy his environments could, if applied with wisdom, enable him to manage the environment for the general welfare.

The emergence of general social concern for the state of the environment is a very recent development in industrial society. It is largely a consequence of the simultaneous convergence of exploding populations, scientific knowledge, and technological enterprise. The world is shrinking rapidly rela-

tive to man's growing demands upon it, and human societies
are confronted with the reality of its finite character. With
the aid of science, technology can enlarge certain aspects of
environmental choice, but increasingly, in a crowded world,
choice in one direction means opportunities foregone in
others. Moreover, at this juncture, science is becoming better
able to measure and describe the systematic interrelatedness
of man's total environment, and to ascertain the ramifications
of his environment-shaping activities. It is enabling man to see
with a new comprehension the nature and consequences of
his impact upon the environment. Science may thus afford
a conceptual basis for public environmental policy that neither
ethics, aesthetics, economics, nor engineering have been able,
thus far, to provide.

THE MEASURE OF AN ISSUE

It would be easy to demonstrate that environmental quality
has become a social issue in the United States. But it is difficult to determine how significant a political issue it has become. Among political scientists, whose profession includes
the study of political issues, environmental quality has
hitherto received little interest or attention. Even the more-
conventional and limited conservation movement rarely has
found a place in the "great issues" textbooks that have been
edited by political scientists for the instruction of college un-
dergraduates. Connections between environmental conditions
and political behavior have been explored mostly by political
geographers, historians, and sociologists. Those aspects of the
environment that have primarily interested political scientists
have been ethnic or economic. "Geopolitics" has been concerned primarily with the politico-economic, military, and
psychological significance of geographical space[4]; "biopolitics" has been given a number of differing interpretations[5];
and ecology has provided a theory-building model for several
political analysts.[6] But little attention has been given to the
political implications of man's interaction with the natural
world. Nevertheless, to understand man in context it is necessary to study man in relation to his total environment, and
this requires knowledge obtained through the physical and

biological sciences. Environmental-policy analysis thus requires a fusion of that knowledge with information derived from the policy, or social, sciences, and from political science in particular. Yet, among the social sciences, political science as a discipline seems most distant from the "natural" sciences, and only recently have the social or political implications of science and technology begun to arouse general interest among social scientists. Until recently, few political scientists had been moved, either by the exhortations of Harold D. Lasswell[7] or by their own assessment of priorities, to interest themselves in the political science of science. Political aspects of nuclear energy, outer-space exploration, and weapons systems did, however, attract the attention of some political scientists, and a growing interest in policy studies is evident. But the previous state of indifference to the natural sciences may perhaps explain why political scientists generally were slow to concern themselves specifically with the political consequences of the impact of science and technology upon the human environment.

Were environmental quality to become as politically decisive an issue as foreign policy, economic stabilization, or civil rights, one could assume that it would receive more attention from political forums at all levels of government, but seldom in the past have the destinies of political parties and candidates turned on the outcome of an environmental issue. Nevertheless, the quality of the environment appears to be a growing social concern in all parts of the United States, especially in California and the northeastern megalopolis. It is becoming a potent although unpredictable issue, capable of reversing the decisions of powerful governmental and industrial agencies.[8] The political strength of the environmental-quality movement still depends very heavily upon the aroused determination of organized citizens. It is not yet firmly based anywhere within the structure of official government. Political systems do not accommodate all issues equally, and environmental quality appears to be one of those areas of public decision to which the institutional arrangements of American government and politics are not especially favorable. The conceptual problem is basic to the development of environmental quality as a social or political issue. If one may judge by the public response to political controversies over environmental questions, environmental quality, as a general proposition, is still only vaguely perceived in the minds of most people. As with many propositions of virtue, there is an easy bias in favor of the idea of "quality"; but public opinion does not so easily support the strictures of "do" or "don't" that are required to give environmental quality operational meaning. When, for example, environmental quality has meant damage to the business of roadside advertising or restriction on the speculative sale of land, popular willingness to support the "quality" concept has often notably diminished.

Although "environmental quality" lacks operational relevance in the minds of many people, the fact that the term can be made operational in specific instances may not always be a political asset. If the values implicit in a particular case are sharply disputed or are not widely shared, politicians may prefer a strategy of deliberate vagueness. Lack of operational relevance may not weaken a social issue that people *think* they understand, but divided opinion over what the issue really is may render it unable to mobilize politically significant support. From the viewpoint of opinion leaders, an "ideal" issue is understood by the public to a degree sufficient to elicit support, but not to the extent of arousing doubts and questions concerning all its implications and possible consequences. The successful political issue sounds a call to action, and is not necessarily or even probably a proposition for scientific investigation. Environmental quality in the abstract does not as yet possess generalized emotive power for political effectiveness comparable to national defense, full employment, civil rights, or educational opportunity. To overcome counterforces in politics, environmental quality must somehow come to symbolize a widely shared and deeply felt attitude toward life itself. Environmental quality may be quite as specific and far more operational than those symbolic words—peace, justice, freedom, and equality—for which men have fought, bled, and died, and paid heavily in material wealth. The difference lies not in the actual substance of the issues, but in the beliefs of men. The "great issues" of the political scientists have often proved in fact to be great illusions. But men thought they knew what the "issues" meant.

They had an image or model of the issue that was often distorted or incomplete and, conveniently for the political leaders, seldom corresponded to reality and could not be put to practical test. It was thus seldom possible to hold leaders accountable either for failure to achieve the unrealized goal of a pseudo issue or for misleading people into an effort to resolve an issue that could not be resolved within the terms in which it had been politically defined.

The environmental concept is burdened by whatever political disadvantage concreteness and ubiquity carry. The problems growing out of man's environmental relationships cannot be exorcised by political magic, although they have often been temporarily evaded by recourse to the magic word "progress." Nevertheless, the task of the politician as symbol manipulator is complicated by the obdurate and pervasive nature of the environmental predicament of modern man. The poorly formed state of man's understanding of his environmental relationships has until recently deprived the politician of an environmental issue sufficiently coherent or emotion laden to easily symbolize. The terms "conservation," "environmental health," "natural beauty," and "city and regional planning" have been employed (with resulting mixtures of success and failure) to capsulize particular aspects of environmental policy. It may be, however, that the condition of the environment, conceived in qualitative terms, is a feasible object for political action only with the maturation of civilization and with the advancement of scientific knowledge.

If scientific evidence and reasoned argument are the appeals that are really required to arouse support for environmental quality as a public policy, then efforts toward this end may move no faster than the speed with which the level of popular understanding and preference with respect to environmental relationships can be upgraded. It would seem to follow that public policies based on a science-derived understanding of man/environment relationships would diminish the role of the politician and augment the policy roles of scientists, engineers, and planners. But this is a conclusion too easy to be accepted without examination. It seems probable that comprehensive environmental policy and administration would change the roles of all these participants in the policy process and that the new roles would in many cases be less differentiated from one another than the old.

EMERGENCE OF ENVIRONMENT AS AN ISSUE— THE AMERICAN EXPERIENCE

Unlike such policy areas as national defense, full employment, civil rights, and educational opportunity, no generally accepted common foundation in political principle or popular belief has underlain the growing number of environmental issues. Until recently, absence of an explicit public commitment to maintain the viability of the human environment has been a major handicap in efforts to protect or improve environmental quality. In the widely prevalent view of the environment as a storehouse of natural resources, advocates of an environmental policy for optimizing the full range of beneficial man/environment relationships have characteristically been perceived as interest-group competitors on a common footing with other natural-resources user groups seeking the exploitation of minerals, open space, grasslands, forests, waterfronts, rivers, or any of the other discrete items in the natural-resources supermarket. The economic concept of natural resources, useful for appropriate purposes, does not provide a fundamental and integrative basis for environmental policy. The concept falls far short of encompassing the full range of man/environment relationships. Nor has the conservation movement provided a concept fully adequate to the need, having at an early age been wedded historically and conceptually to the natural-resources view of the environment.

The difficulties of issue formulation are, at root, perceptual. Environmental policy has been difficult to formulate in comprehensive or generic terms because men relate to their environments in a great variety of ways. In the technologically specialized societies of the modern world, men in the aggregate have seldom perceived a unity underlying these varied relationships. Rarely has there been a common perceptual basis that would afford a foundation for policy consensus on the management of the environment. Conflicting arguments over environmental policies, as, for example, in the use of natural resources in highway construction or in urban planning, often bypass one another. They fail to come to grips with a common set of propositions, because the opponents are arguing from quite different premises and toward quite different objectives.

Those destructive patterns of man/environment relationships that have characterized the American historical experience may in part be traced to behavioral changes or failures of adaptation in the West European peoples who settled and subdued the New World. The Spanish and Portuguese invaded the Americas primarily for exploitive purposes qualified to some extent by a fervor for the religious conversion of the native inhabitants. The initial results of their conquests were almost uniformly destructive, nowhere more evident than in Peru, where the productive agricultural economy of the Inca was disrupted and where the obsessive search for precious metals contributed to a decline in the human ecology of Andean societies, from which they do not appear to have even yet recovered. The North American settlements of northwest Europeans may have been less explicitly exploitive, but they nevertheless resulted in a large amount of inadvertent environmental destruction.

The colonization of North America was coincident with the beginning of the modern era. In Western Europe, the period between 1600 and 1800 was characterized by the breakdown of feudal controls over land and people, by the rise of commercial and manufacturing classes, and by the advent of industrial technology. The era was characterized by a throwing off of the traditional restraints of government upon the exploitation of land and other resources, and by the rise of effective popular resistance to the imposition of new guidelines or controls. During the eighteenth and early nineteenth centuries, the economic doctrine of *laissez-faire* became both theory and widespread practice in American life. Governmental attempts to protect or conserve timber reserves, fur-bearing wildlife, or mineral deposits were defeated by political opposition and popular non-compliance. Conservation efforts by the British Government before independence, and by Washington, Hamilton, and Gallatin during the formative years of the republic, were defeated by political and administrative circumstances.

The guiding objective of American policy throughout most of the nineteenth century was the rapid settlement of the land and the turning of its resources to use by its new occupants. Philosophic concepts of harmony with nature or of ecological balance found no place in the minds of frontiersmen, to whom nature was an enemy to be subdued. The immediate self-interest of the frontiersmen was reinforced by their Old Testament Christianity. For did not God speak to all men through Adam and Eve when, as recorded in Genesis 1:28, he commanded them: "Be fruitful, and multiply, and replenish the earth, and subdue it: and have dominion over . . . every living thing . . . ?"

Throughout the greater part of the nineteenth century, Americans were too busily engaged with the subjugation of the continent to give serious thought to the consequences of their action. Publication of the book *Man and Nature*, by George Perkins Marsh, in 1864 marked the beginning of a new concern among more-thoughtful Americans over the heedless exploitation of the natural environment.[9] This concern was to grow, before the close of the century, into the conservation movement, and was able to stem (although not reverse) the trend toward environmental degradation. There were many skeins of varied motives in the movement; scientific interests were almost always present but were seldom really controlling in the public policy process.[10]

A second current of public concern with the environment emerged with the appearance of the public health movement. The discovery that certain diseases, such as yellow fever, typhoid, and malaria, were linked to specific environmental factors stimulated investigation into what is now called environmental health. Control of the carriers of disease frequently required control of their habitats and, in consequence, the manipulation of certain factors in the environment. By the close of the nineteenth century, public sanitation was a recognized public function throughout a large part of urban America, although the greater part of the twentieth century would be required to make this responsibility effective in all the aspects of the environment to which it should logically

have been applied. By mid-twentieth century, Americans were *
personally the best-sewered-showered-sanitized-deodorized
people that history records, but their public discharge of filth
into the natural environment was equally unparalleled. Sanitary engineering appeared able to prevent the wastes and residues of public affluence from becoming a direct human health
hazard, but the resulting aesthetic and economic blight
aroused public concern over the quality of the environment
itself, and especially with the disappearance of order and
beauty from the American landscape. This concern reinforced
the efforts of architects, planners, and civic-minded leaders,
who sought to beautify the American environment chiefly
through the protection of natural beauty and the embellish-
ment of the cities.

The American experience with attempts to define public
responsibility for the quality of the environment is largely
summed up in these three sociopolitical developments: conservation, environmental health, and public aesthetics. Each
of these developments was distinct in origin, and although
there were interactions among them and some overlapping
participation among leaders and followers, not all interactions
were mutually supportive. A comprehensive public commitment to maintain the quality of the environment would require at least a basic concurrence among the people whose
activities these movements represent. Therefore, a closer look
at the assumptions and objectives of the movements is a necessary prelude to examining prospects for the emergence of
environmental quality as a major concern of government.

CONSERVATION AS A SOCIAL ISSUE[11]

The conservation movement is hard to define in meaningful
operational terms. Among American conservationists, there
has been common opposition to the waste and misuse of natural resources. But even waste and misuse are differently construed, as for example by the scientific forester, who sees
waste and misuse in the "overmature" timber of wilderness
areas, whereas the ecologist and the lover of wilderness aesthetics see the wise preservation of biological "bench marks"
and irreplaceable natural beauty.

The conservation movement might have had greater effectiveness if it had presented a unified front on questions of environmental policy. But its followers sought differing goals: some wished to maximize the economic utilization of the environment and were primarily opposed to waste or "nonuse" of natural resources; others sought protection of aesthetic values in landscape, waters, and wildlife; a third group saw the natural world as a great laboratory of science and tried to prevent its impoverishment through the indiscriminate destruction of living species and of natural habitats. A brief examination of these viewpoints will show why the conservation movement does not necessarily imply the environmental-quality issue.

Like Caesar's Gaul, "conservation" in America appears to be divisible into three parts, symbolized respectively by the terms economic, aesthetic, and ecological; and perhaps, like Gaul, these divisions among conservationists account in part for defeats by aggressive opponents. As with any social movement, it is not necessary (and hardly possible) to fix that place in time when the movement began. The American conservation movement evolved slowly, as perceptive individuals saw with dismay the unnecessary waste and destruction of America's once-great abundance of natural wealth and beauty. The conference of state governors convened at the White House by Theodore Roosevelt in 1908 dramatized the arrival of the conservation of natural resources as a public issue. Very early, however, the commitment to better custody and care of America's natural endowment became divided between two frequently opposing interpretations of the conservation task. The politically predominant attitude interpreted the task as the utilitarian management of the natural environment, and saw the conservation mission as realized in scientific forestry, irrigation of arid lands, drainage of wetlands, and harnessing the rivers for navigation and electric power. The opposing view, while accepting managed environmental change in some degree, was essentially preservationist. It saw the conservation mission as realized in the establishment of inviolate national parks and reservations, and in the protection of wildlife and the distinctive natural features of deserts, coast lines, river valleys, and unique geological formations.

This conflict in values and objectives was dramatized in the break of personal friendship between political progressive and conservationist Gifford Pinchot and naturalist John Muir over the flooding of Hetch Hetchy Valley in the California Sierras by a high dam to provide water and power for San Francisco.

The growth of the conservation movement is indicated by the establishment of voluntary, privately financed organizations to promote general, or more often, specific conservation objectives. Illustrative of a large number are the following organizations established prior to the emergence of the environmental quality movement in the nineteen sixties.[12]

1870 American Fisheries Society
1875 American Forestry Association
1876 Appalachian Mountain Club
1892 Sierra Club
1900 Society of American Foresters
1905 National Audubon Society
1911 North American Wildlife Foundation
1915 Ecological Society of America
1919 National Parks Association
1922 Izaak Walton League
1925 Defenders of Wildlife
1932 National Reclamation Association
1935 The Wilderness Society
1936 National Wildlife Federation
1936 The Wildlife Society
1941 Soil Conservation Society of America
1946 Wildlife Management Institute
1947 Conservation Education Association
1948 Conservation Foundation
1958 American Conservation Association

Public concern with the state of the environment cannot be fully described merely by reference to specific action-oriented organizations. To achieve political goals, the voluntary organizations have found it advantageous to focus their efforts on specific aspects of conservation policy. The interests of their members have often been equally specialized, although a substantial overlap in membership has existed, representing especially those persons with a commitment to a comprehensive public environmental policy. To strengthen the collective effectiveness of the separate organizations, the Natural Resources Council was established in 1946 by several of the leading conservation agencies. Membership in the council now exceeds thirty-five organizations and includes a number of honorary individual members. The council regularly informs its members of developments in the federal executive, legislative, and judicial branches that affect conservation interests. It provides a forum for communication and exchange of information among the separate organizations and undertakes occasional factual studies on specific conservation issues, for example on the proposed Alaskan Rampart Dam. More recently it has analyzed and abstracted the voluminous reports of the Public Land Law Review Commission. Federations or other co-ordinative relationships exist among sportsmen's organizations and among outdoor recreation, camping, wildlife-protection, and soil- and water-conservation groups. Some of these societies have professional leadership and orientation, but nearly all welcome general citizen participation.

The preservationist aspect of American conservation policy, which focuses on unique, rare, or highly localized natural assets, has not often been allied with movements for the improvement of ordinary environmental relationships, even though some strategy-conscious conservationists have seen the enlargement of general recreational facilities in or near urban centers as a means toward reducing the damaging pressure of overuse on unique and fragile natural areas and parks. Unfortunately, the attitude that has sometimes been called the "conservation ethic" has barely begun to touch the consciousness of the mass of people anywhere. Americans favor protection of remote and spectacular national parks such as the Yellowstone and the Grand Canyon of the Colorado, but have rarely shown equal interest in conserving natural assets in their own communities. Too often, the mass public treats the spectacular protected areas such as the Yosemite Valley as "natural amusement parks" and acquiesces in the vulgarizing of the Sierras, deserts, and everglades by man-made amusement parks. In fact, from the colonial era to the present, all efforts to conserve the natural environment, if they involved public control over the use or sale of land, have had to reckon with some degree of popular opposition.

Efforts toward public preservation or protection of unique or unusual areas has been almost uniformly greeted by the protests of local landowners, reinforced by the objections of local public officials. Far from accepting the "conservation ethic," the protesters voice moral indignation over a government "take-away" of every American's "God-given right" to make money from the buying and selling of land. As John Ise observes in his book *The American Way*, "As a result of their historical conditioning, Americans are land value animals. For 300 years they have been moving Westward seeking titles to land that they hoped would rise in value; for 300 years they have been following the lure of the unearned increment, the beacon light of 'something for nothing' . . ."[13] From the conventional viewpoint, to be bilked of an American's birthright by a small band of organized, fanatical nature lovers or bureaucratic planners and, adding insult to injury, to have the take-away financed by taxpayers' dollars is about as "un-American" an act as one can imagine. From this viewpoint, one does not see beyond the economic self-interest of the benefiting individual.

In summation, the conservation movement appears to have been the first organized protest among the American people against the degradation of their natural environments. Initially, conservation was concerned as much with eliminating economic waste as with preventing the abuse of nature. Conflict over specific conservation issues (dam building, for example) revealed the cleavage between the economic, engineering, aesthetic, and ecological viewpoints in the movement. In the heat of repeated controversy, these differences tended to widen, and the economic conservationists by midtwentieth century had largely abandoned the "conservation" label for the more appropriate term "economic development" or "natural resources administration." Moreover, advances in technology and the prospect of substitutes for many nonrenewable natural resources made "conservation" a matter of declining urgency and interest among economists. Influential resource economists reassured the American people that the cries of earlier conservationists had often proved to be alarmist and that the nation was not about to run out of essential raw materials. This line of reasoning tended to shift the weight of the conservation argument from economic to aesthetic and, more importantly, to ecological considerations.

Emphasis on ecological factors in conservation often took the form of defense of the balance of nature. It could be shown that harmful results frequently followed changes in stabilized relationships among living species and their habitats. Careless introductions of exotic species afforded numerous examples. Following their casual introduction from abroad; rabbits became rampant in Australia—an obvious consequence of an ecologically thoughtless and unwise act. But the balance-of-nature argument appeared to lose effectiveness in confrontation with the human wish to banish pathogenic or annoying organisms from the environment and by evidence of man's ability to change the balance of organisms in the environment and still maintain a relatively stable and viable ecosystem. By the nineteen sixties, however, a more sophisticated cybernetic feedback, or dynamic homeostatic systems, interpretation of ecology was modifying the oversimplified balance-of-nature view.

These developments and others presently to be described led to the emergence of the "new conservation." In his introduction to Stewart L. Udall's *The Quiet Crisis* (1963), President John F. Kennedy wrote, ". . . we must expand the concept of conservation to meet the imperious problems of the new age." Two years later, in his message to the Congress on natural beauty (February 8, 1965), President Lyndon B. Johnson declared, ". . . new problems will require a new conservation—not just the classic conservation of protection and development, but a creative conservation of restoration and innovation. Its concern is not with nature alone, but with the total relation between man and the world around him."[14] This new conservation was increasingly to merge into the environmental-quality movement. In summarizing its characteristics, sociologist Richard L. Means describes it as a nascent social movement continuing the tradition of conserving the world of nature but carrying the process into other social and political realms. "It deals," he writes, "with a new metaphysics, a new view of the world that, based on the science of ecology, forces the . . . movement into a much more critical stance vis à vis the culture than was true of the past."[15] This metaphysics, symbolized by the image of Spaceship Earth, will be explored in the next chapter. Now, however, it is necessary to examine another current of social development that has entered the mainstream of the environmental-quality movement.

ENVIRONMENTAL HEALTH[16]

The public health movement illustrates a trend toward diversification and division somewhat analogous to that observable in the conservation movement. In both movements, the growth of knowledge led to changes of opinion and policy among leaders and resulted in sharp differences of viewpoint and advocacy. Modern environmental health had its birth in the rapid growth of industrial cities in mid-nineteenth century. Urbanization was not at first accompanied by a corresponding growth of public environmental management. In consequence, disagreeable and unhealthful living conditions characterized the new industrial towns. In the earlier stages of the industrial revolution, biomedical knowledge was not able to segregate the specific agents of disease from the generally unhygienic environmental conditions. In England, the cleansing of the cities was begun in mid-century under the leadership of reformers such as Sir Edwin Chadwick, who chaired the first National Board of Health, established in 1848. In America, the movement for environmental sanitation appeared several decades later. In 1884, the condition of the city of Providence, Rhode Island, was characteristic of urban conditions generally:

The city had obtained a good public water supply—its streets were relatively clean, it was fairly free from offensive trades, and the condition of its houses was comparatively good. On the other hand, fewer than a third of the houses were yet connected with the public sewerage system, many still relied upon wells for water, a majority had badly defective plumbing, backyards often reeked with piles of decaying garbage, and swill carts and nightsoil wagons left trails of filth along the streets. Probably the most conspicuous aspect of the sanitary

environment of Providence (as of other cities) in 1884 was the
stench. It had odors from its hundreds of stables, its polluted
streams, its dead dogs or horses, and its thousands of foul
privy vaults and cesspools. When the odors became so intense
that even the people who lived among them were nauseated,
it is no wonder that many persons associated disease with bad
smells.[17]

The disagreeable filth and odors were not in themselves
the direct causes of the infectious diseases with which public
health officers were then primarily concerned. But lacking
adequate sciences of microbiology and immunology, public
officials pursued the course available to them—the sanitization
of the municipal environment. And so the early stages of the
public health movement were generally supportive of the efforts to improve the quality of the environment generally.

The advancement of biomedical science, however, changed
the perspective of professional public health workers. As infectious diseases increasingly were linked to specific pathogenic organisms, the public health officer began to distinguish
between the agents of disease, which he saw as his responsibility as a practical scientist to control, and the aesthetically
noxious conditions he might deplore as a citizen but could
disregard as irrelevant to public health science. If public
water supplies were free from parasites or pathogens, they
could be pronounced "pure." Disagreeable taste, smell, or
color in the water could be put outside the concern of public
health officers, however annoying these conditions might be
to citizens generally. The capacity of streams to renew themselves and to support fish and other wildlife were not public
 health matters. A polluted beach could be made safe to the
public by posting a sign reading DANGER: NO SWIMMING—
WATER POLLUTED.[18]

A political consequence of this shift of emphasis in the
public health movement was that latterly, when citizen groups
organized to abate and reverse the degradation of public
streams, lakes, and rivers, they frequently found no support
and sometimes faced outright opposition from local public
health officers. An indirect political consequence of the narrowed perspective of the professional public health movement
was the removal in 1965 of the administration of national

water-pollution control legislation from the United States Public Health Service to the Department of the Interior. Slowness of professional public health officers to redefine their mission to include recreational and aesthetic values was a factor in the transfer of responsibility for water quality to an agency better able at the point in time to deal comprehensively with problems of the environment.

Ironically, the collision between conservative officials who saw environmental health sciences as essentially limited to the biomedical fields of toxicology, parasitology, and epidemiology, and the advocates of environmental quality programs who saw health in broader and more positive terms occurred at a time when opinions were already beginning to change in the public health profession. The "rediscovery of the environment" in the public health movement was a consequence of further advancement in biomedical science.[19] The infectious diseases that had long preoccupied public health officials were being brought under control. But it became evident that not all the factors in the environment that were deleterious to health could be linked to specifically identified diseases.

The growth of the biomedical sciences and of psychology and psychiatry provided evidence that so-called chronic, psychosomatic, and mental illnesses were often linked in obscure ways to environmental conditions possibly unrelated to infectious or toxic elements. The incidence of certain forms of cancer became associated with particular sets of environmental conditions. Environmental health factors were increasingly perceived as far more complex and subtle than had previously been recognized. Environmental health scientists began to discover that harmful effects, as, for example, in air polluted by a variety of inorganic industrial waste products, could not be traced to any single source as simple as a diphtheria bacillus. Health hazards began to be identified in complex, synergistic interactions among substances discharged into the environment by industrial society and further interacting in various ways with plant and animal life. New forms of electronic radiation and sharply accentuated forms of traditional radiation, such as noise, light, and heat, created difficult problems for environmental health science, especially as emergent technologies created new hazards and annoyances that aroused cries for political action and public control. Little was known about the effects of continuing low levels of exposure to substances and conditions that could not be found harmful in the short run but could conceivably entail long-range cumulative effects.

By the mid-nineteen sixties, the public health and medical professions, except in their most conservative sectors, recognized that man/environment relationships in all their comprehensiveness and complexity were basic factors in human health. Between 1964 and 1969, the American Medical Association sponsored six major conferences on environmental health.[20] In 1963, the New York Academy of Medicine, the New York City Health Department, and the American National Council for Health Education for the Public jointly sponsored a conference on Man—His Environment and Health.[21] In 1965, the Mayo Clinic chose Man's Adaptation to his Expanding Environment as the subject for its Centennial Symposium,[22] and in 1965 and 1966, the National Sanitation Foundation convened a series of four colloquia and a general congress on man versus environment.[23]

As a result of these and other developments, the environmental aspect of the public health movement acquired a breadth of scope that was nearly synonymous with concern for the quality of the environment itself. This broadened dimension did not receive universal professional acceptance, however. In the opinion of some biomedical scientists, the improvement of human health would be advanced more surely by a focusing on known and specific pathogenic factors in the environment than by extending the scope of investigation to aspects of the environment not presently amenable to the exactness of experimental control and laboratory analysis. These contrasting perspectives on environmental health appear to have complicated the decisions regarding administrative organization of environmental health responsibilities within the Public Health Service and the National Institutes of Health during the nineteen sixties. Comparable in effect to the differences in viewpoint among conservationists, experts in environmental health science did not agree either as to the dimensions of their subject matter or to the extent of its relationship to public policy on quality of the environment. As public policy on behalf of environmental quality could not be based solely on conservation doctrine, neither could it be built altogether upon environmental health science.

ENVIRONMENTAL QUALITY VIA NATURAL BEAUTY

Nevertheless, by the mid-nineteen sixties, a retrospective look at the changing values in American public life might have suggested the emergence of environmental quality as a political issue. During the three hundred years in which Americans were subduing the North American wilderness and peopling the continent, public attention was focused upon exploitation of the natural environment and upon material production. Following the Chicago World's Columbian Exposition of 1893, a "city beautiful" movement gained some following at local levels of American public life. But a national political movement on behalf of environmental quality, one phase of which was expressed in terms of natural beauty, did not appear until the nineteen sixties. Because the public aesthetics movement merged almost imperceptibly into a movement for environmental quality, the two developments may most realistically be described together. Because their outcome has been legislation toward a national policy for the environment, their emergence as social issues merits attention in greater detail.

Concern for environmental quality or natural beauty belongs to a "consumer" orientation toward the environment. A significant consumer orientation in the American political economy did not emerge until the twentieth century. It appeared as a concomitant of mechanization, mass production, mass communications, and urbanization. The growth of surplus increments in the American production economy, and the enlargement of popular choices resulting from increased economic and geographic mobility, made feasible a popular concern for environmental quality. Americans could now afford to move to higher levels of dissatisfaction, and this dissatisfaction was stimulated by a pervasive and accelerating decline in the quality of American environments. Following World War II, galloping population increase, industrial expansion, and the cumulative effects of a waste-producing,

motorized economy were transforming the American landscape in ways that even the least-sensitive individuals could
hardly accept with equanimity. And as often happens in the
early stages of changing values in society, growing popular
dissatisfaction focused upon the obvious symptoms of environmental decline rather than upon the not-so-obvious causes.

Evidence of a changing public attitude could be read during
the nineteen sixties on the front pages of newspapers from
Maine to Hawaii. Citizen groups were making political trouble for "progress," on behalf of natural beauty or environmental quality. In New York, Governor Nelson Rockefeller,
the Consolidated Edison Corporation, and the Federal Power
Commission were under attack by groups attempting to prevent the construction of an electric-generator plant on the
face of Storm King Mountain in the Hudson Highlands. In
the state of Indiana, persistent citizen action impeded (or at
least delayed) bipartisan political efforts supported by the
Corps of Engineers to remove the Indiana Dunes in order
to construct steel mills and a deepwater port. In California,
the village of Woodside was obstinately opposing the efforts
of the Atomic Energy Commission, Pacific Gas and Electric
Company, and Stanford University to construct overhead
high-tension lines through the community. The apostles of
American technological and economic progress appeared to
have oversold their gospel. Arguments on behalf of the limit-
less possibilities and inevitability of technological progress
were turned against the technocrats. Were environment-
disfiguring smokestacks and power lines really technologically
necessary, or was technological feasibility being set aside in
the interest of economic convenience? Many people suspected
the latter. Questions were also being asked about the so-called
price of progress: who, for example, was setting the price, and
on what terms?[24]

Popular periodicals such as *The Atlantic, Harper's Magazine, Saturday Review,* and *Life* encouraged a growing popular belief that ugliness, disorder, and an unhealthy environment were not necessarily the price of "progress." The fault
was increasingly seen to lie in *failure* to pay the costs of progress—failure of the right people to pay in the right way at the
right time the costs of using the air, land, and water for eco-

nomic purposes. Protest literature could be found on almost any bookstand in the early nineteen sixties. Protest not only appeared in the journals of planning, architecture, and conservation, where it might have been expected, but was also prominent in magazines with a conservative bent. For example, in the June 23, 1962, *Saturday Evening Post,* Stewart Alsop spoke out against "America the Ugly"—against "the way we Americans are turning our lovely country into a garish, brassy, neon-lit, billboard-ridden, slummish, littered, tasteless and, above all, *messy* place."[25] In its August 13, 1962, issue, *U.S. News & World Report* published an interview with National Park Service Director Conrad L. Wirth on "What it will take to make America beautiful." The Kiplinger magazine *Changing Times* attacked the growth of ugliness under the headings "America the Beautiful—Heritage or Honky-Tonk?" (November 1962) and "America the Beautiful—Let's Not Lose It" (September 1963). Reprints were widely circulated. The March 20, 1964, issue of *Life* editorialized on "The Creeping Junkyard." Hardly an issue of that perennial best seller in middle-class suburbia *The Reader's Digest* failed to carry at least one article comparable to "The Great Billboard Scandal of 1960" (March 1960) or "Conservation is Everybody's Battle" (July 1964).

A political issue appeared to be emerging, but its extent, intensity, and implications were hard to assess. In 1965, Peter F. Drucker, one of the more perceptive observers of the American political economy, forecast a shift away from the kind of economic issues that had occupied the center of the political stage for the previous seventy years.[26] He predicted the emergence of a new power center dominated by urban youth, in which "non-economic issues may well become the core of political belief and action." Focus of the new power center would be "on the quality of life, rather than on the division of the economic product." For the great majority of Americans, the quality of life would be impaired by the chaotic and rapidly worsening conditions of the urban environment. "A real solution, if one can be found," he wrote, "will have to be primarily aesthetic (or, if you prefer the word, moral). At stake is the environment of modern man, rather than administration. We need a city that enriches and enables rather than degrades the individual. But long before we can hope to come to grips with the city as a human environment, we will have to come to grips with the city as a government."[27]

Drucker was one of the few commentators on the deterioration of the American environment who pointed out the essential connection between environmental quality and public administration. The ugliness, disorder, and inconvenience that an affluent American society was beginning to notice had been unintentionally built into the American system of government, business enterprise, and popular *laissez-faire* individualism. In a satirical essay in *The Atlantic*, "The Polipollutionists," John Kenneth Galbraith said, in effect, that pollution of the environment was not an aberration or failure of the dominant economic system, but was, in fact, an integral function of the system.[28] To fundamentally reverse the trend toward environmental deterioration would require not merely coming to grips with the city as a government, but coming to grips with the responsibilities of government generally for the management of the human environment. The normal operations of the American system produced ugliness, along with many good things. Changes in the system would be required to correct its undesirable effects. As in most systems, however, changes were likely to produce unpredictable effects. Moreover, a direct attack upon the problems of environmental quality would inevitably lead to political and economic warfare with the people whose activities in agriculture, advertising, manufacturing, merchandising, mining, real estate, and dozens of other enterprises would be adversely affected. An attack upon the undesirable effects of the system could hardly be less than an attack upon powerful sections of the system itself, including those agencies of government whose activities significantly influenced the shaping of the environment.

The evident and exploitable popular dissatisfaction, with its formidable politico-economic implications, confronted politicians with a dilemma. The angry remonstrance against environmental decay could be turned into votes, but at the risk of losing the support of those interests whose environment-despoiling activities might be brought under attack. The problem for the politician was to gather, if possible, the environmental-quality honey without stirring up a swarm of economic-interest bees.

By the eve of the 1964 presidential campaign, the stage appeared to be set for the appearance of environmental quality as a national political issue. The two major parties differed significantly in their assessment of its utility. It was a natural issue for the Democrats—a logical extension of the welfare and conservation emphasis of the Kennedy administration. Its appeal was greatest to the suburbanized, middle-class Americans whose expectations of a good life were being frustrated or threatened by pollution, urban sprawl, water shortages, inadequate recreation areas, and seemingly insolvable problems of public transportation. Moreover, the Democratic candidate, Lyndon B. Johnson, had found a way to evade the uncertain dangers of the environmental-quality issue by associating it with the more easily managed expression "natural beauty." The Republican leadership was so unreservedly committed to the support of free enterprise and so hostile to any extension of public authority that it was unable to respond to the popular discontent over the worsening condition of the environment. Individual Republicans were prominent among the leaders in environmental-quality efforts, but the professional party leadership and the rank and file of the party faithful remained as if mesmerized in their hostility to the now obsolete issues of the New Deal days.

The 1964 platforms of the two major parties contrasted sharply in their treatment of natural-resources and environmental issues. The Democratic platform was the Johnson Great Society program, with an emphasis on public intervention on behalf of environmental quality. The Republican treatment was brief and concerned largely with economic factors and incentives for resource developers. It was silent or noncommittal on such environmental issues as outdoor recreation, open space, and air and water pollution. This failure to comprehend the fears and values of the new American suburban middle class may have cost the Republican party the support of the one major and growing sector of the electorate that it had any real chance of winning.

Lyndon B. Johnson, however, anticipated the environmental-quality issue in his Great Society address, on May 22, 1964, which spoke directly to the values of the post-World War II generation that would shortly determine the direction of American politics. His espousal of natural beauty and environmental quality surprised and gratified conservationists, who had not looked for this type of commitment from a professional politician from western Texas. The depth of the Johnson commitment was open to question. But regardless of the President's sincerity, the fact that he had publicly identified himself with the environmental issue strengthened its position in American political life. It added status and dignity to the efforts of those who sought to better the public environment and who had characteristically been dismissed by practical politicians as ineffectual nature lovers and utopians.

During the 1964 campaign, Lyndon Johnson treated environmental quality as a major issue, but did so primarily in the context of "the new conservation" or "natural beauty." On January 4, 1965, Johnson's State of the Union message included a special section on "the Beauty of America," and on February 8, he sent to the Congress a special message on natural beauty, in which he announced a White House conference in mid-May and outlined a comprehensive blueprint for environmental policy.

The White House Conference of May 24–25, 1965, was chaired by Laurance S. Rockefeller, a public-minded liberal Republican who had long been associated with conservation and environmental-quality efforts. Somewhat more than one thousand persons from all parts of the country and representing a broad spectrum of interests attended. Mrs. Johnson actively participated in the conference and became increasingly identified in the news media as the prime mover of the Administration's "beautification efforts." The President was in the advantageous position of making a show of action on the state of the environment through the joint leadership of a wealthy and highly respected Republican and the First Lady, neither of whom held political office in his administration.[29] He could speak vigorously of the need for restoring and protecting the quality of the environment, but he also encouraged the inference that he did not take the beauty business too seriously. In his remarks at the conclusion of the White

House Conference, he recalled with amusement how his after-noon nap had been interrupted "by Ladybird and Laurance Rockefeller and others in the next room talking about flowers, roadsides, and so forth."[30]

During the balance of 1965, follow-up conferences were held in approximately half the states. Conference publicity was generally favorable, but the latent opposition awaited specific legislative action. The clash was not long in coming. When the Bureau of Public Roads held public hearings across the country on the so-called "Ladybird" highway-beautifica-tion bills, the roadside-business and highway-construction in-terests were out in full force and vigor. The issue was almost invariably defined as the right of American enterprise to earn an honest taxable dollar free from the arbitrary, unjust, and economically crippling imposition of garden-club aesthetics.

White House support of environmental-quality efforts was ambiguous. The President signed legislation that resulted in the running of overhead electric power lines through Wood-side, California, although the community had voted to quad-ruple its tax burden to prevent the kind of disfigurement that Johnson's White House Conference had deplored. The Presi-dent's Secretary of the Army continued to issue fill permits in San Francisco Bay in the face of protests from conserva-tionists, planners, and citizens concerned with the rapid de-terioration of the Bay Area. In the Florida Everglades and the Indiana Dunes, the White House authority appeared to be neutral in conflicts among resource users and federal agencies in which environmental quality was a major factor. Were these compromises with professed objectives evidence of naïveté, of hypocrisy, or of those hard but honest compro-mises that politics often requires?[31]

The extent of the Johnson commitment to environmental quality was not fully put to the test, however, because of the deepening national involvement in the Vietnam War. After 1965, although left-handed efforts were made to keep Great Society programs going, the Johnson administration became increasingly preoccupied with the war. As Negro unrest in the cities and student anti-war protest on the college cam-puses became more disturbing, natural beauty continued to lose ground as a suitable vehicle for environmental-quality

efforts. By 1967, it should have been evident to everyone that
natural beauty as a political issue was as dead as that legend-
ary beauty "Snow White." Its revival was possible—almost certain—but it seemed clear that this revival must await a fundamental change in political climate, the date of which could
not be foretold.[32]

POLITICAL PREREQUISITES FOR ENVIRONMENTAL POLICY

The election to the presidency of Richard M. Nixon in
1968 presaged no fundamental change in natural policy toward the environment. Unlike the 1964 campaign, the state of
the environment had not been a major issue in 1968. But the
new President discovered that the environment had become
much more of a social and political issue than he had suspected when he nominated Walter L. Hickel, the Governor of
Alaska, to succeed Stewart Udall as Secretary of the Interior.
From the viewpoint of most conservationists and of many
individuals and organizations concerned with the quality of
the natural environment, almost everything was wrong with
the Hickel nomination. The Governor personified the traditional "development" approach to the use of natural resources
and was believed to favor the commercial exploitation of
the environment over other uses. Under former Secretary
Udall, the Department of the Interior had come to be widely
viewed as the protector of the nation's total environment,
especially in its scenic, wildlife, and recreational aspects. The
sharp contrast that appeared to be implicit in Governor
Hickel's nomination brought a flood of protesting letters to
the Congress and the new Administration. In contrast to most
of the other presidential nominations, which the Senate
quickly confirmed, the Hickel appointment was the subject of
extended and widely publicized hearings before the Senate
Committee on Interior and Insular Affairs. Confirmation followed only after the Committee was reassured that the new
secretary did not intend to turn back the hands of the conservation clock.[33] Editorials, cartoons, and comment in the
news media made it clear that an influential segment of the
American public was now committed in principle to the new
conservation and environmental-quality concept. That this

commitment was gaining in political significance was evidenced by a growing volume of legislation, legislative proposals, and legislative hearings on environmental issues, especially in the Ninetieth and Ninety-first Congresses.

The aggregate effect of popular movements on behalf of the conservation of natural resources, of healthful environmental conditions, and of natural beauty had been to create an influential body of opinion sympathetic to the idea of a comprehensive public responsibility for environmental quality. In each of the three movements, there have been some individuals who oppose more than minimal intrusion of government, or more specifically, of politics, into public measures, leaving environmental management generally in private hands. But the nature of the environmental situation in which the mid-twentieth-century American found himself could not be managed by any means short of the full power of government. By the mid-nineteen sixties it had become evident that the nature and the extent of the problems to be solved in shaping the environment upon ecological principles required a more responsible and more effective public environmental administration.

Environmental quality as a social policy is therefore the result of many specific dissatisfactions with ways in which man/environment relationships have been managed in modern society. In specific political controversies (control of pesticides, or highway construction through the national parks, for example), many of the groups organized to promote conservation, public health, or natural beauty play mutually supportive roles without any formalized co-operative relationship. In attacking specific environmental issues, this shifting pattern of informal collaboration can be a strength. Somewhat varying sectors of the public are mobilized, according to the nature of the issue. This flexibility tends to produce a vigorous popular involvement focused on specific public questions and is one of the more effective aspects of democratic self-government.

Unfortunately, these combinations for civic action do not cover all man's environmental needs. There are, of course, other movements and organizations that extend the range of popular concern over the state of the environment. Among these organizations are those established to promote urban and regional planning. In 1966 and 1967, for example, the American Institute of Planners sponsored, with the co-operation of a number of other civic organizations, two major conferences on the shaping of man's environmental relationships.[34] But the public planning movement tends to be more professional than popular in its membership, and unlike conservation, health, and beauty, the objectives are more in the nature of means to ends than of ends in themselves. Even so, in a society in which technical knowledge and skill are gaining in importance, the planning movement also gains significance. Much of its philosophy and technique would be indispensable to a comprehensive program of environmental administration.

Related in some respects to the planners have been the civic-improvement groups, some organized on a city-wide basis, some covering metropolitan areas, and others confined to neighborhoods. The impact of these groups is largely on local government, and quality of the environment in a general sense is not always a matter of primary concern. Civic and neighborhood groups are often effective in local political battles on specific environmental issues. But they do not easily make common cause with others engaged in similar battles in other neighborhoods or other cities. Except as they may have caused citizens to become more alert to environmental issues generally, these groups do not seem to have contributed significantly to an aggregate nationwide influence on behalf of environmental quality. More promising are more recent local organizations formed specifically for environmental-policy purposes. The Long Island Environmental Council, in New York State, is one of these bodies with the voluntary support of individuals, business firms, and other organized groups.[35] The Environmental Defense Fund is another type of organization that, although nationwide in its operations, co-operates with local volunteer groups in bringing legal action to bear on threats to the quality of the environment.[36] Similarly, the Conservation Law Society of America was organized to provide the services of a legal staff to research and accumulate the laws, decisions, and other precedents relating to conservation problems; to advise conservation groups on the basis of such research; and to represent these groups in court when necessary.[37]

Man is involved with his environment both as producer and as consumer. Environmental quality, in so far as it concerns food supply, living space, health, recreation, and beauty, is of interest to man primarily as a consumer. Producer interests in the environment are specialized, focused on the production of specific products—foods, fibers, minerals, equipment, and services. All share in the "consumption" of the environment, and here the old proverb that "what is everybody's business is nobody's business" seems to apply. Environmental quality as a social issue shares the political weaknesses of consumer issues generally.

Three centuries of effort to transform the American wilderness into a productive industrial economy has left a national bias strongly inclined toward producers' interests. Although the number of people directly engaged in making the environment produce material wealth is now only a small proportion of the total population, the folk ethic of American politics is still dominated by the values and assumptions that prevailed in the age of Jefferson, when the vast majority of Americans drew their living directly from the land. Sustaining this bias in favor of producers is the concentration of influence and of money that they are able to mobilize when their interests appear to be threatened. Thus, economic interests in farms, lumber, oil, mines, transportation, and electric power all maintain tax-deductible economists, legal counsel, and lobbyists to protect and advance their objectives. In contrast, the sometimes tax-exempt environmental-quality groups must depend for support upon the generosity or idealism of individuals who have no direct economic stake in the controversy, and for whom personal involvement means time taken from job, family, and friends. Can environmental quality, then, be more than a vaguely defined social issue with which an inchoate diversity of essentially consumer-oriented groups are differentially concerned?

At least three conditions must be realized in order to give the environmental-quality concept political strength. First, there must be a more cohesive agreement among groups presently concerned with the state of the environment as to the

goals and tasks of environmental policy and the mutual responsibilities of organized groups in the realization of these
goals. Following from this first condition is the second, that
there must be a clearer and more widely diffused concept of
environmental quality than is now generally prevalent. The
third condition is that the structure of public policy making
must be adapted to permit an adequate consideration of policy alternatives in relation to the environment. The structure
of public policy making in this context implies the entire functional structure, non-governmental as well as governmental.

The first and third of these prerequisites for political effectiveness relate primarily to organization and to administrative
action. They will be dealt with in greater detail in Parts II
and III, concerned with the tasks and management of environmental administration. The second of these prerequisites, the integrative concept that provides the rationale for
inter-group co-operation and for governmental reorganization, is the subject of the chapter that follows.

By the end of the nineteen sixties these prerequisites had
been realized to a degree that enabled a report from the
United States Public Health Service to declare that ". . . the
environmental problem is a substantive issue of major public
concern, not only in the United States, but throughout the
world."[38] Yet the issue could be described in colloquial language as a "sleeper"; its significance, popular support, and
ultimate potential being largely overlooked by much of the
ostensible leadership structure of the country—including most
of the social scientists whose competence presumably extends
to identifying social trends. Explanation for this myopia toward the environment as a social issue is perhaps to be found
in the conventional assumptions prevalent in both the academic world and the higher echelons of government and
business. It was an intuitive sensing of widespread popular desire, and not the counsel and endorsement of important people nor the pressure of political activists, which moved the
Ninety-first Congress to bi-partisan adoption of the National
Environmental Policy Act of 1969.

3

ENVIRONMENTAL QUALITY:
AN INTEGRATIVE CONCEPT

Controversies over the appropriation and use of resources in the environment characteristically have been fought on a case-to-case basis and only seldom with effective consideration of the fundamental issues. The consequence has been massive environmental deterioration despite occasional victories for environmental quality. But a comprehensive and unified environmental quality can provide this basis if the meaning of "quality" can be made substantive and explicit. Derived from the life sciences and in particular from ecology, its symbolic expression would be "Spaceship Earth," its focus the maintenance of a life-sustaining and life-enriching environment as a fundamental public responsibility. But to be operational, "environmental quality" must be referenced to objective criteria by which the state of the environment can be measured in relation to demonstrable human needs and preferences. Only in this way can the quality concept be both evaluative and integrative and thus provide a coherent basis for public policy.

All intentional action is guided by some vision or concept. Ideas, or that special class of ideas called "concepts," have changed man's perspective on the world and its events, and have shaped the transformation of nations. In changing man's perspective on reality, new concepts have altered the expression of old values, and values have themselves been changed under the pressure of events seen in new perspectives.

Efforts to govern man's behavior in relation to the environment necessarily involve control over a wide range of common forms of human activities—notably in agriculture, business, natural-resources development, transportation, and in the adjudication of disputes through law. Environmental *policy* is, by definition, an aspect of politics. In its more general meaning, politics is a contest to control the decision-making process in the governing institutions of a community. The political community may range in size from village to superstate, but the essential elements of the political process do not change, even though the forms through which they find expression vary considerably. Policies that express the intentions of politically dominant groups or combinations are intermediate products of political action. These policies are the guiding decisions to which the more specific decisions of organizations and individuals are expected to conform. If these subdecisions and the pursuant action fail to correspond to the actual values of the community, then the formal policies are merely those of the government of the day, and their administration will probably encounter difficulties in obtaining popular compliance. The really significant public policy, whether formalized or tacit, is that which actually influences the behavior of people. In so tangible a matter as the state of the environment, the policies, if any, that determine what *actually* happens are those most accurately described as the "true" public policies.[1]

In large, complex, and rapidly changing societies, it is seldom easy to determine exactly what policy prevails on a given social issue. This is especially true of public policy relative to the environment, because of the large number of activities and interests that affect man/environment relationships and the changing character of circumstances. The texts of laws or of judicial decisions seldom provide a complete picture of how a policy is interpreted. What people actually believe and do are essential parts of public policy as it is defined in this book, and popular attitudes and behavior are frequently contradictory, necessitating explicit and implied exceptions to general policy statements. The most powerful unifying force behind a policy, other than a perception of imminent danger, is a commonly shared, simple, persuasive idea. To be commonly shared and persuasive, the idea or concept must relate directly to the perceived "needs" of people. The time must be right for the idea, and the idea must fit the "needs" of the time. The most effective governmental policies are those that embody such widely accepted integrative ideas, and these policies are strongest when the integrative ideas represent a substantial consensus of the community.

AN INTEGRATIVE VIEW OF ENVIRONMENTAL RELATIONSHIPS

The absence of a common view of the human environment and of how man should relate to it has been a major obstacle to public environmental policy. Realistically, near unanimity on the varied aspects of so large and complex a subject is not to be expected. Yet there must be some underlying consensus in opinion or belief before communities can act on any proposition. The preceding chapter was largely an account of how several environment-related social issues developed as potential components of a general environmental policy. That they had not combined earlier to form such a policy may be in very large part attributed to the lack of a catalytic agent— in this case an integrative concept that could provide the flux that could make each of these presently separate aspects of social policy parts of a larger, comprehensive policy of environmental quality.

There may be skeptics who doubt that such an integrative concept is feasible. It may be argued that man/environment relationships embrace almost everything; and to have a policy about interactions among everything is an obvious absurdity. But from this viewpoint the problem is misread. It would be equally sensible to conclude that, because almost every human activity has economic implications, that the idea of a national economic policy is unmanageable. The problem is not to cover every aspect of economic activity or of environmental relationships in some monstrous code of laws and regulations. That task would be impossible and could not be a feasible objective. The goals of environmental policy would be to formulate the principles by which, through various means, the multitude of man/environment relationships could be guided.

Critics of the idea of environmental administration tend to overlook the processes of generalization and subdivision through which public affairs are governed in a pluralistic, decentralized, democratic society. The scientific approach to organization and management may increase the effectiveness of public administration, but an important part of the process

of policy application can still be described in the words of
Thomas Jefferson, who wrote: "In government, as well as
every other business of life; it is by division and sub-division
of duties alone, that all matters, great and small, can be managed to perfection."[2] And it also still seems reasonable to
believe, as Jefferson did, ". . . that government to be the
strongest of which every man feels himself a part."[3]

An integrative concept for the administration of man/en-
vironment relationships is one that will identify the concern
common to all men in the condition of the environment, and
in so doing will provide a basis upon which disagreements
can be resolved. The need is for a concept that will provide a
new set of boundaries within which political maneuvering can
occur without endangering the stake that all men have in the
state of their environment. In the absence of such a concept,
it is difficult to see how government can cope effectively with
the growing number and urgency of environment-related
problems.

Many ways of understanding man/environment relationships no longer correspond to contemporary realities. In contrast to times past, the realities have become more exceptional,
more interrelated, and more dynamic, not only because the
environment has changed, but because the ways in which men
relate to the environment and depend upon it have multiplied.
The generally unfavorable consequences of segmental or dis-
parate policies with respect to the environment increase at
least proportionately to man's ever-increasing demands upon
it. The holistic outlook, advocated in the nineteen twenties by
Jan Christiaan Smuts,[4] has today become a practical necessity. The technical function of the integrative concept is,
therefore, to make manageable a holistic view of the environment.

This holistic, or comprehensive, view of environmental relationships is in the nature of surveillance, or "map making,"
rather than of management or operations. An objective of the
holistic approach is to define the dimensions of the comprehensive tasks of environment administration so as to make
them manageable (i.e. comprehensible)—to guide the operating programs so that they are effective and do not counteract
one another. A second objective is to avoid the dangers of in-

advertent drift, which may carry a program away from its intended purposes. The process of day-to-day, incremental decision making, sometimes called "muddling through," is especially vulnerable to errors that result from too narrow or too short-range a perspective.[5] In defense of muddling through, it may be argued that when the wisest course of action is not clear it is better to make small incremental errors than to risk colossal mistakes from comprehensive planning that attempts to project policy beyond the time horizon of safe conjecture.[6] With respect to the environment, however, it is comprehensiveness of surveillance that is needed. Planning need be no more comprehensive than the environmental problem requires (or permits). The justification for comprehensiveness extends only so far as it enables the planner or administrator to minimize inadvertent errors of commission *and* omission.

Conceivably, unintended results may be beneficial as well as harmful. But as with genetic mutations, the inadvertent consequences of ad hoc environmental policy are seldom in the public interest. This may be because to any set of problems there are infinitely more wrong answers than right ones. The holistic, or integrative, overview, assuming that it is valid —that it is faithful to reality—serves a preventative or a corrective function. It helps to protect the administrator from locking onto a course of action in which one thing leads to another, and the end result, reached by logical, step-by-step decisions, is neither the goal originally sought nor one presently desired. The concept of holistic surveillance does not preclude short-range tactical decisions, nor does it prevent day-to-day program adjustments to accommodate changing circumstances. It simply increases the prospect that these pragmatic, disjunctive administrative acts will ultimately add up to the attainment of intended and beneficial policy objectives.

QUALITY AS A FEASIBLE CONCEPT

As noted in Chapter 2, the expression "environmental quality" came into common use during the nineteen sixties, and for the time being appears to be the linguistic vehicle

most readily available to carry into public life the concept of
public responsibility for the state of the environment.

The term "environmental quality" has the advantage of
subsuming the more traditional and specialized aspect of
public environmental policy and thus serving an integrative
function. But is it the only or the best concept available? An
answer to this question begins with an examination of the
merits of the environmental-quality concept itself, and especially of the meaning of the word "quality." There is a semantic bias in the expression "environmental quality"; it tends
to focus attention on the substance of the environment itself
rather than upon man's behavior in relation to it. This is
partly a matter of linguistic convenience. Our use of language
is filled with shorthand expressions, usually abstractions to
facilitate the expression of our thoughts. When, for example,
the expressions "environmental administration" and "environmental management" are used in this book, it is not so much
the direct actions upon the environment that are implied;
these expressions refer rather to the guidelines and controls
over the actions of men. The environment is managed primarily through the management of men—by self-management,
by corporate management, or by governmental management.
Direct changes in the environment itself are the work of
farmers, miners, engineers, and all who use the environment
in ways that alter its patterns of relationship or self-renewal.

There is one important difference, however, between an
environmental concept that focuses on behavior and one that
focuses on substance. Purely substantive concepts incur a
higher risk of utopianism, in the sense that they too often
fail to formulate a feasible operational connection between
the present state of the environment, its ideal state, and the
probable behavior of men. They are also vulnerable to
changes in knowledge or in material circumstances that might,
for example, make quality mean one thing to one generation
of men and another thing to another generation separated
from the first by time or culture. There is also danger that,
in an anti-utopian effort to be practical, qualitative standards
for the environment might be set unnecessarily low.

The validity and operational feasibility of qualitative standards for the substance of the environment depend greatly

on how the standards would be obtained. It is evident that men seek to realize many differing values in the environment. Personal standards of environmental quality differ widely and are often highly subjective. In the open, democratic, pluralistic American society, any feasible standard of environmental quality must accommodate as much variety as this cosmopolitan society demands. It may, indeed, wisely provide for more variety than the society presently demands, as an investment on behalf of future needs and opportunities.

It is not necessary to have actual standards of environmental quality in order to have a policy to the effect that it is a public responsibility to establish and administer such standards. But if they are to be applicable and their application to be justified by generally beneficial results, the standards must be based on objective and reliable knowledge of man's needs in relation to the environment. This kind of knowledge is called scientific, and the science primarily concerned with it is called ecology.[7]

Ecology is a logical source of scientific environmental standards, but it does not provide all of them nor provide them ready-made for the political decision maker. In some respects, ecology is a middleman science, gathering data from other sciences and synthesizing the findings regarding the systematic relationships that ultimately link all living things together in the planetary biosphere.[8] Original investigations are, of course, undertaken by ecologists. But ecology is almost uniquely fitted to occupy the field of learning between the physical and biological sciences on the one hand and the social and behavioral sciences on the other. Among the present-day disciplines, geography and psychology share this position.[9]

Environmental-quality standards tend to reflect cultural values, which may or may not be influenced by scientific knowledge. But if their application is to improve the condition of the environment, they must be consistent with scientific facts. Unfortunately, ecology has been an underdeveloped science, for reasons related to those that explain the underdeveloped state of public policy in relation to the environment. We see evidence in abundance that industrial man has seldom known how to relate to his environment

without impairing or destroying it. From ecology, we may
hopefully obtain the knowledge that will enable us to manage
our environmental relationships in ways that will satisfy our
needs and permit continuing satisfaction from an environment
that is self-sustaining and self-renewing. Environmental quality is a feasible concept around which to develop public policy, provided that the standards of quality are derived from
ecology or at least are consistent with verified ecological
knowledge.

Acceptance of the feasibility of "environmental quality"
as an integrative focus for public policy does not preclude
the possibility that preferable alternatives may be developed.
The traditional areas of environment-related public policy described in the preceding chapter (conservation, health, natural
beauty, and planning) are in a sense a composite alternative.
Even though they do not provide a common focus for public policy, they might be brought into a co-ordinated relationship for administrative purposes solely on the basis of their
common relatedness to the human environment. Yet as we
have seen, mere concern with some aspect of the environment has not in itself afforded a compelling argument for
interagency co-operation in government, or for a general
public policy to guide agency action. Social and political issues do not arise out of the simple fact of environmental
relatedness, but are generated by the "how" of this relatedness. The quality concept has the merit of being extensible
to almost every aspect of man/environment relationships, but
to have a common meaning, the word "quality" must be
given a common content. We have indicated the science of
ecology as the primary source of this content. Why not, then,
seek an integrative concept for the environmental responsibilities of society directly in the subject matter of ecology? Is
it useful to try to cope with the problem of giving substantive
meaning to "environmental quality" if the substance of quality can be identified directly?

AN ECOLOGICAL BASIS FOR ENVIRONMENTAL POLICY

If ecology must provide much of the substantive content
of environmental quality, the question of the adequacy of

ecology for this task logically follows. Applications of ecological knowledge to environmental management will be discussed at length in Chapter 7, "Environmental Management as Applied Science." Our concern with ecology in this chapter is with its adequacy as a source of organizing concepts. It is not feasible to attempt an enumeration of all ecological concepts of direct relevance to public environmental policy. A basic ecological concept, however, concerns the self-maintaining character of dynamic natural systems, and it is this aspect of ecology that is of greatest general relevance to environmental policy.

The popular version of this systems concept has been the "balance of nature" idea. The balance concept in science is not the oversimplified interpretation sometimes encountered in popular writings. It is moving equilibrium, or dynamic homeostasis. In physiology, this concept summarizes the "condition" of an organism that takes in energy-producing materials, processes them to maintain itself and to provide energy for its behavior, and extrudes waste products. The organism may be active, growing, and competing with other organisms in its environment but maintaining essentially the same state of being, in relation to its competitors and its environment: This condition is also sometimes called a "steady state."[10] Homeostasis might perhaps better be defined as a steadying tendency than as a steady state. Unstabilizing forces are at work in and upon all organisms and systems—most fundamentally those summarized by the second law of thermodynamics. But because of the stabilizing tendency, organisms and organizations retain coherent form and resist disintegrating influences for a time sufficient to perform whatever functions are necessary to their continuing existence.

In ecology, the homeostasis concept is extended to a systematically interrelated world of organisms converting inorganic matter into living energy through complex food chains leading from life forms that can draw sustenance directly from sunlight, water, and minerals, through myriad plant and animal species. The sum total of these interrelationships, which in the aggregate are infinitely complex, is called the planetary ecosystem. There are, of course, a vast number of specific ecosystems, interrelating and overlapping, and yet preserving a degree of stability that makes it possible for us to recognize a specific environment day after day and year after year. But although the ecosystem is in balance in the short run, it is nevertheless in constant change. Over periods of geologic time, changes have occurred that have completely transformed the surface of the Earth. Even the composition of the atmosphere is believed to have changed since the appearance of living organisms. It has been further changed by man himself since the mass use of internal combustion engines began. Thus the balance of nature concept implies neither a static world nor one in perfect equilibrium. In some respects, the ecosystem is always out of balance; it is the particular character and degree of imbalance, the possible consequences of the imbalance, and the costs and conditions of the maintenance or restoration of relative stability that are of practical concern to man.

The concept of dynamic homeostasis underlies or is related to almost every proposition or theory in ecology. It has been reinforced in recent years by findings and hypotheses growing out of cybernetics and general-systems theory. In the systems sciences, including ecology, theories of stress in systems, of oscillations, of control mechanisms, and of the utilization of information have been developed for many different forms of organizations; and comparable processes among organizations and systems have been observed.[11] Relatively few of these systems studies are of human societies. In time, more-effective ways to study behavior of human social systems will probably be developed. The present state of social and behavioral science is not yet adequate to give us the kind of information needed to guide the behavior of men in relation to their ecosystems in ways that would insure, as far as human insurance is possible, the continuing viability and self-renewal of the human environment. It would nevertheless seem wise to make the best use of what we already know while endeavoring to extend our understanding of human ecology.

The extraordinary adaptability of man, and his exceptional ability to manipulate his environment and to substitute one set of conditions for another, contribute to the difficulty of assessing the consequences to human society of changes in its ecosystems. The outcomes of ecosystems change are more difficult to predict for man than for the many living species that have relatively short life spans and may be studied in statistically significant numbers under control conditions. Our knowledge of ecosystems behavior is therefore based more upon observation of insects, birds, rodents, ungulates, and primates than upon information regarding human animals. The applicability of these observations to human behavior has been questioned by social scientists wary of reasoning by analogy, and by technologists confident of man's ability to manipulate his environmental relationships. It has been denied by those persons whose religious beliefs place man outside nature.

The inadequacy of our knowledge of human ecology based directly and explicitly on verifiable studies of human behavior may be explained, in part, by the way learning has been organized in our society. Except in relation to physiology and disease, the biological sciences have not primarily concerned themselves with man. The social sciences, heavily influenced by their origins in moral philosophy, law, and the humanities, have largely avoided the biophysical factors in human behavior. There has thus been a gap in the structure of knowledge that none of the older scientific disciplines have considered it their responsibility to bridge. If the thesis of this book is valid, it is important that the gap between the present state of the biological and social sciences be closed, and ecology appears to be the discipline most likely to accomplish this task. But the need for the growth of ecological knowledge does not necessarily mean that it will happen. In part, the undeveloped state of ecology (particularly the study of man/environment relationships) is attributable to a lack of popular understanding of the need for the growth of this field of knowledge. But, more importantly, leaders in the world of science and education have not heretofore considered it of major importance, at least not relative to many other fields of knowledge.

It is not easy, even for the scientist, to escape the non-scientific implicit assumptions of the society into which he is born and within which he lives. Language itself, infused with prescientific concepts, can easily channel the scientist, along with everyone else, into built-in perceptual error. As

J. H. Woodger has pointed out, the concept of environment is particularly susceptible to the tricks that language plays upon thought.[12] The tacit assumption of a natural environment is so deeply imbedded in thought and language that the significance of its presence is easily overlooked. Terms such as heredity and environment have been treated as separate and distinct factors in life processes, in disregard of the fact that the concept "heredity" embodies the assumption of a suitable environment.

Religious thought, and especially Christianity, has tended to separate man from his earthly environment, but not from an environment of some kind. The separability of man from Earth was a theological concept, and the universality of a tolerable, although not necessarily agreeable, environment was assured by divine intent. Wherever there were men, whether on Earth, in heaven, or in hell, there was an environment in which the human personality, in some form, could exist. The separability of man from the earthly environment was, however, seldom joined to the equally valid proposition that the Earth was separable from man. Theologies pictured the world as created for man; they had no reason to postulate environments or, more precisely, natural conditions totally unrelated to man or to his destiny.

Not until the time of Darwin did men begin to perceive the meaning of vast geologic epochs in a world without man. This meaning, reaffirmed by the discovery and probing of outer space, was that all life, including the life of man, is contingent upon the fitness of the environment. The logical inference, not always drawn, however, is that there is a direct relationship between the state of man's environment and his present and future welfare. As more has been learned about the environments of the past and of those in outer space, the present environmental conditions on the Earth appear to be most exceptional. Space probes of Mars and Venus have indicated that the probability of environments on these planets that would be suitable for man is very low. The statistical probability of environmental conditions throughout the universe comparable to those of the Earth is of little practical relevance to the welfare of human society. No extraterrestrial environments suitable for men have as yet been discovered.

Except as man contrives artificial environments in outer space, the environment of the Earth is the only suitable one that he has any present prospect of experiencing. This means that human society is confined within a finite ecosystem. For a long time to come, the finite Earth will be an indispensable base for whatever alternative environments may be contrived in outer space.[13]

Before human populations occupied all of the readily inhabitable niches on the Earth, man's environment had a semblance of infinity. Human societies could follow a course of milpa culture—moving from place to place, exploiting the environment, and moving on.[14] Prehistoric human stress on the environment was seldom so severe or so prolonged as to destroy its capacity for self-renewal. In historic times, however, multiplication of populations of man and of his domesticated animals, and the advent of agriculture and of urbanism, increased the stress on the environment and continued the duration of localized pressures of human use until, in many cases, irreversible environmental changes occurred. Plant and animal species frequently disappeared, becoming extinct or being displaced by other species. Geological processes of land erosion were accelerated. In modern times, toxins and waste products of industrialized societies have been allowed to flow into the ecosystem with effects that often threaten its capacity for life support or self-renewal.

The customary method of dealing with undesirable environmental conditions has been to move away from them. But with the occupancy in some form of nearly all habitable space, this historic practice has rapidly become less feasible. Slowly, but inevitably, human societies are being compelled to face the implications of life in a finite ecosystem.[15] They can no longer afford to remain indifferent to their relationships with the environment, because their stress upon it, their exactions from it, and their reshaping of it to satisfy immediate objectives alter its capacity to respond to present and future demands. The responsive capacity of environments may in some respects be improved, as through well-considered efforts in agriculture and engineering. But impairment of the environment has been the more frequent result of human enterprise. The present-day prognosis of endless increase in

demands upon a finite environment does not suggest an indefinite increase in human welfare. On the contrary, if the
present state of ecological knowledge has valid application
to human societies, man/environment relations are dangerously out of balance over large parts of the Earth, and ecological disaster is more than a theoretical possibility for large
numbers of mankind.[16]

Modern man has let himself into a game of ecological
truth or environmental consequences. If he ignores or mis-
reads the ecological facts of life, he must endure the consequences of existence in an environment that can no longer
respond adequately to his needs. In plainer language, the
penalties for ecological ignorance include impoverishment in
all respects—crowding, lack of privacy and of many other
personal freedoms, deficiency diseases and behavioral ab-
normalities, and perhaps the loss of the will to be civilized
or even to endure life's miseries. Prophecies of gloom and
doom are seldom well received. The successes of modern
technology encourage optimistic assumptions that human ingenuity will find ways to permit man to evade the penalties
that would otherwise be exacted for exploitation of his environment. But no evidence confirms the belief that evasion
can be continued indefinitely, and meanwhile the "technological fix" may exact costs of its own.

A great deal of public law and policy rest upon assumptions that are unverified by history or by science. Yet the argument that what holds true for ecological relationships
throughout nature generally might be assumed, in the absence
of contradictory evidence, to be applicable to man, is often
decried on the grounds that "man is different." The adverse
effects that follow from unlimited growth, crowding, or social
instability among animal populations afford more empirically
demonstrable bases for human population policy than are,
for example, available to support the belief that every man is
entitled to an opportunity for remunerative employment or
that plural marriage is socially undesirable. The cavil that
optimum levels of human population or of population densities and of the stress upon the natural environment have not
been established through science does not seem sufficient
reason to reject guidance from the more pertinent knowledge

available, even though that knowledge is not conclusive for all classes of animals, including man. The indications of ecology, even in its present underdeveloped state, are clear enough to justify a course of caution until our understanding affords a more reliable basis for policy choices. But this counsel is hardly more helpful than "look before you leap." It becomes operational only when one knows what to look for. Specific indicators of danger to the environment are needed to implement environmental policy. But the general tendency or direction of change may also be estimated and would be better than an indiscriminate commitment to "progress," or to the assumption that man can satisfactorily adapt to almost anything.

The concept of environmental stability, which implies a continuing process of environmental dynamic homeostasis or of self-renewal appears, in some respects, to be a feasible alternative to environmental quality as a focus for policy. Stability is no less a tangible concept than quality; it is more objectively definable and hence more easily measured. It is a concept based almost wholly on science, however, and does not seem to provide a convenient standard for qualitative differences defined by artistic or cultural perception. An environmental policy that afforded no basis for aesthetic judgment would not be adequate to cover an important aspect of man/environment relationships. But it would be presumptuous to assert that aesthetic values have no basis in human biology or psychology merely because causal connections have not been clearly established. At present, however, science is generally unable to substantiate aesthetic judgment, and the aesthetic aspect of environmental policy must rest largely upon other grounds. But not exclusively so. In so far as diversity and stability, for example, are general aesthetic values, ecology tends to support aesthetic judgment. Monocrop agriculture, carried to extremes, may be unsatisfying aesthetically, and it is unstable ecologically.[17] Many of the complementary relationships among plants, animals, and their environments that seem aesthetically satisfying to man, also, in the main, represent "good" ecological balance.

Of course, not all ecological relationships are aesthetically satisfying to all men. Nor are all of them ethically pleasing.

The mystery and grandeur of life include predation, death, and decay. Man does face an intellectual and moral dichotomy in his need to accept nature as it is and his desire to change those aspects that affront his sense of purpose, justice, or compassion. Man can imagine a "better world" than the one in which he lives. But it is not certain that he would be happy in any world that he could create unless man himself were changed into a very different creature.

SPACESHIP EARTH, AN ECOLOGICAL MODEL

Among alternative concepts upon which to base a public policy for man/environment relationships, that which is the most fundamental and therefore the most inclusive would in most senses come closest to being the best. It would be best because it would afford the most reliable guidance to specific legislative and administrative action; it would enlarge the area of common ground upon which specific political differences over environment-related questions could be decided. In a manner analogous to the so-called laws of science, the integrative power of a concept grows in direct relationship to its universality and essential simplicity. The spaceship has the properties of such a concept and provides a framework for systematically interrelating ecological and environmental-quality considerations in an operational context.

What are the ideas that the spaceship integrates into one comprehensible image? The essential ideas are these: The spaceship (Earth) is a unified system dependent upon the co-ordinated and continued functioning of interrelating systems and parts. It has surpluses, redundancy, and backup capacity, but its resources are nevertheless limited. Because carrying capacity is one of its limits, it must so far as possible recycle its resources unless it can obtain them at feasible cost from external sources. Changes in the system must be studied in relation to their total effects, because altered relationships among the parts, even intended improvements, may adversely affect the performance of the whole. Maintenance of the system and its subsystems must be watched, for failure at any critical point could lead to the destruction of the entire enterprise.

To a visitor from another planet, it would probably seem strange that circumstances so obviously important to human welfare should have so seldom been perceived as a matter of public concern. To us, it does not seem strange that fish show no evidence of concern regarding their relationship to the sea, for they have no way to conceptualize that relationship or to influence its development. But an intelligent visitor from outer space would be able to see man as man can see the fish—as absolutely dependent upon the continuation of a very delicately balanced and exceptional set of ecological conditions that are statistically very rare throughout the universe. Unlike the fish, however, the human animal has learned to temporarily circumvent natural ecological controls governing his numbers and behavior. He can and does manipulate his environment, and unlike most fish, he can and has destroyed its viability at particular times and places.

Human society has now reached a point in population growth and technological skill at which it can destroy the viability of the environment in a dramatic nuclear holocaust, or more slowly, but just as surely, through unwise ecological behavior in ordinary affairs. To the extraterrestrial observer, man might appear as a clever savage, technologically ingenious but as unself-conscious as a fish in relation to his ecological situation. This ecological innocence, harmless in fish, is dangerous in men. Rambunctious adolescent naïveté and a powerful, science-based technology are poorly matched companions. There being no prospect of a return to a more primitive technology, the only rational alternative remaining to man is to become less primitive in his relationships with nature. But until the advent of the space age, man had no means for taking himself out of his ecosystem and viewing it with an approximation of the objectivity of a visitor from outer space. Imaginative individuals have been able to do this, but, for the mass of people and their leaders, a simple, tangible, and attention-compelling symbol of man's ecological relationships appears to be a necessary prelude to ecological maturity.

The spaceship may provide this symbol. Now, for the first time, man has viewed his natural ecosystem from afar. To explore outer space, he has had to contrive an environment that conforms to the essential parameters of his life processes as circumscribed by nature. He has therefore had to learn the extent to which his psychophysiological make-up can tolerate variations in temperature, humidity, gravity, sound, light, and cosmic radiation. Space exploration has prompted research into human tolerances with respect to abnormal environmental conditions. For example, the effects of isolation, close confinement, abnormal diets, and continuously programmed behavior are highly pertinent to the success of space missions.[18] But all these factors have relevance to life on Earth; in the spaceship, they appear in sharp and simplified profile. The laws of nature are the same in space and on Earth, and the needs of man hold constant, although when the parameters of the environment are changed, as on the surface of the Moon, the requirements for survival and capabilities of man are changed in certain respects also.

In the spaceship, we have, at last, an operational microcosm. It is not a true facsimile of the Earth, but in greatly simplified form, it illustrates relationships between man and his environment that are basic to his welfare and survival. Ecological facts that man prefers to evade on Earth are universally acknowledged for the spaceship. For example, no one doubts that there is a limit to the number of passengers that the ship can accommodate, and the need for reserve capacity to meet unforeseeable contingencies is not questioned. It is obvious that the spaceship cannot indefinitely transform its nutrients into waste. If extruded from the ship as waste, energy sources are irretrievably lost; if accumulated as waste, the viability of the ship is ultimately destroyed from within. There is no escape from the necessity of recycling waste materials. For the duration of its voyage, the ship must remain in ecological balance. Disruption of any of its systems may mean disaster for the mission and the crew. Systems maintenance is therefore one of the essential components of a program of space exploration.

The demands of the artificial ecosystem of the spaceship upon human attention and effort afford an instructive contrast to the far less severe maintenance demands of natural systems.[19] A recurring point of emphasis in this book is the great advantage man enjoys in the automatic operations of a self-renewing natural environment. Work is required to obtain the benefits of a natural system, but only in the event of localized disasters or exhaustion of the environment by human abuse, is human effort required to keep it going. In so far as artificial systems and environments liberate man from the greater efforts that would otherwise be necessary to cope with natural conditions, their contribution to human welfare offsets their maintenance costs. For massive shifts from natural to artificial environments, however, a realistic assessment of advantage would attempt to weigh the costs of maintenance (including alternative allocations of effort) against the benefits of the artificial ecosystem. If man can devise indefinitely self-maintaining artificial ecosystems, he will, of course, have achieved an enormous technical advantage in the shaping of his preferred environmental conditions. The prospect of this accomplishment on any scale other than one of great simplicity and restricted size seems at present no more plausible than the achievement of perpetual motion.

The analogy between the Earth and the manned space vehicle has become readily apparent to thoughtful observers. In his final remarks before the Economic and Social Council of the United Nations, Adlai Stevenson, retiring ambassador from the United States, spoke of human interdependency in relation to the planetary environment: "We travel together, passengers on a little spaceship, dependent on its vulnerable reserves of air and soil: all committed for our safety to its security and peace; preserved from annihilation only by the care, and the work, and I will say the love we give our fragile craft."[20]

The spaceship analogy has been employed by economists Barbara Ward[21] (with respect to international affairs) and Kenneth Boulding[22] (with respect to economic and ecological relationships). Margaret Mead employed a functional variant of the spaceship in an article entitled "The Island Earth."[23] She wrote of the moon-landings of 1969 that "mankind. . . . saw the earth in all its isolated diversity. . . . an island in space. The earth seen from the moon was a whole in a new sense, no longer simulated by a globe, but seen whole."[24] It is plausible that the lunar explorations of 1968–69 exercised a subtle but powerful effect upon American and indeed upon worldwide perception of man's environmental situation. Had there not been an Apollo Program there might not have been a National Environmental Policy Act in 1969.

Nevertheless the spiritual and intellectual implications of space exploration troubled the theologian Paul Tillich. He believed space exploration to be, in principle, desirable and to hold potential for an enlarged spirituality in man. But he foresaw a psychological effect of the view of Earth from outer space that appears to differ from the thesis developed in this chapter. Commenting on the spiritual consequences of space exploration, he wrote:

> "One of the results of the flight into space and the possibility of looking down at the earth is a kind of estrangement between man and earth, an 'objectification' of the earth for man, the depriving 'her' of her 'motherly' character, her power of giving birth, of nourishing, of embracing, of keeping for herself, of calling back to herself. She becomes a large, material body to be looked at and considered as totally calculable. The process of demythologizing the earth which started with the early philosophers and was continued ever since in the Western world has been radicalized as never before. It is too early to realize fully the spiritual consequences of this step."[25]

The inference in the observations of Paul Tillich is that the objectification of the Earth may cause man to view the Earth as he views his spaceship—nothing more than a physical object to be manipulated for his convenience by science-based technology. This outcome, however, is not what present experience would seem to indicate. The American astronauts of Apollo 9 were moved by the sight of the Earth rising above the horizon of the Moon on Christmas Eve 1968 to recall the poetic description of the creation in the Book of Genesis, and Anne Lindbergh, in writing of their adventure, spoke of the new sense of responsibility that the view from space should bring to man on Earth:

> "No one, it has been said, will ever look at the Moon in the same way again. Far more truly can one say that no one will ever look at the Earth in the same way. Man had to sever his umbilical cord to Earth to perceive both its diminutive place in a solar system and its unestimable value as a life-fostering

planet. As earthmen, we may have taken another step into adulthood. We can see our parent Earth with detachment, with tenderness, with some shame and pity, but at last also with love. With adult love comes responsibility. We begin to realize how utterly we are Earth's children. We can accept our responsibility to Earth, and our heritage from it, which we must protect if we are to survive."[26]

Even persons insensitive to ecology might also be persuaded by the view from space to adopt a more responsible attitude toward the Earth. Men have lavished loving care upon mechanical objects—antique automobiles, for example, and endowed them poetically with personal attributes that they knew in fact were fictions. Men have "religiously" maintained mechanical systems when they understood the necessity. If the Earth has been man's mother, man has often proved to be an ungrateful son, capable indeed of matricide. The alienation of man from Earth has been most effectively accomplished by otherworldly or anti-natural interpretations of Christian theology. If man gave Earth the careful, calculated care he gives his spaceship, there would be a greatly reduced need for concern over the future viability of man/environment relationships. But if the spaceship model were applied to terrestrial life and if environmental quality were defined in ecological terms, far-reaching changes in society and government would necessarily follow.

To spell out what these changes might be would require another book, and not all effects of this reorientation would be foreseeable. There is deep and wide division between the assumptions of a Spaceship Earth philosophy and those that have been dominant throughout three centuries of American history. There also appears to be a widening gap between public expectations and the performance of government and the economy on environmental-quality issues. Federal pronouncements and promises have not been effectively implemented. In effect, science and government have shown the people that their welfare is threatened, and have convinced them that public action can restore and protect the quality of the environment. But having done this, the implementing agents have failed to act or have acted to arouse hopes that have then been disappointed. The political situation that has resulted corresponds to the classical model for political radicalism, for a militant ideological attack upon an "establishment" in which waste, pollution, and environmental decay are inherent. Whether, in fact, the American "establishment" can transform itself to meet the circumstances of a new age, and whether or in what form a new, ecologically oriented political ideology might challenge prevailing institutions, are at this point in time conjectural.

❧ II ❧

TASKS

The variety and complexity of man/environment relationships has made it difficult for people to think about or act upon environmental problems with system, foresight, or comprehensiveness. Efforts to manage the environment have often miscarried because of inadequate understanding of the factors involved and because of failure to explore alternative methods of meeting objectives. And the complex multiplicity of man's interactions with his environment appears to exceed human capacity for formulating or administering a public policy for their governance. In this view, the only feasible method for dealing with environmental problems would be either case by case or upon the basis of arbitrarily defined categories of relationships. But the alternatives for public action are not restricted to choice between efforts of an unmanageable comprehensiveness on the one hand, or, on the other, a disjunctive incrementalism that fails to cope effectively with the elements of large-scale, complex ecosystems. A more feasible approach is to define the tasks of society in relation to the environment in terms of the three following ways in which man relates to his environment: (1) in dependence upon the surrounding ecosystem for the support of life itself, (2) in purposefully adapting the environment to better serve carefully evaluated needs, and (3) in shaping his cultures and thereby simultaneously reshaping his environment. Within these interrelating categories, general policies and standards can be developed to guide the specific options of men. But the tasks of formulating and applying these measures imply new duties and responsibilities for scientists, administrators, and citizens alike—and seem certain to induce new theories of social organization, law, and government.

PROTECTING THE ECOLOGICAL BASIS
OF HUMAN LIFE

Man has hitherto enjoyed the advantage of a self-renewing, automatic, life-sustaining system (the biosphere) and has been able to develop his civilizations without the necessity of devoting much of his time and effort to keeping the system going. In contrast, were he to colonize the Moon, a major task in that unviable environment would be to keep the artificial ecosystem functioning. But man's situation on Earth has been rapidly changing. His burgeoning populations and the insatiable demands of his economy and technology have begun to stress the earthly environment beyond its capacity for recovery. Environmental deterioration is becoming widespread, and the viability of the entire planetary ecosystem will be threatened if present trends continue. Protection of the ecological basis of life has therefore become a minimum essential of responsible public policy. The concept of individual human right to a safe and healthful environment is now being advanced as a point of law and a principle of international policy.

At the close of the preceding chapter, the spaceship was cited as an ecological microcosm, a highly simplified but basically valid model of the human condition on the planet Earth. In detail, there are, of course, many differences between life on Earth and life in a spaceship. But certain absolutely basic conditions govern the persistence of life in both environments. Each environment is spacially finite and can accommodate no more than a fixed number of human passengers; each environment requires a balanced recycling of nutrients and wastes; each environment has limits to the amount of stress it can tolerate without ceasing to be life supportive.

The price of survival in outer space is the maintenance of the life-sustaining capabilities of the spaceship ecosystem. On Earth, however, man has behaved as if the terrestrial spaceship were infinite in carrying capacity and in ability to absorb abuse. The conceit that science and technology give man a free hand to manipulate his environment with impunity has caused him to neglect the cumulative and long-term effects of his impact upon the Earth. Convinced that technology can bail him out of any difficulty into which he might blunder, he has not greatly concerned himself with preserving the viability of the terrestrial environment. But time is running out. Accumulating evidence records accumulative abuse of the Earth to a point, in some instances, of irreversible destruction. Man has multiplied himself and his demands upon the Earth to an extent that requires prompt and effective ecological management if his voyage through space is not to be drawn to an untimely end.

The first major task of environmental administration is therefore protection of the ecological basis of life itself. If this life-support system fails, man and all he represents fails with it. And it need not wholly fail, but only weaken at some critical point, to place man in a state of anxiety, ill health, frustration, and despair that could lead to the decline of civilization and to the bitter defeat of human hope and promise. Long before the Earth is no longer viable for man, he would, in all probability, have destroyed his kind in a dog-eat-dog struggle for control of the life-sustaining scraps and niches of an impoverished environment.

If this conjecture seems unduly dire, its plausibility may be tested by comparison with historical human behavior in competition for resources and commodities in comparative abundance. Through technological innovation, it may be increasingly possible to provide substitutes for many things in short supply, but not all resources (notably territorial space) can be simulated. To provide alternatives for all man's natural-resource needs is a very large order for technology. For many materials and commodities, no substitutes or alternatives seem possible.[1] For example, metallurgy might have provided (although it did not) a substitute for the nickel of the mines of Petsamo that Finland lost to the Soviet Union in the war of 1939–44. But technology could provide no substitute for the strategic physical space that Finland lost in the same war. This transfer of territory was a loss to one political jurisdiction and a gain to another, but there was no loss to the planetary biosphere. In the extinction of species or destruction of topsoil, an absolute loss occurs.

The relationship between territory and human population is, of course, not wholly a matter of area in relation to numbers. The carrying capacity of any area is in part determined by the technology that man applies to it and in part by his patterns of behavior. Territory adequate to sustain pastoral nomadism may be vastly greater than that required for intensive agriculture or manufacturing. But there is a point at which a given area becomes saturated with people. The fit of the environment to human society becomes tight by any criterion. Rigid personal discipline becomes necessary to permit society to function, and environmental amenities are foregone as the pressure of society on its environment continues to grow. Environmental planning gives way to improvisation in accommodating the needs of sheer numbers.[2]

If man is a territorial animal by genetic inclination, efforts to curb his territorial possessiveness through cultural conditioning may fall short of success.[3] In fact, cultural factors have usually reinforced whatever genetic predisposition to territoriality is present in human societies. Spatial preferences of human beings appear to be in part culturally conditioned, but there is also evidence of innate spatial and territorial responses in human behavior that are not dissimilar to those discovered among other animals.[4]

Evidence from the study of animal behavior and human history fails to support an expectation of continuing altruism among men where life's necessities are in short and uncertain supply.[5] Regard for social stability and civilized values might therefore be cited, in addition to the urge to survival, as justification for care and prudence in the treatment of man's terrestrial environment. Objectors may, of course, argue that we understand too little of the ecological basis of human society to presume to manage it in the public interest. Moreover, they may allege, the human animal and "mother earth" are tough and resilient and will survive disasters in the future even as they have in the past. This is specious optimism, however, because the condition of the world today resembles less and less the environments under which man moved from the Stone Age to the present. Man is, in any case, a terrestrial late-comer, and his toughness (meaning capacity to survive at all costs) has not yet been fairly tested in comparison with numbers of more ancient species—with cockroaches, for example. Moreover, man and all other organisms are not exposed to environmental hazards unexperienced in the past. The introduction of chlorinated hydrocarbons (pesticides) and radioactive isotopes (nuclear energy) into food chains and ecosystems has occurred only within the present generation. The cumulative effects of these and many other technoscientific innovations in the terrestrial biosphere have yet to be ascertained.[6] Human survival through millenniums of natural hazards is not evidence of ability to survive unprecedented, man-made ecological disasters in the future.

As for the toughness of the Earth, an examination of the universe leads to the opposing conclusion—that the terrestrial environment is indeed highly fragile.[7] The range of conditions suitable for life, especially for human life, is very narrow in comparison with the range of physical possibilities. In proportion to the magnitude of the known universe, the statistical probability of life is very low—even if life-sustaining planets should number in the millions. Some exobiologists now believe that life will always appear when environmental conditions are propitious. But the highly improbable combinations of conditions required make the appearance of life a near miracle even though it may be a wholly natural, statistically predictable event.

For all practical purposes, there is today only one world suitable for man. Measured by nature's standards rather than by those of historical man, it is at present a delicately balanced, highly perishable world that has evolved over long geologic epochs of environmental change. And man, acting as if he owned this world or at least had come into leasehold possession of it, has played his role as lessee very indifferently. In certain respects, he has improved the capacity of the environment to serve his needs—as in animal husbandry, agriculture, forestry, and in the contriving of artificial environments. But he has also proved to be a careless and indolent tenant, guilty at times of arson, pillage, and wanton murder.[8] It will no longer suffice for man to exploit the environment and leave the cleanup and repair to nature or to God. This irresponsible behavior worked (when it did) only so long as man did not unduly stress the environment. But the unremitting pressure of modern technology and multitudes of people allows insufficient margin for the recuperative powers of nature. If man elects to play God with his environment, he must then assume the responsibilities for its maintenance that he has heretofore left to God or nature.

THE TASK OF PROTECTION

Before protection of the ecological basis of a society can become an explicit responsibility and function of government, it is necessary that there be some measure of public understanding of what the task involves. This understanding is of primary importance at the higher levels of public policy leadership and planning, since it should be apparent that we cannot reshape or invent administrative means to accomplish the objective until we have not only a designation of purpose but also some notion of what must be done in order that the purpose be realized. Definitions of the task of environmental protection occur on two levels of discourse. The first of these is essentially instrumental. It is concerned with what is necessary to sustain specified conditions of ecological stability and diversity and to support specified qualities of human life. This level of discourse is concerned not only with ecological necessities but equally with the practical means by which these necessities are or may be realized. The second level of discourse is institutional; it is concerned with the public policy, law, and administration through which the foregoing aspects of the total task are legitimized and organized in society. This essentially political level will be discussed in Chapter 8, "Environmental Management as a Public Function." The balance of this chapter will proceed at the level of ecological operations or applied ecology. For society to cope with its environmental problems and to protect its environmental base, both levels of discourse must be conceptually congruent. This is to say that policy must be consistent with the ecological facts of life, and ecology must be made applicable and provided with an informed policy capable of guiding it toward the ends of application.[9]

Just as the management of a spaceship ecosystem calls for co-ordinated direction at high levels of managerial, scientific, and technical skill, so responsibility for management of the ecological basis of modern society requires a systematic inter-relating of the most advanced state of knowledge and technique. Ecosystem maintenance would challenge the competence of the most highly developed science and engineering now available and would require massive new inputs of knowledge and technique. Much work must yet be done before the science of ecology would be prepared to provide the guidelines that might insure a wise management of the planetary life-support system. Nevertheless, protection of the ecological basis of life could be greatly enhanced by intelligent use of information now available.[10]

The primary contribution of ecology to the practical task of environmental protection would be to establish ecological base lines—parameters, ranges, and gradients for sustaining life at various conditions of stability and diversity. The skeptic is entitled to question the validity of the ecological base concept: Has the possibility of a generalized ecological base been established through scientific investigation? Can one composite ecological base be conceptualized, or is it preferable or necessary to work with many and varied "ecobases"? If environmental scientists accept the ecobase idea, do they agree as to its constituent parts? Honest answers to these questions are conditional. The idea of an ecological base is complex, and if treated honestly, must be treated with the scientific caution that tempers confidence in what we know with recognition of the large areas of uncertainty. The concept of the ecobase is essentially one of fitness of the environment.[11] Strong evidence supports an inference that there are ultimate and absolute parameters for life in general, and for human life in particular. But until ecological research, exobiology, and outer-space exploration fill in missing pieces in the configuration of our knowledge, we cannot be absolutely sure of the exact point (or if indeed there is an exact point) beyond which life in any form becomes impossible. We can be more confident regarding the unfit nature of environmental extremes.

Where human life is possible, we find a range of tolerance among human individuals and physical types, and our concern with ecological suitability may now become more broadly relativistic.[12] If we wish to protect our environmental welfare, we will need to consider what kind of ecobase is necessary to sustain what type of society. The technological and demographic level of society will obviously make a difference in assessment of ecobase requirements. If we try to estimate the ecobase requirements for an uncertain future state of society, we must at least imagine a range of possibilities. In this calculus of possibilities, not only must the various probable states of society be projected, but, in addition, some estimate must be made of the ecological limitations governing future developments. This appraisal would include, of course, ecological changes resulting from application of science and technology to environmental conditions.

The ecological-base concept is therefore not absolute. As an adjunct of public policy, the ecobase includes all the environmental conditions required to sustain a given level of human welfare. The adequacy of the ecobase is partly determined by the demands upon it. The more-varied, numerous, and pervasive the demands, the richer, more extensive, and more resilient the required ecobase. And it logically follows that those social systems that demand most from the environment both qualitatively and quantitatively are often those that exploit the environment most severely—destroying the very values they seek. A characteristic pattern of human behavior is the overexploitation of a rich and varied ecosystem. A favored region, the San Francisco Bay Area of California, for example, induces a flourishing society, which, as it grows and spreads, increasingly consumes and destroys the ecological values that first made it attractive.[13] Stress on the environment for industrial and commercial purposes and for high population densities impairs its value for residential, aesthetic, recreational, and health purposes. In situations where demands upon the environment are numerous and varied, to suboptimize (emphasize a few selective values at the expense of the whole) may alter the ability of the environment to respond to the full range of demands upon it. By maximizing one set of demands upon the environment of San Francisco Bay (the economic), its total ecobase has been diminished, and its ability to respond to other demands has been impaired. Those qualities of life or civilization that have depended upon specific or combined elements in the ecobase have correspondingly diminished.

The concept of an ecobase is thus applicable to a number of levels of existence. At the most fundamental level, it would identify the essential environmental conditions for the survival of the human species. For more than mere survival, the adequacy of the ecobase depends upon the demands of the society upon its environment. The extent of these demands is, of course, influenced heavily by cultural factors and most notably by technology in the service of economic enterprise. The character of social demands depends also upon the extent to which a society attempts to provide, in some measure, for all of the environment-related interests of its people. The more varied the demands, the more varied the conditions required to satisfy them. But lacking an ecobase concept, modern societies arrive at priorities for use of the environment by other criteria. Military demands and successfully aggressive economic interests appear to gain the upper hand in the ordering of priorities, and their dominance is evident in a wide range of political economies, including the United States and the Soviet Union.

A rational approach to public environmental policy would seek, therefore, to establish ecological base lines to meet the known needs and values of the society. It would also, however, attempt to provide an uncommitted margin within the ecological base lines to provide for future needs and unforeseen contingencies. All other things being equal, the more ample the margin between the resources of the ecosystem and the demands upon it, the greater the capacity of the system for flexibility, variety, and self-renewal. But societies have rarely made the preservation of natural ecosystems a public or collective responsibility. The necessity for a buffering of human impact upon the ecobase assumes the continuation and growth of far-reaching demands upon the environment to serve the needs of civilized man. The ecobase concept represents an effort to establish guidelines to help man avoid overdrawing his environmental bank account. It is an effort to protect his ecological solvency and to help him budget his drafts upon nature in relation to what nature is able to provide in satisfying his desires. How this task may be undertaken belongs to the subject matter of applied ecology and will be discussed in Chapter 7, "Environmental Management as Applied Science."

Before identifying more specifically the several aspects of the task itself, it may once more be useful to emphasize two points that are critical to the thesis. First, the task of environmental protection has not confronted most societies in the past, because the degree of stress upon the environment was seldom so widespread, continuous, and severe as to require it. That situation no longer exists. Second, incomplete evidence regarding ecological processes is not necessarily a good argument for failing to adopt a protective environmental policy. Incomplete evidence is not necessarily insufficient evidence for public action, for if incontrovertible data were required in every instance of public action, there would be almost nothing upon which governments might legitimately act.

The first phase of a protective policy would be to designate the general level of civilized existence toward which the efforts of society are to be directed. Stated in this generalizing manner, the task may appear unfeasible. But a level of civilized existence, like a standard of living, can be specified through its component parts. Moreover, a level or standard may have many aspects and alternatives; it need not be highly prescriptive, and it may be as comprehensive and detailed as the human mind can manage. More will be said in Chapter 6, "Shaping the Environments of Civilized Societies," about the specification of standards of living. The important point to emphasize at this stage of discourse is that ecological base lines for human welfare cannot be defined in the abstract except at the minimal or basically physiological level. Beyond the ecological conditions essential to man's physical existence, there appears to be no way to specify ecological or environmental parameters apart from specified levels and qualities of culture. Men have lived contentedly in caves and have subsisted on diets that most moderns would find unacceptable. In the past, either men adapted their wants to what the environment could supply, or the environment was sufficiently ample and diverse to provide for most of the demands that it occurred to men to make. The necessity for a comparative assessment of social goals and ecological resources has arisen because of the rapidly disappearing margin between what the societies are exacting from the environment and what the environment can provide.

The second phase of a protective policy would be the establishment of ecological base lines beyond which the environment would be protected (in so far as possible) from more stress than it could accommodate. These base lines should not be viewed as immutable, except as this judgment is confirmed by weight of evidence. This evidence would include determination as to whether the naturally evolved ecosystem could or should be preserved from specified changes and intrusions. It would also include estimates of the impacts of the various forces stressing the ecosystem and of probable future stresses. The administrative implementation of ecological protection would be to prevent stress levels from exceeding the ecobase lines. In many cases, this action would be primarily to safeguard the capacity of the ecosystem, its subsystems, and its components, for automatic self-renewal. It would be a task of maintaining the environmental life-support system in a state of dynamic homeostasis.

This policy does not preclude the total extirpation of selected organisms in the ecosystem. Protection of the ecological basis of life need not be extended in principle or practice to all life. But it is good sense and good science to avoid remedies that might cause more troubles than they cure. And so the protective task can be wisely performed only upon the basis of the best ecological knowledge available. Interspecific relations in the natural world are often complex, with ramifications impossible to fully perceive. Moreover, there may be future utility even in organisms pathogenic to man and his domesticated plants and animals. Immunity may (or may not) be a wiser goal than the extermination of pathogens in the ecosystem. The pathogenic villain of today might become the public-health hero of tomorrow, but the calculus of probability and risk is a task of biomedical science.

Defense of the ecological base lines calls for at least four types of effort. The first is to monitor the state of the environment against both standards of specified quality in relation to human welfare and the requirements of the ecosystem for self-renewal. The second is to check any breach in the base line—to stop deterioration as soon as it can be identified. The third is to prevent the breaching of the base line wherever possible—to facilitate self-restoring processes in the environment and so to free man from unnecessary burdens of environmental administration. The fourth type of effort is to restore degraded or impoverished environments—to bring ecological conditions back again to a standard represented by ecological base lines. These aspects of the environmental protection task are technically feasible. They can be made specific and operational, but for this to become possible, appropriate policy authorizations and administrative implementation would be required. Detailed recommendations have been made for the surveillance and monitoring of the environment, notably by the Environmental Pollution Panel of the President's Science Advisory Committee, by the Committee on Pollution of the National Academy of Sciences, and by the Subcommittee on Science, Research, and Development of the House of Representatives Committee on Science and Astronautics.[14] There is now a very large literature on environmental surveillance, standards setting, and control. The problems are more those of the will to implement than of the adequacy of the technology.

SOCIAL IMPLICATIONS OF ENVIRONMENTAL PROTECTION

Only recently have efforts been made to specify the human right to a safe and healthful environment. Measures to protect public safety and health have historically been functions of government, but the characteristic feature of these measures has been their isolated and often ad hoc administration. They have been taken as responses to specific threats in the environment, but seldom have been extended to consideration of the environment as a whole.

For example, there are environments, especially in large cities, that are generally conceded to be dangerous in several respects.[15] Yet rarely have governments been authorized or organized to deal with these areas ecologically. Within the dangerous areas, police surveillance and insurance rates may be increased, but the environment is accepted for what it is, and little if any effort is made to transform it. The more-enlightened efforts toward urban renewal might be cited as moving toward change in the human ecology of an area, but these projects seldom have had the comprehensiveness required to alter fundamental ecological tendencies. Too often they have created a new set of environmental problems replacing the old ones. And the former problems have not been solved, but have merely been displaced, reappearing in some other locality.

Rural environments present equally difficult problems of human ecology. There are many areas of the Earth in which no foreseeable technological or economic innovation can provide an adequate ecological base for present levels of population. In some of these areas, depletion of natural resources has resulted in ecological near bankruptcy. In others, the development of available resources would require inputs of capital and technological skill disproportionate to any general benefit to be derived. By way of example, there are areas in Appalachia, northeast Brazil, and the Middle East, where restoration of an adequate life-support base would seem first to require removal of the present human inhabitants and their domestic animals. But the inhabitants are seldom willing to be removed, and governments are seldom willing or able to remove them. It is easier, in many cases, to subsidize rural poverty and ecological decay than to overcome it through fundamental ecological reconstruction.

Public health services afford the most clearly marked aspect of public and individual responsibility for protective measures in the environment. The arts and sciences of sanitary engineering and epidemiology have been applied in all modern countries to protect the ecological basis of life. National efforts have been assisted and supplemented by the World Health Organization, UNESCO, and private philanthropic efforts. The most articulate expression of basic ecological protection to date may be found in the environmental health aspect of the public health movement. Environmental health as a field of professional practice has undergone, as noted in Chapter 2, several major changes of orientation and emphasis since its beginnings in the mid-nineteenth century. Professional focus has at times narrowed to problems amenable to medical treatment and then widened to include considerations of a broadly ecological character. Campaigns to stamp out malaria and other diseases in tropical countries, unaccompanied by population control and land-use reforms, have resulted in ecological disasters perhaps as great as those that were remedied. Malnutrition and starvation are not acceptable substitutes for malaria and dysentery, nor has any public health administration proposed that they should be. Yet, unanticipated difficulties have too often followed from unbalanced attacks upon environmental health problems.

The present trend in environmental health appears to be toward a broader ecological investigation of health-related factors in the environment. The trend may be explained, in part, by growing evidence that the incidence and severity of many well-defined diseases are influenced by environmental factors that do not always in themselves appear to have direct medical significance.[16] The cost of illness, given new meaning through Medicare and Medicaid programs, is another major incentive to improve environmental health. A society that commits its resources to open-ended programs of medical care cannot afford to have too many people ill. Environmental health measures are primarily disease-preventive, and there are obvious economic as well as humanitarian arguments for preferring them to reliance upon curative health measures.

Emphasis on environmental health and disease prevention leads logically to an examination of the health relatedness of the structure and behavior of society itself. Concepts of social health and illness are widely prevalent in modern society, but are seldom well defined.[17] The extent to which the concept "health," as applied to organisms, may also be usefully applied to organizations, is open to question. Attempts have been made to understand or interpret the behavior of social organizations by analogy to organisms and specifically to the physiology of the human body. One of the most explicit of these efforts was made by physiologist Walter Cannon, who during the nineteen thirties, authored a political theory based upon analogies to the homeostasis, or stabilizing tendencies, of living organisms. In the concluding chapter of *The Wisdom of the Body*,[18] he developed his concept of "biocracy," a theory of government intended to maintain social and economic stability and to redirect creative forces of man toward qualitative improvement.

Cannon's biocracy joined a larger and older body of writings on equilibrium societies that did not interest the people of a day and age committed to unending quantitative growth. The expansionist and competitive orientation of American society in mid-twentieth century were uncongenial to Cannon's biocracy, as it had continued to be to Herbert Spencer's "moving equilibrium." By the late nineteen sixties, however, growing apprehension over population growth was beginning to give these rejected concepts a new relevance. Efforts to retard or to stop population growth were often advocated without adequately considering the social, economic, and political consequences that could be expected to follow their success. Although the problems of population stability were ultimately in every respect preferable to those of exponential population growth, they were real and disturbing problems nevertheless. America and the modern world have had pervasive ideologies to legitimize unending growth; they have lacked adequate political theories of dynamic stability or of ecological self-renewal. Material for such theories has been available in numerous hypotheses that, being counter to the main currents of their times, were relegated to comparative obscurity.[19]

The revival and development of theories of societal homeostasis (including the spaceship paradigm) would seem to be an inevitable concomitant of efforts to protect and maintain the planetary life-support system. The unlimited multiplication of any species is an ecological monstrosity, and must ultimately be checked. If societies are to avoid wide-swinging oscillations of numbers, damaging to health, happiness, and the ecological basis of life, social stabilization will become necessary. An important task of environmental policy is therefore to discover and apply concepts and procedures that would not only stabilize society where stability is necessary, but would also enable society to cope with the problems that this stability would induce.

IMPLICATIONS FOR ADMINISTRATORS AND CITIZENS

As suggested in Chapter 1, the dilemma of the public decision maker in attempting to reconcile political preference and ecological truth could be greatly eased by a generally accepted, ecologically valid view of man/environment relationships. If protection of the ecological basis of life were to become a governing principle of public policy, a number of specific political consequences could be expected to follow, in addition to the more general reorientation toward social stability. Among the more interesting of these would be the possibility that ecological policy might become one of the more objectively definable aspects of the public interest. If the ecological basis of human existence (as distinguished from cultural preference) were found to be essentially the same for all men, and if its parameters could be discovered through scientific investigation, there could emerge a sector of public policy in which the scope of opinion and of interest-group competition could be minimized. Yet, inasmuch as all that needs to be known about basic human ecological needs is not likely to be known in the foreseeable future, and because the evidence now available indicates a range of conditions rather than absolutely fixed parameters for human survival, it seems safe to conclude that science will not enable us to take environmental policy out of politics and to make of it a wholly executory function of government.

Accepting the inevitable limitations of knowledge and rationality, it is nevertheless possible that the latitude for political differences regarding the protection of the ecological basis of life might be greatly narrowed by validated knowledge and general acceptance of the protective policy objective. Whether this narrowing in fact occurs, depends to a large and not easily predictable degree upon human perceptions and moral values. The consequences of major environmental change characteristically are deferred to the future. To forestall undesirable effects in the future frequently requires restraint in

the present for which no immediate pay-off occurs. Thus altruism, or regard for man's posterity, is often invoked on
behalf of conservation or protection policies for which the
present generation must pay so that future generations may
enjoy. Self-denying policies have usually been hard to sell except when (as in the case of war or pestilence) they have
been linked to a tangible present danger.

Strategy for success in obtaining popular acceptance of a
comprehensive policy of ecological protection would be to
link current and future dangers, so that present fears may
provide sufficient political force to carry future-directed measures along with measures answering present exigencies. This
is, of course, a conventional political technique, but it gains
pertinence in environmental issues as a result of the fore-
shortening of time by technology. The rapidity with which
man can now alter the environment with the aid of new forms
of air and sea craft, giant earthmovers, nuclear energy, chemical agents, and sheer multiplication of his species, means that
increasingly the future is near. Since men may expect to experience within their own lifetimes most of the environmental
changes that can now reliably be projected, perhaps altruism
need not be heavily relied upon in motivating protective
policies.

If what men perceive to be their self-interest were to square
with what the best evidence indicates to be the public interest,
the path of public policy development would be greatly
smoothed. Unfortunately, the immediate self-interest of individuals is not necessarily consistent with the public interest,
now or in the future, a circumstance brilliantly explicated by
Garrett Hardin in his essay "The Tragedy of the Commons."[20] Individual self-restraint is not alone a reliable means
of protecting the environment. Nevertheless, an internalizing
of ecologically valid behavior patterns could greatly facilitate
the administration of public environmental policy. If protection of the ecological basis of life is both self-interest and
public interest, then the first major task of policy development
is to maximize public understanding that this is so. In a literate
and democratic society, this task implies public understanding
of *why* it is so. Widespread understanding of ecology is a nec-

essary precondition of a protective ecological policy in a technologically advanced society.

The American people, relative to their ability to manipulate the environment, have been dangerously deficient in ecological sophistication. Measured by the needs of society, the formal structure of education has been slow in responding to the circumstances resulting from the explosive growth of population, knowledge, and technology. Alarmed by the widening gap between public comprehension of the ecological facts of life and the threat to the viability of the environment posed by the unprecedented stresses of a burgeoning population and technology, groups of scientists, lawyers, physicians, and informed citizens generally have undertaken voluntary efforts to arouse public concern and to assist the people and their political representatives toward understanding their collective ecological self-interest and what must be done to protect it. The work of the Environment Defense Fund, the Conservation Law Society, and other citizen action groups have been described in Chapter 2 as indications of the emergence of the environment as a social issue.

Among the efforts most specifically directed to the protective task has been the Scientists' Institute for Public Information and its associated Committee for Environmental Information.[21] Established in 1963, under the leadership of biomedical scientists, many of whom were associated with the highly regarded Rockefeller Institute (now the Rockefeller University), this group has mobilized scientists in communities across the country to bring before citizens generally, but particularly before the civic and business leadership, the implications of present and impending crises in the American environment. Beginning in 1958, a monthly journal (*Environment* since January 1969) has been published as a part of this effort. The journal was an outgrowth of the concern of the Greater Saint Louis Citizens' Committee for Nuclear Information with public education regarding the hazards of radioactive fallout. Its concern broadened to include hazards to the human environment generally, and in 1967 the journal became an official publication of the nationwide Scientists' Institute for Public Information.[22]

Other organizations, with more-generalized objectives, have

focused more specifically during recent years upon public understanding of the need for protection of the ecological basis of life. The Izaak Walton League has emphasized broad ecological viability quite as much as the status of game fish and wildlife, and the National Audubon Society is as concerned with the state of the American and global ecosystems as it is with the preservation of birds. In both organizations, the viability of the ecological base for life generally has been perceived as essential to the survival of fish, of fur-bearers, and of birds. The cumulative effect of these efforts is difficult to assess directly. No reliable data inform us regarding the numbers of persons or the percentage of the population actually reached by these efforts, nor of the extent to which the attitudes and actions of those reached have in fact been changed. A large part of the public audience represents persons already persuaded to an ecological outlook. For these people, the work of the organizations is to reinforce and mobilize action on behalf of ecologically desirable objectives.

We are not, however, without evidence that a change of public perception has been occurring. The evidence may be found where its political significance is most clearly evident—in the political process itself. Major governmental inquiries into any state of public affairs do not continue to be made very far in advance of a clear and substantial public concern. Since publication of Rachel Carson's *Silent Spring* (Cambridge, Massachusetts: Houghton Mifflin, 1962), numerous and extended investigations, hearings, and reports, sponsored by the executive and legislative branches of the government of the United States, lead to the conclusion that the viability of the environment is indeed a public and national responsibility.[23] The collective findings of these reports are comprehensive in scope and specific in detail. If put into effect, which implies Congressional acceptance and adequate staffing and funding, their recommendations, which in the main are mutually consistent and reinforcing, would comprise an impressive public commitment not only to protect the viability of the American environment but to restore damaged portions of it that are amenable to repair. The political and administrative action required to put these recommendations into effect will be discussed in the third part of this book.

In the Ninetieth and Ninety-first Congresses, more than thirty-five bills were introduced (not counting reintroductions) that would have provided for, defined, or reinforced protection of the ecological base of the nation. There are implications for both administrators and citizens in efforts to establish and define individual rights and responsibilities in the environment. For example, Senate Bill 1075 in the Ninety-first Congress declared (Section 101b): "The Congress recognizes that each person has a fundamental and inalienable right to a healthful environment and that each person has a responsibility to contribute to the preservation and enhancement of the environment." Other measures before the Congress have similarly declared the rights of individuals to safe and healthful environments and, in the instances of Representative Richard Ottinger's Conservation Bill of Rights, and a subsequent proposal by Senator Gaylord Nelson, would amend the Constitution of the United States to attain this objective.[24]

It cannot be certain in advance of actual experience what effect these declarations of rights might have. Under the American system of adjudication, the practical meaning of such provisions would ultimately be interpreted by the courts. Their meaning would also be interpreted through administrative practice. To an important degree, both judicial and administrative interpretations would depend on the extent to which people take these declarations of right seriously and use political pressure to back up their beliefs. To the extent that people do not believe that they really have a right to a sanative environment, or even to complain against degrading intrusions upon their surroundings, these declarations would be dead letters. But the history of judicial interpretation in the United States demonstrates the skill of the courts in finding, when the time is right, new and enforceable doctrines of law in long-moribund or innocuous statements of principle. Taken in the context of other legislation, it may be that the American citizen will one day obtain as much right to the protection of his environment as despoilers have previously enjoyed in their presumed right to destroy it.

Meanwhile, international recognition that the Earth has in a practical sense become a spaceship with a vulnerable life-support system has begun to receive practical expression.

Since 1948, the International Union for the Conservation of Nature and Natural Resources has undertaken to persuade governments and international organizations to recognize and support ecological values and to protect rare and endangered species of plants, animals, and habitats. Membership in IUCN consists of national governments, governmental agencies, conservation and scientific societies, and individual benefactors. It has been associated with UNESCO and has also had co-operative relationships with the Food and Agriculture Organization and the United Nations Secretariat. The IUCN works through a series of commissions (on Survival Service, Ecology, Legislation, Education, National Parks, and Landscape) and holds general assemblies triennially. Technical meetings are organized in conjunction with the general assemblies and at other times as needed. Associated with the IUCN is the World Wild Life Fund, an organization formed to assist the protection of endangered species. But the objectives of IUCN extend beyond protection, to include ". . . the rational use of Earth's resources to achieve the highest quality of living for mankind."[25]

In September 1968, an international conference on the use and conservation of the biosphere was convened in Paris by UNESCO. The recommendations of the conference stressed the need for protection of the planetary life-support system, and the very use of the word "biosphere" in the designation of the conference indicated the arrival of the concept in the politics of international affairs.[26] On December 3, 1968, the General Assembly of the United Nations provided positive evidence of world-wide concern for environmental protection by adopting a resolution offered by the representative of the Swedish Government calling for a World Conference on Problems of the Human Environment to be held in 1972.[27] Pursuant to this resolution, a report prepared for the Secretary General and General Assembly under the direction of the Advisory Committee on the Application of Science and Technology to Development stated: "It is apparent that if current trends continue, the future of life on Earth could be endangered."[28] The report specified the tasks that the 1972 conference would confront, and summarized the current activities and programs of the United Nations and its affiliated organizations relating to the human environment. Referring to the growing stress of man upon the environment, the report declared: "No nation can any longer be isolated from these global pressures. It has become clear that we all live in one biosphere within which space and resources, though vast, are limited."

The numerous reports sponsored by United States Government agencies, along with the environmental policy documents of UNESCO and the United Nations, reaffirm the conclusions of ecologists that the ecological basis of human life cannot be protected by concern for man alone. For man as a species does not and cannot live alone. The basis of *human* life is the basis of life itself. Man's existence depends upon maintenance of the fabric of what John H. Storer[29] has called "the web of life" and which throughout this book has been less poetically described as "the planetary life-support system." Yet perhaps Storer's poetic description is more accurate than the language of bio-engineering. Life supports life, and no manipulation of inorganic nature would be sufficient to sustain human existence in anything like the form in which it has hitherto existed. By protecting the Earth's endangered species, man not only shows respect for the vast creative process that made possible his own birth, but he takes practical action toward maintaining the conditions that will permit his own survival.

5

ADAPTING NATURAL ENVIRONMENTS
TO HUMAN NEEDS

The alteration of environmental conditions to meet human purposes better has been a characteristic form of human behavior, but its significance has changed under the influence of science and technology. Goals of environmental adaptation that once appeared to be obvious to most men have now become less certain and are frequently confused and contradictory. This is partly because of the vastly wider range of choice made possible by science and technology. And the problem of deciding how to shape (and also whether to shape) the environment has also become complicated by the pressures of rapidly expanding populations and technologies. Adapting natural environments to human needs thus becomes less a matter of engineering or of economics and more a matter of social policy. And in adapting the environment to his purposes, man must perforce adapt himself to the changes he induces. He would therefore benefit from greater wisdom concerning the potential costs of adaptive change.

Ever since evolution toward civilization began, a very large part of man's activity has been directed toward changing the conditions of the natural world. Civilization is, in one sense, the result of this effort. When man cannot obtain what he wants directly from the natural environment, he frequently seeks ways to change the environment to satisfy his demands. The more obvious of these modifications of the environment are illustrated by such activities as agriculture and animal husbandry, forestry, engineering, architecture, and city building.

To be civilized, man must in some measure modify and control the natural environment. Medicine, art, science, and freedom from unremitting servitude to the basic needs of the body, are possible only through major man-made changes in nature. At the beginning of history, the changes that man could induce in his environmental relationships were for the most part slow-moving and slight compared with those now possible. So universal and commonplace have been man's efforts to modify nature that, except in its technical or engineering aspects, the process of environmental adaptation has not received study proportionate to its importance. There is now need to remedy this neglect. For in freeing himself from past dependence on the produce and processes of nature, modern man risks involuntary servitude to the artificial systems developed through technology. Moreover, as he has become more dependent on his artificial systems for life support, he has behaved as a species in an increasingly thoughtless and short-sighted manner in his treatment of natural systems.

Perspective on the situation may be gained by recalling that man's environment-shaping propensities are not unique. A large number of animals modify their environments. Certain insects (for example termites, wasps, bees, and ants) are well-known environmental modifiers. Birds' nests, beaver dams, and prairie dog colonies illustrate the propensity of "natural" creatures to adapt environments to a more satisfactory meeting of their needs. Interaction between organism and environment involves modification of both. The geneticist Theodosius Dobzhansky writes, "Man is a part of his own environment: he influences his environment, as well as being influenced by it. The organism and environment are really parts of an interacting system."[1] In this ecological process, natural selectivity and, sometimes, cultural evolution operate to restrain maladaptive practices.

An organism that alters its environment in a manner prejudicial to its continuing welfare loses advantage in the selective process of evolution. Its impositions upon the environment may destroy other creatures, upset ecological equilibrium, and trigger off disastrous aberrations in the environment. Organisms may safely modify their environment in many ways, but only in so far as they are capable of changing their own physiology through adaptation can they transcend natural parameters that otherwise condition existence.

Through science and technology, man has been able (perhaps only temporarily) to suspend or evade some of the penalties for misuse of the environment. He has been able to compensate through technology for certain deficiencies he experiences in the environment. He does this not only by modifying the environment or through altering nature in agriculture or weather modification, but by contriving artificial microenvironments, as in space suits and air conditioning. To a very limited extent, natural selection, interacting with environmental factors, appears to have led to modifications in the human physique. Enlarged lung capacity among peoples long resident at high altitudes, and resistance to heat and sunburn among peoples long exposed to strong direct sunlight, are among the more-apparent instances of physiological adaptation by men to their environments.[2] Biomedical science may enlarge this adaptability in the future. Nevertheless, the environmental parameters of man, as of all living things, are not indefinitely expansible.

Man now has the unique ability to alter his environment with a speed and thoroughness that often exceed the capacity of the cautionary responses of nature to come into action. Lacking an ecological early-warning system, man can do irreversible harm to his environment and ultimately to himself before the consequences of his maladaptive behavior become apparent. Modern man can, therefore, no longer afford to wait for nature to lay a restraining hand on his shoulder. He must be able to assess the consequences of his environment-shaping action *before* the event. Afterward may be too late.

SEPARATING POLICY FROM TECHNIQUE

Until the twentieth century, the principal challenge the natural environment presented to man was how to cope with it. The tasks appeared obvious; the challenge was technical. Technique remains a challenge and will continue to be one in the future. Man has by no means solved all the problems of adapting the natural world to his desires and his needs. The new adaptations often bring new problems. For example, release of atomic power through fission raises serious problems of protection against radioactive radiation and especially the disposal of radioactive and thermal residues. But the technical problems of how to adapt the environment to get what is wanted from it have now diminished relatively to the political problems of determining priorities with respect to what kind of environmental conditions should prevail. Not all men desire the same environments.

To earlier generations, the tasks of environmental administration were essentially those of engineering. Today the tasks of engineering are, or should be, secondary to those of policy. Yesterday the tasks of environmental adaptation seemed self-evident. Economic productivity was the overriding objective of Western technoscientific industrialism. The environment-shaping powers of technology were placed almost exclusively at the service of economic purposes. There was little debate about this, for the prevailing assumptions in industrial societies in the nineteenth and early twentieth centuries stressed the primacy of economic values. Capitalism and Marxian socialism differed primarily with respect to the legitimate beneficiaries. In both camps, there was agreement that economics was the determining arbiter of human affairs. Thus the industrializing commissars of the Soviet Union showed little more concern for the full range of values that might be realized in the environment than did their capitalist counterparts, the captains of industry in the Western world.

The new environmental challenge to man is obviously not mastery of the environment (a task that has required most of his efforts since the Stone Age), but mastery of his desires and his judgment with respect to his use of the environment. The objectives of man in the environment are now no longer obvious. Science and technology have made possible new goals, in which the traditional rationales of production are neither mandatory nor sufficient. The public and economic benefits of the exploration of outer space, of the marine depths, of the inner structure of the Earth, may be real but they are not self-evident. Their economic pay-offs are highly uncertain, and the penetration into these environments is costly to a degree that only public subvention can support. The question of allocating public resources to penetrate and perhaps to exploit these hitherto inaccessible environments thus becomes foremost a question of values and priorities. If the growth of human populations could be drastically slowed or stabilized, there would be less compulsion of circumstance to use technoscientific capabilities of modern society in one direction as against another. The need for criteria upon which to base social choice would thereby become even more acute than at present. And population control is one of the options open to society today, so a decision as to how many people a society is to have necessarily carries with it implications with respect to the possibilities for the future environment of that society. The opportunity costs of "people unlimited" can be very high.

The task of adapting natural environments to human needs has now become increasingly political and controversial, because the priorities among needs are no longer popularly accepted as obvious, and the range of possibilities for shaping the environment has enormously increased. Countries not severely constrained by insufficient food, water, or physical space, or immediately threatened by military insecurity, have the greater range of choices in how they shape their future environments. In the absence of generally accepted rational criteria for making environmental choice, conflicts in this area will be settled as they now are, through trial by political combat. The outcome of this method is probably as wise and as just as it was when individual men settled their differences in this manner in primitive and medieval societies. But where the future of society—of all individuals—is at stake, this time-honored method is neither satisfactory nor safe.

Adaptation of the environment to human needs unavoidably becomes a matter of public policy. But wise policy decisions cannot be made unless the nature of human needs in the environment is known and can be defined or measured so as to permit assessment of alternatives and some estimate of priorities. This analytic process, to be valid, must be able to measure or at least identify intensities of need or feeling, and must be able to factor out incompatible from mutually compatible environmental decisions. A vast new area of public administration now opens, for which people and governments have heretofore had little conscious preparation or experience.

ADAPTATION AND INTERACTIVE PROCESS

Before examining the task of environmental adaptation as an aspect of policy, it will be useful to review the ecological implications of the interactive adaptive process. The primary implications of adaptive change in nature is that its effects may extend throughout the ecosystem in which it occurs. Minor and circumscribed changes may have only a localized effect upon a system—but the ecosystem in an absolute sense has been changed. Adaptive effects extended over time may cumulate to decisive changes in the future. When man changes his environment in some significant way, he will probably also change himself or his successors. Man's self-image is projected against an environmental background, and he is seen by himself, as well as by others, as related to this background in some specific way or ways. We thus identify and categorize many groups of men by their environmental relationships, as, for example, astronauts, firemen, seamen, farmers, woodsmen, and miners.

Adaptation is one of the processes necessary to the survival of living organisms. We have emphasized its dual character, in which both organism and environment and their relationships are in some degree altered. The process may also be physiological or it may be behavioral—the latter including learned behavior that extends from "institutional" to individual and technological adaptations. Adaptation of organisms to environmental stresses may occur when circumstances (perhaps insufficiency of time) prevent an organism from repelling or avoiding a stressful environmental situation. In some cases, physiological responses may be automatic: an organism may shiver in response to cold, or may regroup white corpuscles in response to a lesion in its skin.

An adaptive response intermediate between involuntary physiological reaction and manipulation of the natural environment is to contrive an artificial environment—as when primitive man began to wear clothing, and insects, birds, and some mammals (notably man) built artificial structures to protect themselves from the instability and severity of their natural surroundings.

Compulsion toward adaptive change increases as organisms sense discomfort or threat to their continued existence. Adaptive strategies may be sought as a consequence of this awareness or of a desire to reach some goal that prevailing man/environment relationships appear to prevent. Thus, adaptation, in any of several aspects, represents the price that is paid for obtaining a better fit between an organism and the environmental conditions that prevail. For the human animal, a special problem is created by the diversity of tolerance, value, and imagination among people. Value differences in clothing, housing, and in larger-scale environmental adaptation have been continuing sources of interpersonal and social conflict. When imagination supplements instinct as a prompter of environmental adaptation in human society, the scope of potential political conflict becomes enlarged.

One of the ecological implications of the adaptive process follows from the ecosystem concept. It is the possibility of adaptive chain reactions caused or necessitated by some critical change in the system. To categorize change as voluntary or involuntary, intended or inadvertent, is to view it from the perspective of man rather than to conceptualize it as a *system* phenomenon. Implicit in the idea of adaptive change is "purposefulness," or teleology. Possibly the term adaptation should be used only to describe intended modifications of the environment or of organisms, classifying all other adaptive reactions simply as responses to stimuli.

Obviously, not all responses are adaptive. And among involuntary responses or reactions evidencing an adaptive effect, not all are successful. The chain reactions may entail the hazard that, even if the primary adaptation is successful, subsequent subadaptations may lead to unwanted consequences. The advantage of the so-called systems, or ecosystems, approach to environmental policy making and administration is that it helps to place the adaptive process in its proper perspective. In examining a proposition to change the environment in some particular, a systems approach examines not only what is intended, but what happens throughout the system (assuming that the boundaries of the system are known). Adaptive strategies can be understood adequately only within the context of their organisms or ecosystems. But unfortunately for the welfare of man and his environment, the selected adaptive strategies of humans in relation to their environment have rarely been premised on this ecological assumption.[3]

There is, however, a growing body of argument that the ecosystem is the soundest conceptual tool for analyzing and managing the adaptive actions of man in relation to the environment. Among others, Arnold M. Schultz, Professor of Forestry at the University of California at Berkeley, has endeavored ". . . to show that it is logical, both on practical and philosophical grounds, to consider the manageable unit of human culture and natural resources as an ecosystem."[4] B. Riley McClelland, of the National Park Service, has advocated the ecosystem as a unifying concept for the management of natural areas in the United States national park system.[5] What, where, and how to adapt man/environment relationships are questions that should be asked together. But before they are asked, the more fundamental questions of Why? and To what purpose? should be answered.

HOW NECESSARY ARE "NEEDS"?

The strategies by which man copes with his environment are embedded in cultures, which have evolved through time. Man does not act upon his environment with hypothetical free rationality. His sense of reasonableness is only in part derived from empirical test or from science. It is also conditioned by concepts of rationality prevailing in his cultural milieu. Conventional tests of reasonableness in human societies are so thoroughly infused with cultural and semantic biases that it becomes difficult to find any firm basis for truly rational discourse. It is hardly feasible here to undertake a philosophical analysis of "reason," and so the test of rationality that has been premised in this book will be taken as the measure of reasonableness in the specification of human needs. This test is essentially ecological: that which is consistent with continuing health and happiness of man and with the self-renewing tendencies of the planetary life-support system will be taken as "reasonable."

By this test, a large part of human behavior, especially in

relation to the environment, is highly irrational. But human mentality and motivation can be intermeshed in complex ways, and very rational human purposes are often expressed in irrational or counterproductive action. Man's imagination leads him as often into error as into positive achievement, but unfortunately, success in doing the wrong thing may nevertheless be socially evaluated as success. Perhaps if man better understood his own nature, he would restructure his values and behavior patterns to accommodate his real needs rather than to invent plausible, but often harmful rationalizations for his motives and his conduct.[6]

In its present rudimentary and compartmentalized state, social science does not provide us with an adequately tested theory of human behavior in relation to the environment. Following pioneering work by Kurt Lewin, a field of ecological psychology has developed and may in time enlarge our understanding and opportunity for insight into this aspect of human behavior.[7] But meanwhile an examination of human behavior, detached from conventional assumptions, reveals factors in human impact upon the environment that are both discouraging and reassuring. The discouraging aspect is the seemingly infinite capacity of human beings for self-delusion, and the ease with which people can be persuaded to accept as inevitable or irresistible, policies and practices that are in fact arbitrary, unstable, and self-destructive. The encouraging aspect is that no ecologically destructive course of action is *required* by any genuine human need. An ecologically "stable," diverse, and healthful world could have been, and may yet be, compatible with advanced industrial technology. But this possibility is contingent upon a degree of rationality and self-control that the species "man" does not appear to possess.

It is axiomatic to say that man adapts his environment to his needs. This process occupies a large part of the business of civilization. Yet the diversity of civilizations throughout historic time suggests that men have not perceived their needs in the same ways. Modern man tends to accept an implicit teleology in which past cultures move spontaneously toward the now prevailing types of technological societies. Cultures incompatible with modern technological society tend toward acculturation or physical extinction. But this view of history may be misleading. Its time dimension is very short—measured in centuries or decades rather than millenniums. And it conceals an assumption that the culture that gains dominance and survives must possess continuing survival capabilities. Yet it does necessarily follow that a culture that eliminates all competing or separate social systems is itself invulnerable. Unless a widely pervasive or universal culture has built-in mechanisms to assure critical and detailed evaluation of its own behavior, the assumption that whatever is, is right, is likely to prevail. If what everyone believes to be "right" turns out in fact to be "wrong," so much the worse for society, depending upon the seriousness of the error. Cultural diversity could provide a corrective mechanism through comparison of the consequences of environmental management, but because man is not accustomed to examining his environmental relationships in ecological terms, such comparisons are not made, or if made, are confused by cultural biases.

The way in which culture determines the socially accepted meanings of "need" may be illustrated by the influence of human "play" in the environment. Now play is a "natural" form of behavior, observed by ethologists in many animal species in addition to man. It is not always easy to distinguish play from work, even by using the criterion of necessity. Many preindustrial societies institutionalized play in various forms, often associated with religious, sexual, or communal events. In the modern industrial world, however, play and work intermingle in complex ways. Mass cosmopolitan societies are characterized by the commercialization of play, and play becomes confused with entertainment. Especially in America, as David Riesman has observed,[8] play has become compulsive—Americans work at the business of playing. Recreation has become big business and a big factor in environmental policy and administration.[9]

Play has presented a psychological difficulty to modern industrial society. For reasons that need not be explored here, it has been difficult for modern, science-based technological societies to legitimize play or play-related needs growing out of physiological necessities. When a mass market for entertainment developed in the twentieth century, play became legitimized by money, and only then did it begin to become a positive concern of modern government. Human needs for play, recreation, or aesthetic satisfaction were poorly served in the building of cities. The principal provision was through parks and thoroughfares. But it is doubtful that the Americans of the early twentieth century were as well provided with recreational facilities as the citizens of first-century Rome, Athens, or Alexandria, with their public baths, theaters, forums, and accessible open countryside.

If play represents a genuine human need, its expression can be only partially suppressed. It may assume forms that are socially disapproved, but it may also cover itself with the respectability of serious business. Small boys building sand castles and mud dams are obviously at play. Less obviously at play are the engineers, politicians, and developers who have learned how to put a long face on levity and to delude themselves concerning the kind of human needs to which they are responding. There seems to be no end to the list of dams, bridges, highways, and other public works that have been built so that grown-up men may play. The argument for public works is invariably "human need" as defined by those who "need" to do the building. The adapting of the environment to human needs is not the simplistic proposition that is commonly advanced by the Earth's developers. Many of the needs served by what is actually done to rivers, coast lines, lakes, mountains, marshes, and deserts are "needs" only within a very selective context of argument. They are "needs" only if one accepts limiting premises as to *who* needs *what, when, where,* and *why!*

A major aspect of the adaptation of natural environments to ostensible human needs is the group of processes called "development." This term means many things, and to attempt a critical exposition of it here would be a diversion from the main issue. But the development process commonly refers to the extension of human habitation and resource exploitation into hitherto undeveloped or underdeveloped areas. Seldom does it refer to the rehabilitation of degraded environments. Perhaps "development" is the consequence of a compulsive human drive to bring all of wild nature under direct human utilization and control. The term "waste land" is often given to unoccupied natural areas, although it might be applied with more true meaning to land that man has wasted. The "development" concept ought to receive a very hard, critical look from any person concerned with the quality of the human environment.[10]

Although "development," in a broader socioeconomic sense, has become an international movement, it was in the United States that the process became a way of life. It has been associated from the first European settlement in North America with the ideas of land speculation and economic growth. The Great American Developer evolved as an occupational species as distinctive as any typed in modern society.[11] Historical circumstances combined to make the development of the continent unnecessarily destructive ecologically and to reward the most self-centered and rapacious forms of human behavior. The orderly and well-considered adaptation of the wilderness to human uses was inconsistent with the intense individualism of the pioneer and the ineffectuality of the government for large-scale or long-range public management. There were always some men in public life who argued for a more conserving course of settlement, but their voices were scarcely heard in the clamor for free land, internal improvements, and development.[12]

The paradox of the American environment is the obvious inconsistency between precept and example—between an articulate awareness of the possibilities of an environment of order, beauty, freedom, and health, and the more-common reality of disorder, ugliness, frustration, and decay. "No people," writes Peter Blake, "inherited a more naturally beautiful land," and "We are about to turn this beautiful heritage into the biggest slum on the face of the Earth."[13] "What kind of men," asks Marya Mannes, "can afford to make the streets of their towns and cities hideous with neon at night, and their roadways hideous with signs by day, wasting beauty; who leave the carcasses of cars to rot in heaps; who spill their trash into ravines and make smoking mountains of refuse for the town's rats? What manner of men choke off the life in rivers, streams and lakes with the waste of their produce, making poison if water?"[14] What manner of men? Ordinary, taxpaying, churchgoing citizens who join in singing "Amer-

ica, the Beautiful" at the noonday luncheon club, in whose
schoolboy memory America is still the land where the air is
full of sunlight, although it may also be filled with carcino-
genic smog. It has rarely happened that men in America, or
elsewhere, have deliberately set out to destroy environmental
values in the name of development. Yet this, too, has been
done, as when political and economic interests combined to
bulldoze the irreplaceable beauty of the Indiana Dunes, thus
removing an attractive obstacle to "progress."[15] A paradoxi-
cal ecological blindness rather than deliberate destructiveness
appears to be the more common deficiency.[16]

Development enthusiasm and specious debate concerning
human needs in the environment are almost invariably premised upon unavoidable massive and continuing increases in
human populations and upon corresponding projections of
growth in human mobility and indiscriminate consumption of
goods and services. To the extent that needs so defined depend upon actual growth, they are only conditional needs and
would not be needs at all if the growth did not occur. One
way to cope with such conditional needs is to prevent their
emerging. A determined and effectively pursued policy of
population control could be the easiest and most economical
method of meeting many "needs" now furrowing the brows
of perplexed economists, statesmen, and technicians. Thus,
human beliefs and values confuse the identification of need.
Governments expend their energies on pseudo needs, because
they are, or believe themselves to be, unable to deal with the
"real" ones.[17]

Economic "needs" are among the most widely accepted
rationalizations of human behavior. Not only does alleged
economic necessity cover otherwise indefensible projections
of self-expression onto the environment; it also "justifies" exploitive uses of the environment in the name of progress,
growth, or public demand. Congested megalopolises which
cannot "afford" open space or the conservation of aesthetic
amenities, exemplify this aspect of the nonsense of economic
necessity. For example, the value of land in mid-town Manhattan is no more than what the society that controls its use
wishes to impute to it. It has no intrinsic value that an economist can measure. Its worth is socially determined, and a

modified market is the mechanism that American society has chosen to establish its value. One could argue that human needs for open space in the heart of a populous city could make some land too valuable to be built upon. But modern society, at least in the United States, has no generally accepted or operational way of making this need effective.[18]

Although some economic "needs" are specious, others are very real. But even real needs are sometimes artificially induced. Even if one accepts population growth as "natural," the same cannot be said of taxation. Administration of the American valorem tax upon land and its "improvements" has been the source of some of the worst misuses of the environment, both natural and artificial. Twentieth-century Americans have witnessed the pulling down of buildings of artistic and functional merit that would have continued indefinitely to serve public needs except for their failure to yield sufficient earnings to satisfy their temporary owners. This insufficient margin is often explained by heavy taxation on the property itself. The response of the owners, which may indeed improve their economic circumstances, may be costly to society.

An example of this economics of expediency may be found in the displacement of railway passenger stations in large American cities by multistory office buildings.[19] The railway passenger business having sharply declined as a consequence of irrational public transportation policies, owners of large and monumental passenger facilities found it advantageous to destroy them—thus sacrificing the original cost plus the cost of wrecking and replacing them with structures yielding higher private incomes. The taxation on these stations was one of the reasons for their becoming burdensome to their owners. But their multistory successors frequently burdened the surrounding area with an overload of new office workers, customers, and clients. The owners proceeded unilaterally to change the environment of the area and to push the "externalities" of their enterprise in the form of transportation and other user services onto the public. The reduced railway services continued with greatly reduced amenities, and the entire area, while technically becoming more productive, became so at the price of lowered environmental quality and greater interpersonal and environmental stress.

An ecological tempering of short-range and self-centered economic thinking might produce a more generally satisfactory adaptation of the environment to a more valid set of human needs. But it is unrealistic to expect people to act upon long-range and socially beneficial considerations when society itself, through its systems of reward and punishment, favors those interests that are devoted to self-seeking over those that would implement the public good. A political economy oriented toward indiscriminate increase of the gross national product is poorly oriented to make a rational assessment of its own needs.[20] The flowing, interlocking systems that are now the basis of the American economy are still misunderstood by large numbers of Americans as exemplifying "private" enterprise rather than "social" enterprise. The focus of policy, law, taxation, and administrative practice is atomistic rather than comprehensive. The anti-trust syndrome continues to dominate political thinking. Thus, the same conceptual failure that explains many bad judgments with respect to the environment operates also to confuse public understanding of the economy.

RATIONALIZING NEEDS AND PRIORITIES

If man is willing to pay the price of a stable, mass-production society based on scientific technology, his basic needs for food, clothing, and shelter can be met with relatively little individual thought and effort. In primitive societies, social and individual goals were nearly identical and obvious beyond argument. In modern industrial society, however, the amount of energy available exceeds the immediate demands for basic necessities. Most of the so-called needs of modern man are not of this basic, life-support character, but are postulates of cultures. Individuals and groups may and do differ over the definition and evaluation of second- and third-order needs. Political controversies over public services in "advanced" countries fall largely into these categories, for modern industrial societies have not found ways of making obvious the priorities necessary to their own survival. This is the reason that the political slogan "from each according to his ability, to each according to his needs" has no intrinsic meaning. Someone or something must identify the abilities and the needs before the words have any substance.

If the abilities and needs of individuals could be fully specified, the tasks of politics could be more systematic and rational. Unfortunately, our understanding of these attributes of individuality is as yet inadequate.[21] Beyond basic biological factors, abilities and needs are culturally defined, and even biological needs are culturally interpreted. As with estimates of life expectancy, it is easier to specify abilities and needs at the societal level than with respect to particular individuals. Indeed, the diversity of human personality defeats efforts to determine conclusively what any particular individual is able to do or what that individual (by whatever criteria employed) might "need." Provision for the expression of individuality can be made only at the societal level, at which the range of opportunity and limits of social tolerance are set. Society shapes the environment in which the individual can establish his personal identity and find fulfillment for his subjectively defined needs and preferences.

Therefore, an environment is best adapted to human needs when it provides the widest possible range of diversity consistent with its continuing self-renewal. When the fit between man and milieu is loose, voluntary individual adaptations are possible. When social pressures on the environment are severe and the man/milieu relationship is tight, politics replaces individual choice, and priority, rationing, or some other form of social decision overrides voluntary behavior. No political system can cope with the subtleties and diversities of individual choice, and to the extent that political decisions become necessary, they must deal with matters by category. Considerations of individual freedom are heavily influenced by the judgment of persons in authority as to what latitude a society can afford. Many considerations may enter into such judgments. Among the most coercive are overt social pressures upon the environment, especially for basic necessities. For this reason, popular movements for environmental quality have been almost invariably related to movements for stabilizing or reducing growth of human populations.

It would be difficult to find a spectacle more illogical or ironic than the conservative advocate of individual rights, especially in property ownership, business enterprise, and personal mobility, who opposes public efforts toward population control on grounds of individualist and traditionist principle. It is difficult to imagine a concept more self-destructive than that of unlimited growth of any sort. Keeping open the doors of opportunity is an essential element of any policy in which individual freedom is valued. To the extent that flexibility is preserved to meet "needs" that may emerge tomorrow or in the more distant future, to that extent also a society will be capable of providing the latitude needed for individual choice. But it appears that in most modern societies it is among the advocates of individual freedom that one will find the most assiduous engineers of its destruction.

Considering the many obstacles to rationality surrounding the processes of public decision making, what prospects are there for a more rational ordering of human priorities in the use of the environment? A contingent answer is necessary, because the prospect depends upon how much the people of influence in any community care about its present and its future prospects. Before the environment can be adapted to meet a people's needs, those needs must be identified and understood. Too often, they are dogmatically postulated, and no real effort is made to examine their validity, their implications, or the alternative ways in which they might be met.

But needs cannot realistically be specified in the abstract; they have meaning only in relation to conditions that must also be specified. Needs are experienced in relation to something, and that something may be as specific or as broad as the conditions or circumstances required to fulfill the ostensible need. The question of needs is one of needs for *what* in relation to the *total context* in which the "needs" are fulfillable. As the answer involves society, the question becomes political.

Environmental adaptation is thus a task of great complexity and variability. It must take account of various levels of needs in the environment—some universal, many specialized. The level of existence and the demands of circumstance make for differences among the specialized needs of astronauts in space, patients in hospitals, and office workers in the megalopolis. The environmental needs in these and other categories are combinations of general and particular requirements, and if these are adequately analyzed in relation to the total matrix of human needs, some rational allocation of priorities among needs might be determined. Priority decisions are in any case being made, and it would seem sensible to substitute, wherever possible, a greater for a lesser degree of rationality, even though a thoroughly rational calculus cannot be achieved and may not even exist. The basic task is to learn what environmental adaptations are required in order to meet those human needs that can be demonstrated and evaluated, not merely those that are asserted.

We return inevitably to the question of the kind of choice man is to have with respect to his environment and related style of life. There are many current attitudes that in their stereotyped extremes will obstruct any rational answer. Among these are biases toward compulsive development, angry equalitarianism, uninhibited speculative profit taking, self-centered indifference toward environmental and social trends, and unlimited political expediency. These attitudes share an unawareness or disregard of man's cosmological and ecological predicament. To this extent, they are small-minded biases and defects of morality. They do not contribute to the shaping of a civilization worthy of man's best hopes.

6

SHAPING THE ENVIRONMENTS
OF CIVILIZED SOCIETIES

A civilization reveals the nature of its goals and values in the environmental conditions that it creates. The environmental consequences of social change have often been indirect and seemingly contradictory. Deterioration appears to follow more from failures of perception and incompleteness of value structure than from inadequacy of protective or corrective technologies. Technoscientific advancement has created a dual condition, *first*, of unprecedented human stress upon the environment, and *second*, of reliable knowledge about man/environment relationships. But modern society has not yet developed, internalized, or articulated a set of goal-directed institutions capable of using science and technology to prevent the destructive overstressing of the environment. The further development and survival of a humane civilization depend upon the selective "editing" of modern technoscientific culture in accordance with ecologically based criteria. This effort requires the analysis of existing behavior patterns and the synthesis of new cultural attitudes and institutions.

With the insight of the poet, Matthew Arnold spoke for his time, but not ours, when he wrote of "wandering between two worlds, one dead, the other powerless to be born."[1] In Arnold's time, the loss of tradition could be regretted, but the shape of the world yet unborn was unknown. Neither poet nor man of science could know how to relate to it. But the world in gestation in the nineteenth century is now emerging. Its initial outline and its character are beginning to appear, and it is a task of our generation to consider what it may become. Can it be a better world, or will its already evident tendencies toward the monstrous prevail? Is this new world ours to shape, or are we powerless to arrest or reverse the forces that are carrying the modern world toward self-destruction?

We begin with these questions, not to consider if or how they may be answered, but as reminders that our practical way of dealing with the world poses for us a moral obligation to act as if we could shape its future. As a practical matter, we resolve the question of our role in evolution by assumptions of human autonomy and competence. We may reject the teleological question of predetermined ends for man and his civilizations only to confront the ontological question of the future development of human society.

We view the future with an implicit assumption of our self-actualizing power. The logic of this position implies a corollary responsibility to consider and to evaluate the purposes toward which our efforts are directed. We are not *compelled* by logic to determine the ends of our efforts or even to forecast their unplanned outcomes. But it seems irrational to concern ourselves with means, to the neglect of ends. For we have already seen the harm that can come from the unprecedented and inadequately considered use of power. If there is meaning in the word "wisdom," it surely implies an attempt to use the resources of knowledge and material wealth not only for immediate purposes, but to shape a future in which human happiness and welfare will be possible.

MAN: A MANAGEABLE FACTOR IN HIS OWN ENVIRONMENT?

The shaping of man's future implies the shaping of his future environment. His ability to plan his future depends largely upon his capacity for reason. Disagreement over whether planning of the environment should be comprehensive or incremental reflects differing assessments of human capacity for rational conduct.[2] The difference is one of degree, for no one contends that rationality is unlimited—and few would argue that human behavior is totally irrational. Rationality is always bounded, but incrementalists doubt man's capacity to deal effectively with comprehensive, complex, and long-term developments. They contend that, because individual man cannot foresee his future, and because societies of men differ among themselves as to what the future ought to be, man as a species is doing the best that he can. He cannot purposefully shape the course of environmental change, nor should he attempt to do so. His environmental correctives should be confined to specific, immediate, and manifestly harmful effects.

This attitude tends to the conclusion that, whatever its failures, ours is the best *possible* world. It may not be the best of *all* possible worlds, but it is the best that is possible for us. We are what we are as a consequence of an evolution over which human rationality has had little or no control. Our expectations of shaping our future, if realistic, must be modest. One may regret that, in pursuit of his perceived self-interest, man so often degrades the environment that sustains his life— but then, *ecce homo,* this is the kind of creature the human animal is!

The empirical evidence in support of this conclusion is formidable. We see it on all sides. Continuing disregard of the known causes and consequences of man's misuse of his environment is discouraging. But any conclusion regarding the potentialities of man is tentative. It is a current thesis that man has taken over direction of his evolution. This conclusion appears to be premature; but ultimately man's survival may depend upon his controlling both the biological and cultural aspects of human evolution. There is no conclusive evidence regarding human capacity for collective self-control; yet there is abundant evidence to indicate that human behavior is bringing about environmental changes that are highly threatening to man's biological and cultural future.[3] The cardinal question regarding man's future is whether, as a species, he is capable of bringing his destructive tendencies under control. And this test primarily concerns his unintended and inadvertent destructiveness—the harm he does in pursuit of presumed good. Man seems capable of coping with threats when he actually perceives them. History indicates that human societies are capable of planning and sustaining massive, complex, and relatively long-term efforts. Were this not so, world wars and space exploration would never have proved feasible. Yet the fact is that we have no verified knowledge regarding man's potential intellect, and no satisfactory scientific explanation for the evolution of human values and for the rise and decline of civilizations.

We are as yet unable to explain the process by which the human brain evolved, separating man from his primate relatives; and we have no firm basis for assuming that man's evolution is complete. Our knowledge of human evolution is fragmentary and covers so brief a period of geologic time that we cannot plot a reliable trajectory of man's development. We do not even know what concept or process of evolution or cultural development is valid in relation to man. But our knowledge of the forces of evolutionary change is growing, and our technical understanding of man's mental processes, although still rudimentary, is much greater than that of our forebears. If self-understanding is a key to self-control, then progress is being made toward a point in human development when man may be able voluntarily to push outward the bounds of his rationality.

In order to improve the quality of man's environment, the quality of man himself must also be improved. The upgrading of man and of his environment would be aspects of a single great and complex process: advancement of the quality of civilization. And it may be argued that neither aspect of the process can occur to a significant degree without the other. The phenomenon of man occurs only in context, and whether one looks outward from man toward his environment or inward from the environment toward the nature of man, the field in which inquiry takes place is the same. The viewpoint, or perspective, changes, and the focus of attention shifts. But the man/environment universe, although infinitely extended and complex, is integral and holistic. The amenability of the human factor to purposive self-control is discovered through tests of action. Environment shaping is one of these tests and one of the more significant of them because of its contextual relationship to the human condition. Forethought, restraint, and a considered appraisal of alternative means to socially desirable ends are characteristics of the civilized aspects of man. They are qualities of mind and personality that will be emphasized in the education of any people who seriously attempt to shape their civilization.[4]

THE CIVILIZING PROCESS

Civilizing is the process of achieving civilness or civility. The forms and substance of civility are not things upon which all men agree. But the essential or basic meaning of civilization is the attainment of relationships under which culture-creating men are able to live together in communities. Animal and plant communities exist without the assistance of civilization. There are communities of men in which the state of civilization is rudimentary. Yet the psychobiological distance between the most primitive living men and the most advanced non-human social species appears to be far greater than the distance between the most primitive and most advanced human societies. Man, unlike his fellow creatures, has an aptitude for civilization. His imagination and ambition impel him to refine and complicate his social arrangements and his technology in order to attain his objectives. Given time and an appropriate environment, primitive men have shown that they can become "more civilized," but no ape or insect has as yet demonstrated this capacity.

In the process of becoming "more civilized," man has developed elaborate technologies that are sometimes erroneously identified with civilization itself. Clearly, technology is a major aspect of civilization, and it is through technology that man undertakes to reshape the natural environment better to satisfy his wants. It is what man wants that determines the quality and direction of his civilizing efforts. Technology is the knowledge of means. In a society of self-imposed limitations on perspective, the advancement of technology may become an end in itself. The result is the technological society that Jacques Ellul describes and that humanists deplore.[5]

The dominant impulses of a civilization are revealed through its uses of technology, and the consequences of this usage may be seen in its effects upon man/environment relationships. Throughout historic time, deterioration of the viability or self-renewing capability of an environment has usually presaged a decline of civilization. Evidence from Central Asia, the Middle East, the Mediterranean littoral, and Central America appear to substantiate this hypothesis; and yet, paradoxically, the spectacular advancement of techno-scientific civilization in the nineteenth and twentieth centuries has also been accompanied by measurable, verifiable decline in many aspects of man/environment relationships. Skeptics are therefore moved to question the reality of an environmental crisis. Some technologists now argue that the environment, in its natural, evolved form, can almost, if not wholly, be ignored. Man can make his own environment. Under plexiglass domes, he can lay out golf courses on the Moon.[6] This optimism may follow from a misreading of history. The technological society of the twentieth century "exploded" with a speed unprecedented in historical experience. The environmental damage accompanying its expansion has been enormous, but its cybernetic, or feedback, effects may require more time than the initial impacts. It is much too early for present-day man to congratulate himself on having outmaneuvered history.

A civilization reveals the nature of its internalized goals and values in the environmental conditions it creates. Obviously, the environment of a civilization does not express all the values and conditions implicit in a civilized society. Yet, if read perceptively, the environment reveals much more than the untrained eye sees. The science of archeology is based upon the reconstruction of past environments and upon the extrapolation from them of the activities, attitudes, and institutions of the people of past civilizations. We cannot be sure of the accuracy of these extrapolations, and it is helpful to have written records that verify or supplement material artifacts. We cannot always tell, where natural environments have declined, how much change was caused by man and how much by nature. Did, for example, man-induced stream siltation, continental uplift, or both, destroy the harbors of Ionian cities on the Aegean Sea?[7]

But although the physical environment may not tell all that is to be told about the quality of a civilization, neither does it lie, as written records sometimes do. Man may misinterpret, but the physical evidence does not dissemble. In many societies, and not least in the United States of America, one finds great contrasts among the varied uses of the environment. From some viewpoints, American treatment of its environment appears to be violently contradictory. Like magnificent Asian temples rising out of filth and misery, the contrast between the "best" and the "worst" of the American environment is so marked as to suggest a national schizophrenia in environmental attitudes. The analogy may not be inapt. There is ample evidence to suggest that America, as a social system, does express contradictory attitudes toward the environment. But this trait is not uniquely American; and it is also true that these contradictions exist within a system that, however complex and contradictory its components, does function as a total society. The contradictions are within the system; they reflect subsystems of the totality. Inconsistent as they may be with one another, such contrasts are not wholly incompatible. The system has accommodated itself, at least temporarily, to the stress of its contrasts. In a vernacular phrase, they are "built into the system."

It is this built-in nature of human behavior in relation to the environment that will make the effort for environmental quality in America a difficult and frustrating, uphill fight. An attack upon environmental pollution, for example, is in some part an attack upon the prevailing social system. The attack is, of course, focused upon specific, and from some viewpoints harmful, aspects of the system. But as John Kenneth Galbraith has remarked in a satirical but all too candid essay, pollution is not a casual or spontaneous activity: "On the contrary, it has deep and penetrating roots in the body politic."[8] And in describing the environmental deterioration of present-day America, Paul Ylvisaker writes:

> "Call it by any name—chaos, unplanned growth, ribbon development, social anarchy, slurbs, the decline of American civilization, the resurgence of *laissez-faire*. But recognize it for what it is—a people's *laissez-faire*, which sinks its roots down past any rotting level of corrupt and cynical behavior by the few into a subsoil of widespread popular support and an abiding tradition of private property, individual freedom and 'every man's home's his castle.' "[9]

The environment of a society as shaped by man is thus not merely an expression of social values; it is a function of the society itself. It is a part of what the society is. To shape the environment of a civilized society means nothing less than shaping the nature of the society. Those who undertake to alter or direct the process of environmental change thereby take a hand in shaping the course of civilization. But it is one thing to initiate a change and quite another to sustain it. Many a well-conceived environmental improvement has been made only to be destroyed because its sponsors did not or could not provide means for its continued maintenance. Unless even relatively slight environmental changes are integrated into the functional processes of society, the probability of their survival is not high. The flowers will wither in their planters in the downtown mall unless their presence has become a part of the value structure and operational system of the city that sought to improve its image by planting them there.

FREEDOM AND CONSTRAINT IN ENVIRONMENTAL CHOICE

The anonymity and uniformity of contemporary man-made environments contrasts sharply with the distinctiveness and variety of traditional cities and countryside. Contemporary style in office buildings, airports, luxury hotels, factories, motor expressways, bridges, and increasingly, in the patterns of agricultural settlement, tend to a highly similar, almost common, set of qualities. Planned distinctiveness is often attempted, but the leveling logic of technique is not easily offset. It appears that technoscientific culture generates its own environmental style, freed from the assumptions or constraints of traditional cultures. Gestures contrived to provide "atmosphere" in tourist hotels or airports often confirm the leveling effect of technoscience as man has applied it. Symbolic distinctiveness is often emphasized where loss of real diversity threatens business based on human interest in change and variety.

Distinctiveness and variety do appear to be human values, but one finds an apparent paradox in contemporary society. Architects, artists, and designers often go to great lengths to assert the individuality of their work. Whether the results are pleasing variety or disturbing discord are perhaps only matters of taste or preference. One result, however, is that eclecticism, rampant at the community level, creates a nondescript sameness as between communities. In traditional societies there was a much higher degree of stylistic uniformity *within* particular communities. But as *among* communities, there was greater contrast. By way of example, new additions to older buildings nowadays characteristically contrast violently in style. Variety is added to the immediate environment, but its integrity and distinctiveness are often lost.[10] Widespread, uninhibited heterogeneity results in a generalized sameness. Buffalo, Detroit, Denver, and Seattle are different primarily where nature is still visible. A once-distinctive Boston is becoming more and more like Houston. There have been some successes in accentuating civic distinctiveness. The great arch at St. Louis is one of them. But, with few exceptions, all large American cities appear to be the same place. As Robert Sommer puts it, the shapers of America's contemporary environment appear to be planning "Notplace for Nobody."[11]

The implications of this paradox of eclecticism and monotony are significant for the task of environmental planning and administration. Implicit in the differences between traditional and technoscientific environments are contrasting latitudes of choice. The constraints upon choice in traditional societies were relatively severe. Yet environmental styles were as distinctive as the images of environments associated with Brittany and Cambodia. The choices that men made in shaping their environments were limited by religion, technology, availability of building materials, patterns of settlement, methods of transportation, agriculture, and trade. These constraints still limit choice, but the latitude of choice has expanded with unprecedented rapidity. Today, that latitude is so wide that contemporary society has hardly begun to explore seriously the significance of the range of possibilities available to it.

Traditional society was relatively stable because the choices available to it were few and frequently obvious. In contrast, the choices available to technoscientific society are vastly greater, but many of the possibilities are not perceived by the mass of people or by their leaders. Yet there is also a widespread belief that almost anything can happen. Potential conflicts of interest thus multiply. Growth in technology, in economic wealth, and in population create new opportunities for the enterprising, and new threats to established values. In shaping the environments of traditional societies, man appears seldom to have been self-conscious about his choices. The limitations of circumstance, the strength of customary ways, and the relatively low pressure of population enabled environment shaping to assume an almost natural evolutionary course. In the world today, no environment is secure. There is hardly an acre of Earth anywhere that is not vulnerable to someone's plans for change.

More than any other factor, science-based technology has enlarged the scope of man's environmental choices. But more than technology is involved. The uses of technology in processes that have altered environmental conditions have been highly selective. Technological feasibility is seldom the real criterion by which the choice is made in the uses of technology. The actual scope and application of technology lies in its combination with other things—with economic, industrial, or military activities. Technoscience enlarges choice but does not guide it. The effect of technological innovation in combination with other elements is determined by the interactions among the elements. The synergistic effects depend upon the nature of the combination, seldom upon technology itself. For example, the automobile in so-called less-developed countries has not had the impact upon the environment that follows when economics, industrialism, and public policy permit the operation of automobiles by the millions. It was not technologically foreordained for American society to use technology to promote transportation by privately owned automobiles instead of by public carriers. The "decision" was a consequence of interacting economic and political forces. The impact of technology is a total systems effect; it is seldom an isolated event.

The environmental conditions of any society, but especially of contemporary technoscientific societies, are perhaps best understood as composite results of converging causes. This synergistic effect of technology plus economics, plus other factors in society, provides the energy that levels mountains, moves rivers, and creates smog. But this convergent power is usually organized through interrelationships and combinations that are highly resistant to competing interests. Opponents of the public-works policies of the United States Army Corps of Engineers, of the Bureau of Reclamation, of the Bureau of Public Roads, of the Federal Aviation Agency, or of the public utilities corporations have hitherto confronted the formidable strength of these technical-economic-political combinations and have learned how seldom their behavior can be changed by direct frontal attack. Environmental preservationists have fought battle after battle over specific decisions and policies, but the combination that is the force behind the actions of the public-works agencies has remained close-knit and strong, seldom successfully challenged as an environment-shaping system by any equally powerful combination.

These technoeconomic and technopolitical combinations have evolved as the primary forces in American society in the making of environmental choices. The choices are those of interested parties but become, by institutional or political default, the choices or non-choices of the whole society. But even as their policies and actions have been modified in the late nineteen sixties by growing public opposition to their past disregard of environmental amenities, technoeconomic forces raise new threats. In response to the opportunities presented by a society of mass affluence, leisure, and boredom, vast amusement enterprises have been moving in upon the natural environment.[12] Their vulgarization of the environment on behalf of mass popular entertainment poses new and difficult problems for public policy. Thus, the freedom of choice that wealth and technology confer (in theory) upon contemporary man often in fact becomes disillusioning. Much of the frustration and anguish of the idealist who would see technoscience used to create better environments, results from this paradox. The means that could shape a more healthful, aesthetically pleasing, and convenient environment are used instead in ways that destroy or impair environmental assets. The latitude of real technological choice in meeting the needs of modern society is decreased by political and economic considerations. The location of factories, dams, highways, harbors, housing developments, and amusement parks, or the necessity for their construction in particular instances, are decided through the application of criteria that do not begin to avail themselves of the full range of socially relevant values and possibilities.

It is evident that publicly acknowledged criteria for what is good, bad, tolerable, or preferable are largely functions of the total society. These criteria may be, and some have been, influenced by science. In the main, they are manifestations of conventional culture, and the tendency of society is to apply them uncritically to novel situations. Moreover, the fractionalization of the total culture as a consequence of the impact of technoscience has deprived society of general guidelines or standards by which the results or desirability of technoscientific innovations can be appraised. Freedom of choice thus becomes inability to make discriminating choices. Weakness of constraints on technological choices gives an open field to aggressive and purposive politico-economic advantage seekers. To oversimplify for emphasis, it may be asserted that the two-culture cleavage in modern society (technological and humanistic) adds to the difficulties of coherent direction of its future. Expediency thus continues to be a prevailing characteristic of contemporary policy making at a time when available knowledge and techniques are rapidly diminishing the great historical justification for expediency—ignorance.

EDUCATION AND THE ENVIRONMENT

Can we really elect to have a high-quality environment? Does the structure of American society—pluralistic, democratic, historically biased in favor of an "everyman's *laissez-faire*"—permit the shaping of its environment in any way other than by combat and compromise? The question is not whether conflicts of interest in the environment can be eliminated; there is no prospect, in a finite world, that they will be. The practical questions are rather, *first,* how conflict can be reduced without compromising environmental quality, and *second,* how the levels of information and social concern at which the process of bargaining and accommodation occurs can be raised. To improve the human environment, both man and politics must be improved. Men make politics; political institutions influence human behavior; but behavior is also influenced by attitudes, beliefs, and values. Purposeful shaping of the environment involves the purposeful shaping of outlooks on life. The quality of the future environment depends therefore upon the shaping of attitudes, beliefs, and values through present education.

Some aspects of human conduct are expressions of psychophysical nature. It is natural for man, as a civilizing animal, to substitute reason and culture for subrational drives, but rational behavior may serve irrational motives. It is, therefore, important to our welfare to understand the nature and effect of physiologically conditioned behavior. If man is a territorial animal or if he displaces onto the environment aggression generated in his social relationships, knowledge concerning these circumstances could greatly assist development of feasible strategies for effective environmental policy. Yet neither all men nor all societies project destructive impulses against the environment. The improvement of man can proceed through education in the broad sense, while efforts are made also to understand and perhaps to improve the psychophysical tendencies of the human species.

What are the implications for an educational process that will help to build better environmental relationships in the future? The structuring of the entire process of formal education around man/environmental relationships is not necessarily indicated. Many of the attitudes, beliefs, and values that would improve prospects for better environments in the future are equally relevant to other aspects of life. Yet not all educational orientations are equally suitable to help society to set goals and establish priorities for the future. Education limited to information is of little help. The question becomes one of what attitudes, beliefs, and values the system inculcates. In the broadest sense, the issue is what kind of civilization the process of education will produce.

Within this broader context of educational policy, an increased and, in some measure, new focus on environmental relationships and policies will be necessary. Recent moves to establish centers or institutes for environmental studies in a number of colleges and universities indicate intention to remedy past neglect.[13] Through the organization of new courses of study and the reorganization of old ones, higher education is better equipping today's youth to perceive and to assess the meaning of environmental change. Only a beginning has been made, and much more needs to be done. It is especially important that basic environmental concepts be built into secondary education, where they have heretofore generally been lacking. Education is more than schooling, but it is through formal systematic mass education that the greatest organized impact on attitudes, beliefs, and values can be made.[14]

In a technoscientific age, there is no end to the need for learning. Planned systematic education now continues through adult life and is increasingly civic as well as vocational in character. With the displacement of traditional culture by technoscience, we are confronted with the necessity of working throughout life to maintain our civilization. We can no longer merely inherit it. To preserve the heritage of the past, whether in art, in ethics, in historic sites, in landscapes, or in social institutions, requires unremitting effort. It also requires reappraisal; for not all that we inherit is necessarily good.

The concept of an "administered" environment or of consciously shaping a civilization suggests the idea of an "edited" culture, described by Chad Oliver in his science fiction novelette *Rite of Passage*.[15] In the course of the story, the question is asked, "What happens when a culture is so complicated that one person can't possibly learn it all?" Two answers are given: (1) infinite multiplication of specialization and (2) deliberate selection of cultural attributes. Modern technological society has accepted the first answer. The method described in the story is ". . . to learn a small core of culture and then specialize with increasing minuteness in a technical field." The results of this method of "advancing civilization" are sometimes painful: ". . . scientists who neither knew nor cared about the effects of what they did in their labs, soldiers who fought without knowing why, governments that legislated in mental darkness, writers who wrote glibly about problems which they were incompetent to understand."

Detailed accomplishments of this approach to culture have been prodigious, but society has become increasingly unstable, stressful, and incoherent. It has no adequate rational means of setting priorities or selectively accepting and rejecting technological innovation. The official standard of living rises, and the actual quality of life declines. The techno-economic system becomes increasingly complex and demanding, increasingly vulnerable to disruption, increasingly incomprehensive to the mass of people. The system adds to its own difficulties and seems unable to service its own basic needs. The society needs inexpensive, coherent mass transportation; instead it receives supersonic transport and "jumbo jets." It needs to cleanse its polluted lakes and streams; instead it receives vast and costly irrigation and water-transport schemes to produce crops that are not needed and to promote population growth where the pressure of numbers has long since impaired the quality of life. It is willing to commit indeterminate funds to "doctoring" the ailing, provided their ailments can be classified by medical specialists, but it appears unable to conceive a public effort toward social health—toward the prevention or reduction of illness. As noted in the preceding chapters, modern society has been failing signally to establish adequate criteria to determine what its needs really are.

A contrasting solution to the problem of making civilization manageable and responsive to human needs is that of "editing"—of selectively editing a culture down to agreed-upon essentials and learning to live with it. In Chad Oliver's novelette, the concept of "edited" culture raises the same problems that would be encountered in a systematic effort to protect the ecological basis of human life and civilized society: What is essential, and essential for what? The concept is not necessarily utopian, but it *is* highly rational and sophisticated. The idea of allowing self-renewing natural systems to serve human needs as far as possible is a manifestation of this rationality, but it is feasible only if rationality is extended to limiting human numbers to levels that natural processes can supply with minimal intervention through human technology. Chad Oliver's world of "edited" culture was very lightly populated, its inhabitants enjoying a highly stable and secure environment. In contrast, modern technological societies are utterly dependent upon the maintenance of the technology. A massive and sustained breakdown of the technological system in any one of its many critical parts could bring disaster and death to millions of inhabitants of the megalopolises in a period of days or weeks.

We are not yet able to explain why some societies adopt ecologically valid goals and practices, and others do not. Simplified explanations are likely to be wrong, but it is possible, without fully understanding the causal factors, to draw certain general conclusions from the course that contrasting cultures have taken. For example, although no simple explanation seems adequate to account for the decline of the traditional civilization of China, the inadvertent overstressing of the environment by sheer numbers of people seems to have been a significant factor. The ethos of China, less complex and more dogmatic than the ideologies of the West, was more congenial to harmony with nature. Yet neither philosophy, bureaucracy, nor science enabled China to avoid the environmental impoverishment that followed a slowly increasing but unremitting pressure of man on the land. In the West, science and technology enabled society to achieve a more-productive and better-balanced relationship to the natural world, even though, paradoxically, the dominant attitudes toward nature tended as much toward hostility as toward harmony. Industrialization, and the colonization of the Americas, ameliorated, in Europe, the type of inordinate stress of man on his environment that accompanied the decline of Chinese civilization. But we have no assurance that the combination of culture and technology that, with obvious qualifications, has worked well for the West will continue to do so in the technoscientific society of the future.

Two major concomitants of the passage of modern society across the historical threshold that separates the apparent openness of the past from the finite restrictions of Spaceship Earth are exponential increases of people and of power. The danger in destructive or misguided attitudes toward nature has become greater today because of the greater means to translate attitudes into action. Guided ignorance in the form of dogma appears to have been a factor in the decline of the old China; unguided knowledge in the form of technocratic optimism appears to have been a characteristic danger to the West. Today, the establishment of guidelines for knowledge in the application of science and technology to the human environment is a task of urgent importance everywhere. The task is urgent, because until it is accomplished, there will be no adequate basis in theory or principle upon which to base public and international policies for the custody, care, and development of the human environment.

Modern society may be reaching a point at which a choice between unguided development and cultural "editing" is no longer available. In a finite world, some form of "editing" is necessary. Modern men have hitherto largely evaded this necessity or believed that they have avoided it, because many of the former properties or qualities of civilization that have been excised from modern life have been removed "unintentionally." But inadvertent editing is not editing in any meaningful sense. Its excisions are indiscriminate, their effects upon the total socioecological context being largely ignored. Thus in America chattel slavery was excised, but a black-white ethnic problem remained and grew. Numerous species of wildlife have been eliminated from the American environment, but health-hazardous "pesticides" have been injected into the ecosystem with minimal regard to the full range of their effects; in an effort to eliminate harmful species, beneficial plants and animals have been destroyed.

The freedom and ability of modern man in general and Americans in particular to exercise some rational choice over their futures is severely handicapped by a number of mutually reinforcing modern myths. These myths, or perhaps more accurately, patterns of belief, have operated to block or distort man's perception of his actual circumstances. The most pervasive and invalid belief of all is that "freedom" is free—that it exacts no price, that freedom exists when each individual does whatever he pleases, wherever he pleases. It is apparent that this utopian state does not actually prevail; but in the United States there is widespread acceptance of certain assumptions regarding man's freedom of choice that handicaps his rational use of whatever freedom he might have to shape his environment. These assumptions may be summarized as, first, the almost unqualified beneficence of growth, second, the inevitability of uncontrolled technoeconomic "progress," third, one man's culture is just as "good" as another's, and fourth, each individual has a "right" to get whatever he can out of the environment (the everyman's *laissez-faire*).

These attitudes share certain negative characteristics significant for the environment-shaping process. None of them imply or require self-restraint or control, none suggest individual or collective accountability, none concede the existence of criteria for evaluating the use of the environment that are independent of individual interest or preference. All these attitudes suggest resistance to any general pattern of environmental development in society or to any meaningful standards of environmental quality *per se*. They do not preclude the imposition of social control where a clear and present danger to individual well-being can be proved. But they severely retard the establishment of general principles of ecological policy, upon which more-specific standards can be based. More critical attention to their effects is therefore needed.

The "growthmanship" attitude is deeply embedded in American culture. Whether the national obsession with quantitative growth can be transformed into qualitative growth or growth within a self-renewing or an internally dynamic homeostatic system, is conjectural. The most problematic growth of all is that of numbers of people. In America, there are grounds for cautious optimism that the national enthusiasm for numbers may someday be displaced by a concern for the quality of human life generally.[16]

Technoeconomic determinism, or the "you can't stop progress" attitude, is still firmly ascendant in American life, despite critical attack from both science and aesthetics. Supersonic transport, and airports unlimited, are only current examples of a national tendency. It is curious that people vigilantly jealous of their rights in relation to government will permit their privacy, convenience, and possibly health to be jeopardized by costly and unnecessary technological innovation that yields little, if any, social benefit. More strange is the tendency of science-oriented, rational people tacitly to accept the metaphysical assumption of technological inevitability.[17] It is, as we have emphasized, a contradiction of the tacit belief of Americans in the self-actualization of the human personality. It is an example of compartmentalized thinking, against which education and the prevailing culture have not yet provided sufficient countervailance.

Cultural relativism has permeated the social sciences and has strongly influenced ethical and religious thought. This viewpoint, however, has the defect of its virtues. It encourages tolerance of cultural diversity, but also frequently leads to exaggerated attitudes, as for example, that one man's attitude toward or use of the environment is equally as "good" as another's. This attitude is exemplified by certain individuals of high intellect and cultivated tastes who, although they themselves prefer a high-quality environment, are vigorously opposed to the efforts of conservationists or preservationists to "impose" their values on other people. A demonstrably valid set of ecological principles by which public policy could be guided might reduce, if it did not eliminate, the objections of cultural relativists. It could provide a common ground for greater consensus. But it might still encounter objections from those who hold that science has nothing to do with values. Our slowness in exploring the biosocial interface in science has kept us from providing an adequate and convincing answer to arguments over relativity or priority among values in the environment. Political accommodation among conflicting interests therefore tends to occur at too low a conceptual level to give adequate weight to scientific knowledge or ecological wisdom.

The *laissez-faire* attitude toward the rights of individuals in relation to the environment has suffered some attrition through public action on behalf of public health and safety. Land-use planning and zoning, and emerging pollution-control legislation, further constrain individual behavior in relation to the environment. We are beginning to lay a foundation for a legal doctrine of public rights in the environment, as distinguished from the specific and discrete prohibitions that have hitherto characterized our environmental policy.[18] Yet at the local level of government and throughout large areas of the country where pressure on the environment has not been felt acutely, the right to exploit the environment for personal advantage is still very broadly construed. Here again, culture shapes environmental attitudes. The psychology of the frontiersman is still vigorous, and when reinforced by technoscientific capability, can be a very potent force, usually in ways harmful to environmental quality.

A characteristic common to all these foregoing attitudes is that they are highly prejudicial to the effective public control of applied science or technology. They derive from viewpoints formed mostly in the prescientific world, although cultural relativism reflects to some degree an inclination to be scientific. But relativistic thinking that dismisses weight of evidence and insists upon incontrovertible proof of the validity of one environmental attitude as against another has abandoned science for a philosophical fetish. In actuality, these attitudes do not appear as clear-cut or consistent categories of belief or behavior. They are interwoven in the fabric of our social, political, and economic life, and this is why it becomes so difficult to change them. It is why environment shaping becomes culture shaping, and why attack upon the environment abuses of our industrial society readily becomes an attack upon certain aspects of the structure of the society itself.

WHERE SCIENCE AND THE HUMANITIES MEET

These remarks began with an allusion to the concept of two worlds—the familiar but no longer viable past, and the future, which more than a transition from the past, appears to bring a change of state in the human condition. Related to this concept is that of two cultures, popularized by C. P. Snow.[19] Each of these concepts is expressive of the change that science has brought into the world. Both imply discontinuities in culture—chronological, intellectual, and emotional.

The truth of these assessments of contemporary history is perhaps more poetic than rigorously factual, more qualitative than quantitatively demonstrable. A truth may be substantial without being universal. And it seems true that the *means* to shape the environment of civilized societies belong largely to science, whereas the purposes of men—the standards of beauty, of order, of aesthetic satisfaction, of welfare, and even of some aspects of health—belong to the humanities. This separation between the custodians of means and ends in our society creates weakness and discontinuity at the point of social decision. In the process of public policy making, the respective contributions of the "two cultures" are needed to form a mutually comprehensible and coherent unity.

The size and complexity of modern society require specialization. In the absence of integrative forces, occupational differences tend to fractionalize society. Communication across occupational lines becomes difficult, and no common set of assumptions or values provides a meeting ground for differing interests. The openness of modern society is deceptive. Freed from barriers of class and caste, it is more subtly fragmented by technoscientific specialization and by the progressive isolation of the traditional culture from technoscience.

Here perhaps lies an important part of the answer to the question of why contemporary Western technoscientific society has not dealt more effectively with its environmental problems. Means and ends are separated. The wholeness of man and of society requires a synthesis, or integration, in orientation toward the world and life that conventional education has not provided.[20] Thus, as we earlier observed, contradictory tendencies of modern American society are built into its social system. And it is this schizoid tendency that more than any other thing makes it difficult for the United States of America to develop a guiding set of environmental policies or to employ more than a fraction of the potential power of science and technology on behalf of human welfare.

Through science, man has acquired the knowledge and power that make him responsible for his future; it has not given him the moral compulsion to act responsibly. The substantive values that science and technology serve are articulated in the humanities, but are seldom amenable to scientific verification; it is at this interface between science and the humanities that environmental policy is made. And it is at this interface also that higher education can contribute to resolving what some observers call our environmental crisis.

How this educational task can be accomplished is yet to be discovered. There is no master blueprint for the development of ecological understanding that is equally applicable to all educational institutions or to all aspects of the educational task. But these elements in the task are universal: first, it is primarily one of synthesis; its basic data will be derived largely from the established disciplines that individually are unable to bring together knowledge relevant to environmental policy in a comprehensive or coherent system; second, its concern is not merely with the appearance of things, but with the purpose, quality, and worth of man/environment relationships; third, it reinforces rather than dilutes efforts in the separate sciences and humanities, because it establishes or clarifies their relevance to life; fourth, and finally, it emphasizes a truth that is too often forgotten: through education in its broadest sense, the civilization of the future is shaped.

Past generations of Americans, and men generally, have understood education as preparation for life. It is that, but that is its smaller dimension. Its larger dimension and equally important task is to *shape* life as well as to help prepare for it. In some degree, education has always done this, but often without conscious effort or intention. If man is to be the master of his own ingenuity, and not its victim, he will have to find better ways to relate means and ends, and to evaluate the ends that science makes available to him. In summation, the major task of education and politics is to shape a world in which preparation for life is worth while.

≈ III ≈

MANAGEMENT

Until very recently, no major society or national government perceived a need for general or comprehensive policies of environmental administration or control. In the United States, for example, public management extended only to specified aspects of the environment, for which special agencies frequently were created. Characteristically, these agencies have been focused on narrowly defined sets of purposes and have little if any responsibility for considering the broader environment implications of their activities. But if modern society is to cope more effectively with its growing environmental problems, a different structure of policy and administration will be necessary. An ecologically-based environmental policy would be characterized by a comprehensiveness of policy and control for which political acceptability and appropriate operative arrangements are only now beginning to emerge. Rapidly worsening conditions in the public environment, and the growing science of ecology, are inducing the popular comprehension necessary to political acceptability and may also help to formulate a system of ethics regarding man/environment relationships that will add emotional reinforcement to intellectual conviction. An ethics of man in relation to his environment is also an ethics of human relations. To implement such an ethics, a facilitating system of concepts and institutions must be developed. The biosphere concept, symbolized by Spaceship Earth, would appear by force of circumstance to assume an increasingly dominant position in social thought. The spaceship paradigm implies an integrative system of policy, ethics, and management, and would appear to mark a new phase in the evolution of human society.

ENVIRONMENTAL MANAGEMENT
AS APPLIED SCIENCE

Science is not an impersonal force, independent of human purpose. It is essentially a highly developed method of understanding reality that has proved to be more reliable for this purpose than other methods. Man has used science, through technology, to satisfy demands upon his environment. But he has not adequately inquired through science as to the terms upon which the environment is capable of responding to these ever-increasing demands. Scientific knowledge could guide man's environmental relationships, provided he was willing to accede to the self-restraint that guidance implies. Evidence of the practical need for this guidance is increasing, as the pressure of human occupancy on the Earth increases, and conflicts over the uses of the environment multiply. It is already evident that man must apply scientific knowledge to his own behavior in relation to the environment or else incur the inevitable consequences of progressive environmental deterioration to an ultimate point beyond which civilization and life itself can no longer be sustained.

It is a modern myth that science can help man realize his values but cannot help him to choose what values to pursue. This proposition is widely accepted as axiomatic, and there is seldom a call for evidence of its truth. It is evident that human society has rarely sought valid scientific knowledge regarding the implications of its objectives. Pseudo science has often been invoked in support of social policies and political objectives. It has been invoked for and against policies pertaining to education, natural resources, population control, racial relations, and war—and the list could be indefinitely extended. But, to put the matter abstractly, man has seldom asked science for guidance regarding what policies to pursue. And so it has not been demonstrated that science could not help men formulate wiser goals, were it given opportunity to do so. Perhaps man has not asked science the "right" questions.

What questions *ought* man ask of science? It is evident that science is a powerful tool for intellectual and technological discovery. The double-edged character of this tool is equally evident. Experience has demonstrated that the uses of science can be destructive as well as constructive, and that harmful as well as beneficial effects may result simultaneously from the same application of scientific or technical knowledge. What may be constructive for one purpose may be destructive for another. For example, chemical attack upon plant diseases may preserve the plants, but destroy bird and animal life. The dangerous potential of modern technoscience justifies efforts on the part of policy leaders and managers in society to bring its uses under some form of considered and effective control.

Proposals for the social control of the uses of science and technology are alarming to persons who foresee the advancement of knowledge hobbled by scientifically invalid, emotionally inspired policies. But the uses of science are, in fact, everywhere subject to some form of control. Where the political economy permits, as in the United States of America, a substantial part of this control is provided by the operation of the free-enterprise system. Science is applied where it proves commercially profitable to apply it. Science is also applied in efforts that yield no monetary advantage or return. Governmental scientific and technological activities are frequently of this non-profit character, but many of these activities do provide economic incentives to government contractors (as in space or defense efforts) or are indispensable to major profit-earning activities (as in the services of the National Bureau of Standards or the Environmental Science Services Administration). The specialized uses or non-uses of science and technology incident to economic or military purposes may be described as having a controlling effect. But it is questionable if they represent control in the sense of considered social intent. Their effects are more often the accidental consequences of unforeseen impacts upon the operation of our complex social system.

Hostility to the idea of the social control of science is commonly based on the assumption that science can exist independently of a political milieu and that science, free from "political interference," can advance indefinitely even though politics does not undergo a commensurate improvement. The assumption that politics cannot be improved is widespread and not easily refuted. But if politics is incorrigible, it must surely be because people are generally incapable of learning from experience or of paying the social costs of scientific advancement, one cost of which is clearly a more effective management of the natural assets of society. The notion that modern science could exist totally independent of politics has no foundation in actual practice.

The history of science and technology in modern national states records a variety of relationships between government and science. Where government has sponsored and controlled science (as in the Russian Empire and its Soviet successor state) or where benevolent disinterest has been the tradition (as in the United Kingdom and the United States), the prevailing order of politics has determined the relationships. For science to be free from "political interference," it is necessary to have a political order committed to the value of a "free" science. A political regime ignorant of science, its values, or its methods could inadvertently blunder into a crippling infringement of scientific inquiry. More likely, it would deliberately place science under certain prohibitions or restraints intended to protect prevailing dominant values.

The more directly that science impinges upon social and economic interests, the more it attracts political attention. The most free sciences are generally the most abstract ones. The history of science suggests that the more theoretical the science and the further it is removed from any practical application, the greater freedom it will be accorded in society. Advanced theoretical studies in physics and mathematics could be pursued with impunity and indeed with honor in Czarist Russia and the Soviet Union, whereas those biological and social sciences that were relevant to dogma or to issues of the day were vulnerable to political control. In the United

States, the freedom of science is relatively greater. But even in a non-ideological society, the freedom of science, determined more perhaps through legislative appropriations than overt controls, is greatest where its involvement in the social and economic affairs of society is least apparent.[1]

This generalization oversimplifies actual circumstances. In some respects, science applied to weapons systems has enjoyed considerable freedom, although the relevance of military applications to social and economic affairs is widely recognized. Where technology is based upon scientific knowledge, science must be enlisted when (or if) the uses of science are to be controlled with regard to the public safety and interest.

Scientific methods must be used to analyze the substance and scope of scientific knowledge in order to identify the points at which the search for new knowledge must be pushed. It is not safe to employ powerful science-based products and techniques when their effects upon the environment are untested and unknown. Environmental science therefore has a responsibility for analyzing the effects of human action upon the environment, especially when that action is implemented by science and is thus more likely to achieve results. Environmental management is more than applied science. It must apply science not only to the technologies of environmental manipulation, but to be effective, it must also build up a body of knowledge and doctrine about man/environmental relationships that will provide reliable guidance to wise action.

ENVIRONMENTAL SCIENCE AND TECHNOLOGY

If environmental management involves the application of science to environmental problems, its further examination requires, in relation to those problems, identification of both the science that is applied and the techniques of application. But before beginning this inquiry, a look at the characteristics of science and technology may be helpful.

Let us begin with science. It is not synonymous with absolute truth. Man invented science in order to discover the truth of things, but scientific knowledge is subject to obsolescence and to modification by new knowledge. It is further subject to alteration in the course of interpretation or application. Science is a systematic and objective method of seeking truth, but its findings are not always truth itself. Confusion of science with truth leads to scientism—an unscientific belief that science offers an answer to all human problems. The concept "science" is not precise. Scientific work involves imagination, insight, and a large number of techniques and skills that are properly classed as art. And (aside from science fiction) all scientists appear to be human. They are immune to none of the fallibilities of the human mind and personality. Nevertheless, a mystique has grown up around science and scientists that some scientists, with varying degrees of deliberateness, have found flattering to cultivate.[2] It is not in the interest of public responsibility to make a mystery of science, nor is it advantageous to science or the public welfare to have the opinions of scientists (even on science) accepted unquestioningly. Many scientists, perhaps most, agree with these observations. In summary, we would be justified in placing greater reliance than we do on scientific knowledge, but we should also remain aware of the limits of science, which are the limits of human insight, information, and understanding. Fallible man can hardly create an infallible science.

A second point of clarification pertains to technology. Scientific knowledge pertaining to the environment is largely applied through technology.[3] Knowledge may cause man to act or to refrain from acting directly upon the environment. Usually his action will be implemented or mediated by technology. Tools and methods, techniques and machines extend man's capabilities in relation to his environment. Collectively, these devices for implementation are called "technology." They may or may not be based on scientific knowledge, and unfortunately they seldom are provided with monitors that provide the warnings needed to protect man and nature from the harmful consequences of misapplication.

Although technology has sometimes been described as an autonomic and self-augmenting force, it is not necessary to endow it with metaphysical properties to establish its great influence upon society.[4] It is clear that reciprocal relationships exist between technology on the one hand and economic and military activity on the other. It is not necessary to our

purposes to know which is the primary influence. It is clear
that, once discovered, a powerful technology cannot easily
be suppressed. Economic interests seek out useful technologies that may be employed to advance some gainful purpose.
History is filled with accounts of timely (and untimely) innovations, many of which were devised in the hope of material reward. It therefore is plausible to argue that technology
is not a self-directing force, but is instead invented by men
to attain specific goals. While the range of ostensible goals is
great, most of them ultimately are reducible to power and/or
money. Technology is available only in so far as someone's
specific interests are thereby served.

Most advanced modern technologies are costly. Although
simple techniques persist from earlier times, and new methods
are sometimes inexpensive, the characteristic technologies of
modern society require highly developed production skills,
a wide diversity of natural and artificial materials, and elaborate industrial organization. Automobiles, computers, and tele-
vision require an environment of economic advancement
sufficient to support their production and use. But someone
in the society must somehow pay for their use. In the American economy, where a relatively free market prevails, technology is built into the economic system. Control of the
technology therefore entails control of, or at least intervention
in, the economic system.[5]

The expression "economic system" may be understood as
an abstraction summarizing the interrelated ways that people
earn livings. How people earn livings greatly affects all other
aspects of their lives. And so we find that, although the con-
necting chain may sometimes be extended, efforts to control
the impact of technology upon the environment come very
rapidly and literally into the personal lives and homes of
people. This is, of course, one reason why democratic governments in general, and elected officials in particular, are often
reluctant to take a lead in comprehensive environmental controls. As in the case of anti-pollution legislation, they prefer
to be pushed by vigorous public demand. Their reasoning is
understandable and consistent with democratic values. But
it leaves society vulnerable to dangers in the environment

that the public has not, in sufficient numbers or intensity, perceived as a threat.

Some of the most costly aspects of modern technology are not, however, economically induced. The vast and complex apparatus of military technology, of space exploration, of research in astronomy and high-energy physics, are paid for by the public through the agency of government. Yet aerospace, military, and atomic technologies generate industrial investment and production and create an economic interest in the perpetuation of public expenditure on these technoscientific enterprises. A major reason for the public management of these physical technologies is their enormous costliness; no other aggregation in society could afford to support them. Their maintenance and development are, however, competitive with environmental management for legislative appropriation. It is a competition in which military and quasi-military propositions have almost always won. As long as public opinion holds preponderately to the view that the nation is threatened more dangerously by political enemies from without than by social attitudes and practices that are destroying the environment from within, the disproportion between military expenditures and appropriations for conservation and environmental management will be great. Theoretically, the nation could, for example, simultaneously support war overseas and also cleanse the contamination of its rivers and lakes. Practically, it seems unlikely that it will ever do so.

TECHNOLOGY AND THE ENVIRONMENT—
THE PROBLEM OF CONTROL

Technology is controlled most effectively through its uses. To control the method or the machine, one controls the man who directs its use. If the effects of technology were only beneficent, and human employment of technology always adequately informed, responsible, and restrained by consideration for the public welfare, regulatory measures would be unnecessary. But these conditions cannot possibly exist. For example, the driver of an automobile cannot read the mind of another equally reasonable and responsible driver. Rules of the road are therefore devised to prevent inadvertent col-

lisions. In our uses of the environment, however, we have as
yet relatively few general "rules."[6]

The application of science and technology to management
of the environment is secondarily a matter of knowledge and
primarily a matter of values. This rank order of influence
should not suggest that the adequacy of knowledge, because
it is secondary, is relatively a minor consideration. This would
be a serious misunderstanding. Throughout this book, it has
been emphasized that the extent of scientific knowledge that
could be applied to environmental management is much
greater than is, in fact, being used; and there is need for
fuller knowledge of almost every aspect of environmental
science. The factor deterring us from the fullest use of what
we already know and from the extension of science into areas
of inadequate information is the factor of human choice.
Choices relating to the environment are seldom made explicitly by society in clearly stated referendums. They are
choices made inadvertently, most commonly in the course
of action on seemingly unrelated matters.

Choices are frequently institutional ones. An electric utility, for example, may have to weigh reduced returns or higher
rates against the cost of applying the latest technical advances
in the undergrounding of power lines. If the company concludes that its function is to provide the least costly power
with the highest return to the company, it may reject undergrounding. If the community has not made a choice favoring
the use of scientific technology on behalf of environmental
aesthetics, it is hardly reasonable to expect the company to do
so. If, however, public opinion places protection of environmental amenities as a constraint upon the electric-power industry or upon industrial activity in general, a value choice
will have been made that will influence institutional behavior.[7]

Scientific technologies are characteristically devised to meet
some specific need or objective. As noted, they frequently
serve an economic purpose, conferring real or assumed advantages upon their users. To control their use is to control
their users and perhaps to deprive them of advantages they
might otherwise enjoy. The application of science and technology to the environment in pursuance of benefits to the

user frequently has mixed effects upon other people. Some may also benefit, some may experience injury or deprivation, and frequently there will be a mixture of good and bad results. There is no end of familiar illustrations.

For example, if the Tennessee Valley Authority buys coal stripped from the West Virginia and Kentucky hills because (as a consequence of mining technology) its dollar price is low, it makes itself a party to the ecological and social devastation of this area of Appalachia. And if in extenuation of this policy it pleads the necessity of generating electric power at the lowest possible dollar cost, it is exemplifying the linear logic that has led to much of the unnecessary misuse of technology. Its cost accounting is incomplete unless it includes restoration of the environment from which the coal was taken. Failure to do this means that cheap electric power to one group of Americans is being subsidized by both the degradation of the environment of other Americans and the permanent impoverishment of a large area of Appalachia. A similar reasoning applies to hot water and other residues discharged from electric-generator plants, particularly those powered by atomic reactors. Energy systems are not solely matters of science, technology, and nineteenth-century bookkeeping. Their ecological effects must also be factored into any valid calculus of costs.

Agriculture provides many examples of the conflicts that arise when scientific technology is applied to the environment for specific purposes without regard to its effect upon the complexity of the total environment. The productivity of American agriculture has been a notable triumph of applied science. Within the usual context of agricultural economics, the application of science to the production of food and fiber is perhaps the most thoroughgoing example of deliberate environmental management that can be cited. But the achievements of agricultural productivity, when entered on a balance sheet of total effects, must be offset by the damage to the environment that too often results from an overly zealous application of science to agriculture. Human nutrition requires the sacrifice of large areas of the natural landscape to food production. But scientific methods have been widely misapplied in agriculture on behalf of economic concepts of efficiency that have no scientific validity and are often biologically unwise.[8]

Agricultural insecticides, fungicides, and herbicides may increase crop yields, thereby increasing profits to farmers, to chemical manufacturers, and to farm-supply retailers, and possibly bringing lower prices and more attractive fruits and vegetables to consumers. Against these benefits, both real and fancied, are possible dangers to health through toxic substances sprayed on agricultural produce and carried into the soil and water and on into an ecological chain that may ultimately affect human health indirectly. The pesticides may also directly affect animal life, notably insectivores such as birds. Decline or elimination of wildlife populations may have not only indirect ecological effects, but may also result in an aesthetic impoverishment of the countryside. Herbicides may increase agricultural acreage and provide clean fence rows devoid of cover or food for birds or other animals. Populations of pheasants, quail, rabbits, and other "game" animals may be reduced—to the deprivation of hunters and economic interests associated with hunting (and of course to people who enjoy the presence of these animals). Predator and so-called vermin control, still practiced by the federal government and by many of the states, is still another area where the environment is presumably managed through scientific techniques, but not toward objectives that are justified by comprehensive scientific knowledge.[9]

The rural and natural environment affords a further list of examples of indeterminate length illustrating the problems, difficulties, and conflicts resulting from the application of science to human purposes. An illustrative list of instances of environmental management suggests its scope and variety. Included in such a list could be: mosquito abatement, road building, scientific forestry, tree removal as a water-conservation measure, artificial stocking of fish and game birds, surface mining, irrigation, drainage, damming of streams, landfill of wetlands, range improvement by substituting exotic grasses for native forage, fish and shellfish cultivation in coastal waters, weather modification, windbreak planting, wildlife management, and use of fire as a control technique in forestry and agriculture.[10]

In the urban and industrial environments, the conflicts generated by applications of science to society are even more numerous. Mechanized and automated technologies impinge in many ways upon the life of industrial man and increasingly shape his immediate environment. Environmental hazards are more complex, some psychosomatic in their effects. Environmental pollution becomes more acute as more people are crowded together. Crowding itself gives rise to a number of problems, both psychological and physiological. Yet, in some respects the giant cities of our technological society are monuments to the power of applied science. The application of knowledge to sanitation, to water supply, to control of epidemic disease, to preservation and storage of food, to the transportation of people and material, to electric power, and to electronic communication and control, have made possible the megalopolis of the twentieth century.[11] The achievement has been prodigious, even though of dubious ecological wisdom.

And so, in urbanism as in agriculture, the balance sheet of human welfare shows mixed and even contradictory results. In both areas, science has been applied to the solution of specific human problems. Evaluated within the limited context of their specific objectives, some successes have been spectacular. But the applications of science have been made primarily to those problems that yield a pay-off to the applier—usually in money or power. There are consequently neglected areas, economically or politically unprofitable to cultivate, that might yield large social returns. Preventive measures to protect the environment are principal among these. And even in those areas of applied science in which success has seemed so unequivocal, as in certain aspects of agriculture, engineering, and medicine, there is a reverse side of progress.

Untoward or contrafunctional aspects of applied science are part of what is sometimes called "the price of progress." Yet not all of this price is fairly assessable as "payment" for advantages received. A large part of this so-called "price" may be attributed to misapplications of science. Among these misapplications, a large number occur not through want of knowledge, nor because of economic necessity, nor as a result of inadvertency or error. They occur because of the human tendency to focus upon one problem at a time—to act upon the environment in a variety of apparently unrelated ways toward unrelated or unreconciled objectives. The human environment is a single, complex ecological entity, but man persists in acting upon it as if each of his actions had no bearing upon any other aspect of the environment. As a consequence, monumental environmental disasters have occurred, some of them ironically resulting from action taken in the name of science.

The problem of environmental control is therefore basically conceptual. If the environment is not really perceived as a complex, interrelating whole, it will hardly be acted upon from this viewpoint. In a society in which the environment is commonly conceived as divisible into discrete resources such as water power, timber, fossil fuels, minerals, or farm land, it is easy to act in relation to each of these "resources" with minimal regard to their involvement with other aspects of the environment. When conflicts arise among resource users, as inevitably they do, no adequate principle is available upon which to base a sound compromise among the users or to choose one use as opposed to others.

Conflicts over resource uses tend therefore to be reduced to tests of political strength without regard to the environmental or ecological merits of the outcome. As noted in Chapter 1, economists have brought a measure of alleviation to uninhibited political combat through the technique of cost-benefit analysis. The technique has undergone refinement over the years, but is nevertheless susceptible to manipulation through arbitrary assignment of values to costs and to benefits. The fundamental weakness of cost-benefit analysis is, however, a consequence of insufficient knowledge. If we may assume hypothetically that there are "absolute" costs and benefits that exist independently of any cultural system of values—that are essentially physical or biological in character —the most valid application of cost-benefit analysis would be to ascertain the relationships among these natural factors. Knowledge of man's environmental needs and relationships and of ecological relationships generally is not presently sufficient to support this comparative calculus to the extent needed for wisdom and rationality in environmental decision making. More knowledge is needed, and to obtain and to apply this knowledge, some new relationships among the sciences and new emphases in education, in engineering, and in scientific research and development will be required.

DEVELOPING CAPABILITIES FOR APPLIED ECOLOGY

We have not yet attempted to answer the question posed at the outset of this chapter: Can men obtain guidance from science in the determination of social goals? Does the fact that they have seldom done so in the past mean that they will not do so in the future? The same general question may be asked by the query: How rational can man be? For science is not a resource independent of human intelligence. Science is simply a method of ascertaining reality—the most reliable method yet discovered by man. It includes not only the discovery of new knowledge, but the storage, organization, retesting, and dissemination of existing knowledge. Science is not an oracle; it is a method of work, and it must *be* worked if information or guidance is to be obtained from it.

The application of science to management of the human environment requires a reorganizing and refocusing of knowledge for this purpose. This does not mean a change in existing configurations of knowledge for purposes *now* well served. It does imply new formulations of knowledge for purposes not well served by today's science, and indicates new configurations among the sciences of the future. To deal with present problems of man/environment relationships, it is necessary to draw as fully as possible upon the information and methods of conventional sciences and professional disciplines. To reshape this knowledge so that it is applicable to emerging and future environmental problems requires institutional arrangements and synthesizing skills that have not heretofore generally been available. To argue that there is nothing about environmental science and technology that existing sciences and engineering could not supply directly would be comparable to arguing that schools of medicine and engineering were unnecessary because their basic data were already available in the fundamental sciences. Schools of medicine and of engineering do draw upon fundamental sciences, but they have organized this knowledge in ways not found in the basic disciplines, and they have added new knowledge and techniques of their own to that derived from the sciences.

Man cannot deal with matters politically that he has not first dealt with in some measure intellectually. Each of the major aspects of our public life—among them law, business, education, social service, agriculture, medicine, engineering, and public administration—has its counterpart in the structure of higher education and research. There may even be a rough analogy between the strength and prestige of these fields of study in the universities and their status in our popular scale of values. If we were to have a department of the environment as one of the great administrative divisions of the federal government, we would also need schools of environmental science and technology in our universities. But what would be the substance of such schools, and how would they relate to the broader field of undergraduate education in our colleges?

To answer these questions adequately, we must again distinguish between the two levels of concern with the environment introduced in Chapter 4. One of these concerns is conceptual. It does not imply or require technical knowledge or skill in solving environmental problems. It is the level of understanding of ecological relationships and of man's circumstances on Spaceship Earth, and it is also the level of public policy and administrative decision. This level of concern should be common to all informed citizens in a nation prepared to cope with its environmental problems. Our present environmental difficulties are largely attributable to the absence of this concern from the educational experience of Americans both in and out of formal schooling. This is the level of concern at which the liberal arts college and undergraduate university education can make maximum contributions toward popular understanding of man/environment relationships and what these relationships imply for human behavior and for public action.

The other level of concern is operational. It is the concern of the ecologist, the environmental planner, the epidemiologist, and the engineer. It implies varying degrees of technical knowledge and skill, based, however, upon a general systems, or ecological, view of reality. This systems-oriented, ecological proviso is absolutely fundamental to the education and research that will be adequate to meet the needs growing out of man's environmental planning and public health. We need what we have—but it is not enough. Present limitations are not so much in technique as in perspective, and in lack of interrelatedness and coherence in the use of the technical and professional skills needed for successful attack upon environmental problems.

No really adequate schools of environmental science and technology exist as yet. The reason is not wholly lack of appreciation for the need; beginnings have been made in several colleges and universities, and plans are under consideration in many more. At least four deterring factors may be identified. The *first* and perhaps the principal deterrent has been lack of the well-organized reciprocal relationship that must exist between a field of education that is policy and action oriented, and a field of public action. For example, law, medicine, agriculture, engineering, education, and theology have been organized fields both of education and of practice. Man's manipulation of the environment is a large and complex field of action, but it is only now beginning to be perceived as a unified field of public policy. As the tasks of environmental manipulation come to be increasingly perceived in ecological terms (as they must be if man is to maintain or improve his present position on the Earth), the training needed for these tasks will change, and the rationale for the school of environmental science and technology will become clearer.

A *second* deterrent has been the scope of the enterprise needed to deal effectively with the management of man's environmental relationships. The wide range and complexity of the environment and of the ways in which men relate to it makes it as difficult to organize its study institutionally as it is to organize one's thinking about it. Since we have insufficient tested experience upon which to base opinions, we still depend upon "considered judgment" in determining how best to organize the field of study. Because of its complexity and its dependence upon other disciplines, the professional study of environmental science, technology, and management should be organized primarily at the graduate level of the university. Understanding of environmental and ecological relationships is, of course, a critical need at all levels of education, especially at elementary and secondary school levels.

A question debated in many universities has been that of finding a "handle" to take hold of the environmental issue. Understandably reluctant to take on all of man's environmental problems, university committees have often attempted to identify a clearly defined, manageable subject-matter area for attention. But it is doubtful if self-imposed limitations are as practical as they may at first appear. The environment of man, like the universe of the astronomer, is a whole. Specialization is feasible and necessary provided it occurs within the context of the whole. Therefore, the conjecture seems probable that the more successful academic efforts to deal with the environment will be found among those most broadly based in concept. It matters less that all major aspects of the environment may not initially be brought under study than that their study be provided for in a plan that is consistent with the magnitude and complexity of the subject matter. Interuniversity programs or consortiums may help to meet the problem of addressing the broad scope of the field of study, given the limited resources and the special emphasis of individual universities.

A *third* deterrent to environmental studies is the belief that their separate organization would duplicate work now being done elsewhere within the university. If there should in fact be unavoidable duplication (and not merely its semblance), some internal reorganization in the university might be indicated. But the fact of duplication does not necessarily evidence waste or malorganization. Reorganization, like medication, tends to be disagreeable, and its justification depends upon its effecting a cure. Unfortunately, as with medication, justification through results may require time. Universities are particularly difficult to reorganize—and yet their history shows that massive changes do occur.

A *fourth* deterrent to the establishment of graduate schools of environmental science and technology has been insufficient money. The money is available, but Americans have not allocated it for this purpose; high-energy physics, for example, has been preferred. Past expenditure has traditionally been the yardstick by which Americans normally measure the reasonableness of expenditures for any purpose. This is the conventional method of legislative appropriation committees and of budget examiners. For environmental research, protection, and control, past expenditures were little to nothing, and therefore present requests at any figure seem high. A more valid yardstick would be comparable aspects of military defense expenditures. If these were used, present allocations to environmental administration and technology, and especially to environmental research and development, would be seen to be absurdly low. Allocation of vast sums to a dramatic new policy (as in the space race) may appear to contradict reliance on past experience for measures of reasonableness. But examination of Congressional reasoning in relation to the space effort makes evident its close connection to defense expenditures. The yardstick for the space program was not prior appropriations for astronautics or astronomy, but expenditures for war. And this is the yardstick most appropriate to the environmental needs of man and of the endangered ecosystems of North America. The development of capabilities for applied ecology does not and need not depend wholly upon what universities can do. Applied ecology is emerging as a field of professional service or business enterprise sometimes in conjunction or association with universities or research institutions. New forms of action-oriented research and development institutions have been proposed to deal with the social and environmental impact of technology and with research into man/environment relationships. Illustrative of the innovations are proposals for joint efforts between the Argonne National Laboratory and the Argonne Universities Association,[12] and the suggestions of the Conference on Environmental Research of the National Academy of Sciences for a corporate agency to pursue, organize, assist, and coordinate research relating to problems of the human environment.[13] The National Institute of Ecology, proposed by the Ecological Society of America, would contribute to capabilities in applied ecology indirectly, through enlarging the base of ecological understanding, and directly, to the extent that its investigations addressed themselves to practical problems.[14]

SCIENTIFIC TECHNIQUES FOR ENVIRONMENTAL MANAGEMENT

The operational level of environmental management consists of a series of tasks most of which are preventative and restorative. As outlined in Chapter 4, these tasks of protection are: (1) to monitor environmental change, (2) to check environmental deterioration, (3) to prevent such deterioration, and (4) to repair the damage that has already been done to the terrestrial ecosystem. In addition to these tasks of management, there are those directed toward the adaptation or improvement of the natural environment in relation to human needs and purposes. These tasks were described in Chapter 5 and are those with which human society has primarily been occupied in the course of taking "possession" of the Earth. But during man's millenniums-long effort to subdue the Earth, it was seldom the environment *per se* that concerned him, but rather some specific resource or property in the environment, as for example, arable land, building material, or negotiable wealth. The tools and techniques for environmental adaptation have not, until recently, been obtained through science. They were instead derived from experience, and like the axe, the spade, and the spear, have been developed into sophisticated instruments for environmental control into which science has now made inputs.

But environmental administration does not embrace all aspects of all activities that shape or influence the environment. It is not concerned with all aspects of agriculture, forestry, fisheries, or road building; its focus is upon the impact of these and other activities on man's total ecological needs in the environment. The emphasis of environmental management is therefore on surveillance, guidance, and protection, and its tools and techniques are more characteristically those of measurement and analysis (e.g., Geiger counters, gas analyzers, and aerial photogrammetry) rather than of physical impact (e.g., chain saws, bulldozers, and herbicides). The substance of the environmental management task cannot fully be defined until there are decisions regarding what needs to be done. Establishment of ecological base lines and descriptions of their scope and significance require the combined

efforts of scientists, technicians, and adminis
tion, however, cannot be undertaken until me
have been devised and employed for gaugi
and extent of environmental change.

Monitoring systems and devices are established for purposes of detection and measurement of specified environmental conditions (e.g., sulphur dioxide in the air, DDT in
the water, soil erosion on the land). The practical significance of these measurements becomes evident only when they
are projected against standards of quality that represent progressive degrees of environmental change, adulteration, or
hazard. At some state, as in smog alerts in Los Angeles or
as in coeloform bacteria counts on public beaches, administrative action may be automatically invoked, and predetermined legal prohibitions or requirements put into effect.
Stated simply, someone must examine the state of a particular
aspect of the environment, apply the measuring device, and
compare his reading with the standard. There are several ways
of doing this, plus a variety of instruments to facilitate the
analytic process. The principal ways include (1) samples, (2)
records, (3) case studies, and (4) bench marks. Techniques
associated with these methods have been as important in protecting human beings from the natural hazards of the environment as they have been in preventing the viability of
the environment from being destroyed by inordinate human
pressure.

Sampling techniques have been applied to almost every
major environmental phenomenon: to air, water, soil, and
minerals, to various forms of radiation, and to organisms
living and dead. Sampling may be used in combination with
other techniques, as for example, with record keeping, thus
permitting statistical comparisons to be made between different localities and different points in time. It is an essential
technique in air- or water-pollution control.[15]

Recording of environmental statistics, and of numerical
data on tides, floods, earthquakes, the weather, forest fires,
alga "blooms," plant and animal diseases, and population
cycles, for example, enables us to identify environmental trouble spots and, more importantly, to project trends. It is useful
to know the history of flooding in river valleys when methods

mizing flood damage are under consideration, and
orecasting of weather is made more reliable by accurate
storical records. Recordings of environmental phenomena
are characteristically also measurements. The techniques extend from the most simple observational methods to such advanced methods as seismology, geodesy, chromatography,
electromagnetic sensing, and photographic reconnaissance or
remote sensing via airplane or satellite.[16] Devices that monitor and record environmental phenomena are becoming
more elaborate and more common. Tiros weather satellites
are now familiar objects, at least by reputation.[17]

Less familiar, but indicative of the advancing state of available technology, is the electromagnetic fence of the United
States Naval Space Surveillance System. This electronic
"screen" extends across the entire continent of North America and upward into the stratosphere. Objects passing through
the "screen" interrupt a continuous signal from transmitters
and reflect the interrupted signal back to receivers that transmit this information by wire into a series of data processors,
computers, and recorders. The intended function of the system is to detect the presence of man-made objects in the
atmosphere and outer space above the North American continent. These objects may or may not have major environmental significance, but the system itself may be adaptable
to (or may inspire) a more extended range of applications.[18]

Case studies afford still another approach to environmental
surveillance. This method, when applied to environmental
investigation, is usually an attempt to ascertain cause-and-
effect relationships. It has been used to reconstruct past events
for which no systematic recording of data occurred, but
which might offer guidance in coping with future contingencies. Studies of environmental catastrophes are cases in point.
For example, between 1963 and 1965, the Hudson Institute
produced a series of studies of past environmental disasters
such as earthquakes, volcanic eruptions, and insect depre-
dations, as background for civil defense efforts and estimates
of the probable consequences of thermonuclear war.[19] A
more extensive collection of case studies of ecological errors
resulted from a conference on the Ecological Aspects of International Development convened in December 1968 by the

Conservation Foundation and the Center for the Biology of Natural Systems of Washington University.[20] Less-dramatic uses of case studies may be found in such environmentally connected activities as wildlife management, popular reactions to environmental hazards, and urban planning. The case study may therefore be, in effect, surveillance extended backward into time, or it may present a composite or synthesized picture of a contemporary or future circumstance.

For the detection and measurement of certain types of environmental change, it is necessary to identify bench marks, or fixed points in reference, in the environment. These reference points must have stability relative to the changes that are being monitored. For example, changes in land forms, in vegetation, in soil condition, or in specific types of ecosystems are more easily ascertained if full descriptions, or (better yet) living examples, of more generally prevailing earlier conditions are available for comparison with subsequent conditions. All nature is, of course, in a state of continuous change, but, for some ecosystems, a relative stabilization has occurred, so that these systems, or the areas in which they are contained, afford reliable bench marks against which to compare the sequence, timing, and effects of change in less-stable areas. To make a comparative assessment of the impact of human technology upon the environment, the protection of representative types of natural areas is desirable. The effects of overgrazing by wild or domesticated animals, or of ecologically damaging methods of soil cultivation or crop production, can be determined by reference to control areas in which neither grazing nor cultivation is permitted, or where carefully managed manipulation of the components of the ecological situation is carried on, as for example, at the Hastings Reservation of the University of California or the Brookhaven National Laboratory.[21] Permanent signs or markers have been used to assist detection of environmental changes in land and water surfaces (e.g., the elevation of the land above sea level, flood stages of rivers, and the configuration of coast lines) and as warnings to indicate undersurface conditions on the land and at sea (e.g., signs indicating subsurface pipelines or cables, and buoys marking submerged hazards to navigation).

Environmental surveillance serves protective purposes in two ways. It may alert designated officials to the need for action on some specific impending threat from the environment to man, or from man to the environment; and it may also indicate the long-range direction of environmental trends. As previously noted, when monitoring devices indicate a predetermined level of hazard for smog, floods, or forest fires, appropriate previously determined administrative responses are activated. Where highly articulated systems are operative, it may even be possible to automate a response to warning signals. This is seen in simple form in automatic alarm systems for fire, or for dangerous gases in mines. The number of environmental hazards being brought under surveillance and warning systems is being extended and the systems refined. A world weather watch is evolving into a global system of forecasting, and among specific refinements, tornado alerts are now standard operating procedure where these storms threaten.[22] Insect infestations can now be predicted, mapped in advance, and subjected to appropriate controls.[23] It may ultimately be possible to forecast with much greater precision than at present the probable occurrence of earthquakes. Partial protection from the effects of earthquakes and from waves resulting from seismatic disturbances under the sea is already provided through a seismographic monitoring and warning system.[24]

Long-range projection is the second benefit obtainable from environmental surveillance. Measurements of soil erosion, of loss of soil fertility, of quantity of carbon dioxide in the atmosphere, and of the advance and retreat of glaciers and polar icecaps may not trigger off immediate responsive action. But these relatively slow-moving environmental changes may hold important implications for the future. They are often indicators of need for more knowledge, and so may stimulate research.

Environmental surveillance is thus undertaken in order to predict with increasing accuracy the probable state of the environment at some future time. The time factor may be minutes in a tornado alert or it may be centuries for certain geological changes. In so far as a phenomenon cannot be controlled with assurance, warning systems enable men to better prepare themselves to cope with environmental hazards or to flee their onset. For more-generalized or longer-range hazards, the great advantage of surveillance is the evidence it provides for trend projection and thereby for the exploration of alternative ways of altering or coping with the trends. Of special importance is the identification of trends toward irreversible effects that man could not or would not wish to endure. These effects, such as the consequences of unchecked increase of carbon dioxide or other noxious gases in the atmosphere, must be forestalled by action taken long in advance of the point of actual hazard. Laboratory experiments in simulated environments, such as those made possible in the Biotron, at the University of Wisconsin, should enable us to foreshorten time and to manipulate trends. Computerized projections supplementing controlled environmental experimentation may give us the solid evidence needed to shape public environmental policies for the future and to specify by law certain types of behavior or restraint that would otherwise lack adequate basis for legislative or administrative action.

Science and technology are not self-executory. If science is to be invoked on behalf of a better environment, means must be provided to enable it to respond to the call. This means that a coherent system is needed for translating scientific knowledge into purposeful action. No adequate system now exists for environmental problems. Even a "Manhattan Project" for the American environment would be less than what is needed, although an adequately funded and focused effort of the character that utilized science and technology in developing the atomic bomb and in landing men on the Moon could greatly improve the present situation. A great deal of knowledge is already available regarding the application of ecology to industrial society.[25] The problem of applying science is not primarily a matter of knowledge, but of public will, implemented through appropriate administrative organization.

It may be fatuous to declaim about the destiny of man when present hazards to the future of civilized society are so apparent. It is reasonable, however, to point out the things that man must do if his future condition is to be as good as his present, however inadequate that present may appear to be. Present-day man has a science that is good enough to enable him to see the error of his ways and to provide guidance toward a better future.[26] But neither science nor history offers any assurance that the human race will be or can be guided by its own best interests or can agree as to what its "best interests" really are. These interests are not always (perhaps seldom) consistent with the personal or short-range interests of the individuals of whom societies are composed. Over large parts of the world, in Asia, Africa, and Latin America, the coercive pressure of short-range "necessities" may lead to total catastrophe before the end of this century. The possibility of massive and thoroughgoing ecological collapse is conceivable—with social and political consequences that cannot be foreseen. In North America and Europe, and especially in the United States, the opportunity still exists to bring man's behavior and the capabilities of his environment into a dynamic balance—stable and yet creative. One must be an optimist to believe that adequate advantage of this opportunity will be taken. Yet it may be true that the constructive work of the world has been done by hopeful pessimists, and that the vindication of their hopefulness is the best of what we call civilization.

ENVIRONMENTAL MANAGEMENT
AS A PUBLIC FUNCTION

The way in which societies and governments organize to deal with problems of the environment depends not only upon the nature of the problems, but also upon contingent circumstances of history, culture, and institutional structure. At present, these considerations preclude any universal "one best way" to organize for environmental management. The practicable course toward understanding the problems of environmental management, therefore, is to examine them in relation to a particular political jurisdiction. At this point in time, the United States offers an especially challenging opportunity for examining problems of policy and administrative organization. This is not only because of the magnitude and diversity of its environmental difficulties and their complex involvement with science-based technology, but also because the nation is now in the process of establishing environmental management as a defined and regularized public function.

How can modern societies organize to deal effectively with problems of the environment? As with most social questions, the answer depends upon contingent factors. These factors must be specified before any appraisal of organizational effectiveness can be made. Principal among these factors are the goals sought in the environment: If a society acquiesces in the exploitation of the environment for maximum material "wealth" in the shortest time regardless of the consequences, the organizational arrangements could differ greatly from those that would be required if ecological self-renewal were a major objective. In a complex and diverse society, social goals are necessarily formulated in broad terms. To become operational, they must be implemented by specific criteria for policy choice and must be supported by a system for the collection, interpretation, and evaluation of relevant information. It is therefore impractical to consider in the abstract what methods are best for coping with environmental problems.

Environmental management requires comprehensive planning but does not imply a specific form or method. The objective of environmental planning is to obtain a more adequate consideration of alternatives in the protection, modification, and improvement of the total environment than could be obtained through the independent and uncoordinated efforts of separate environment-shaping agencies. One measure of the effectiveness of planning is obviously the extent to which it contributes to the attainment of intended objectives. But an important secondary consideration is the extent to which the net benefits of a plan or method exceed the sum total of the costs it exacts. For no activity of any kind occurs without cost. All actions exact costs in energy and opportunity. Therefore, all policies for the environment represent value judgments; they are, in effect, decisions as to the worth of specified properties or conditions of the environment. Environmental planning that is comprehensive and realistic will require, either explicitly or by implication, the making of social decisions regarding the uses to which knowledge and energy are to be directed, and the opportunities that are to be made available, now and in the future.

If a thoroughgoing social consensus prevailed regarding the uses of the environment, environmental policy would be environmental problem solving. Its business would be largely scientific, technical, and administrative. Controversy would be over means rather than ends; and objective appraisal of means would generally be possible. But clearly the emphasis in planning for society's environmental needs should differ, depending upon whether environmental problems are technical or political. In fact, the environmental problems of modern industrial society today are both technical and political. At this point in time, they are more political than technical because of widely differing social attitudes regarding the values to be sought in the environment and to be implemented by governmental action. The success of a technical innovation may depend upon its social acceptance. For example, the emerging technology of weather modification may make feasible radical new methods for managing the environment, but this feasibility will be contingent upon satisfactory solutions to the social, economic, and legal problems involved.[1]

Problems of policy and organizational choice are further complicated by the fact that not all social values or influences in the environment are equally supported by scientific evidence or by observed experience. For example, a continuing increase in CO_2 in the atmosphere cannot be established to be socially desirable regardless of popular indifference to it or of popular preference for activities that cause it to occur. Environmental policy making that seeks the continuing welfare of society must therefore endeavor to discover and to bridge gaps that separate political feasibility from scientific reality. Yet difficulties further increase, because the state of scientific knowledge is not adequate to answer all environmental questions. It is easier to identify conditions that are incontrovertibly harmful (e.g., ionizing radiation or heavy concentrations of DDT in food chains) than to establish that specified conditions beyond those necessary for health and survival are "objectively" good. Consequently, environmental policy tends to be probabilistic. It must depend as often upon prudent conjecture as upon rigorous analysis. In this, it is no less accurate or objective than in the calculations upon which foreign policy and military strategy are based. In fact, the scientific evidence for environmental policy is more adequate, but psychologically men are more ready to accept conjectures regarding threats from other men than they are willing to admit responsibility for their own damaging impact on the environment. The empirical evidence of foreign hostility weighs more heavily with peoples and governments than the often less evident but perhaps more dangerous threats to national security through damage to a nation's ecosystems. And the enormous costs of foreign policies and military establishments pre-empt throughout most modern states the resources in money and men that might otherwise be directed (among other purposes) toward the protection and improvement of the environment.

The nature of the public function in the environment is

defined by public policy and made operative through public administration. The political character of a public function is colored by the particular historical and cultural circumstances of the society in which it occurs. Policies differ among public agencies in response to the personalities and ambitions of their executive heads, the professional biases of the bureaucracy, the varying interpretations of mission and legal authority, and the relationships with constituents throughout the country and in the legislature. Therefore, discussion of environmental policy as a public function must be at a relatively high level of generalization. Only to a limited extent should it include specific policy formulations or program arrangements. But environmental management is concerned with the real and present world. A highly abstract account of its problems could obscure the relevance of the subject matter and diminish the reader's appreciation of the reality of the issues. For this reason, the following discussion will be focused on certain specific aspects of environmental management as an emerging function in the United States. There is, of course, a risk in dealing with contemporary or very recent political events—it is difficult to assess their long-range significance and to relate them unerringly to particular trends or principles. Therefore, although the point will not be labored throughout this chapter, a certain tentativeness in the appraisals should be assumed. Some aspects of the narrative are distinctively American in character —Presidential/Congressional relations, for example. Many of the basic considerations, however, would be relevant to environmental administration in any modern industrial state.

TOWARD A SUBSTANCE FOR POLICY

Under the political circumstances of the world today, public policy for the environment must be a policy of national government. It must be a policy for people within the context of their total environments, and this means that environmental policy must also have an international dimension. Its foundations must be broad enough to support the full range of those human needs that depend for fulfillment upon the environment. These needs are diverse; some are essential to survival, others are experienced very differently among various sectors of the population. The more-obvious needs are those that we describe abstractly as physiological, economic, aesthetic, scientific, and recreational. An adequate policy for the environment must therefore be shaped to take account of the total needs of the total man in the total environment. The series of unrelated unidimensional policies for the environment around which governmental programs have characteristically been built have not proved adequate to protect mankind's natural life-support system, nor have they adequately protected the diversity of values that men seek in the environment. It is for these reasons that the Biosphere Conference in Paris in 1968 recommended: ". . . that Member States and governing bodies of all United Nations organizations develop comprehensive and integrated policies for management of the environment, and that international efforts and problems be considered in the formulation of such policies."[2]

This need for a policy for the total environment does not imply that government should establish laws and regulations governing all environmental details. It does not mean that national government, or government generally, should itself manage and direct all uses of the environment. The task of environmental management is so vast and so complex that, to be accomplished, it must be widely shared. In the United States, it is a task not merely for the national government, but also for the states and localities, and for neighborhoods, groups, and individuals. It will increasingly be a responsibility of international agencies in co-operation with national governments and with scientific and industrial organizations. But neither individuals nor organizations can work together nor take constructive independent action in the absence of goals, standards, and guidelines. A national policy for the environment is needed to provide these common criteria for independent but mutually consistent courses of action. Government today speaks of environmental problems with many discordant and inconsistent voices. The environmental administration that present circumstances require would be widely distributed and diversified throughout society. But before this can happen, government at the national level must be reoriented for this function, for only as its facilities for national policy making and administration permit, can the full potential of American society for constructive and responsible action for the environment be mobilized.

As noted in Chapters 2 and 3, the transition from a policy focus upon natural resources and conservation to a national policy for the environment was gradual. No clear break in time can be identified as marking the departure from an essentially nineteenth-century relationship of society to the natural world, and the attitude that could become necessary if modern society were to survive into the twenty-first century. Yet the nineteen sixties appear to be a critical period of transformation, marking a change in the character of American public life at least as profound as that which had accompanied the American Civil War a century earlier. The public identification of a crisis in the environment first became evident during the presidential administration of John F. Kennedy. The emergent concept of "environmental preservation" was given a text in a book, *The Quiet Crisis*,[3] written by Secretary of the Interior Stewart L. Udall, under whose eight-year tenure a major transformation occurred in public expectations regarding the responsibilities of government for the environment.

The first legislative effort to establish and implement a national policy for the environment did not, in fact, specify the environment as the object of its concern; but this, in effect, was its substance and intent. On August 20, 1959, Senate Bill 2549 was introduced in the first session of the Eighty-sixth Congress by Senator James E. Murray of Montana, Chairman of the Senate Committee on Interior and Insular Affairs. The stated purpose of the bill was "to declare a national policy on conservation, development, and utilization of natural resources. . . ." The bill contained a statement of national policy ". . . to use all practical means, including coordination and utilization of all its plans, functions, and facilities, for the purpose of creating and monitoring . . . conditions under which there will be conservation, development, and utilization of the natural resources of the Nation to meet human, economic, and national defense requirements, including recreational, wildlife, scenic and scientific values, and the enhancement of the national heritage for future generations." The operational aspect of the bill contained a feature to be included in subsequent legislative proposals—a high-level council for fact finding and review.

A Council of Resource and Conservation Advisers would have been created in the Executive Offices of the President on the model of the Council of Economic Advisers. Its functions were to study natural-resource and development trends and the related programs and activities of the federal agencies to determine their consistency with the declared national policy. The Council was directed to make recommendations to the President to implement the national policy and to report annually to the President, who in turn would annually present a Resources and Conservation Report to Congress. A joint committee on resources and conservation would have been created in Congress to receive and study the presidential report and to guide other committees of Congress dealing with legislation relating to the report.

Hearings were held early in 1960 on the proposed Resources and Conservation Act of 1960. The bill received the support of a distinguished group of Senators and conservationists, and was endorsed in the Democratic platform in the 1960 electoral campaign. During the campaign, John F. Kennedy expressed concern with the difficulties of co-ordinating natural-resource programs—citing as problems, overlapping agency policies, lack of comparability among standards for federal contributions to natural-resource projects, and inconsistency in agency policies on federal fees and user charges. At the time of his inauguration, he was believed to favor the principles of the Murray bill. But as President he abandoned this approach and in a special message on natural resources he stated his intention to administratively redefine resource responsibilities within the Executive Branch; strengthen the Council of Economic Advisers by establishing with the Council a Presidential Advisory Committee on Natural Resources; and instruct the Director of the Budget to formulate general principles for the application of user charges at all types of federal resource projects, and to re-evaluate the standards for appraising the feasibility of water resources projects.[4]

Although President Kennedy convened a White House Conference on Conservation in 1962 and requested the National Academy of Sciences to undertake a comprehensive study of the nation's natural-resource base, his major interests lay in other directions. His concern with natural resources appears to have been primarily economic rather than ecological.[5] The focus of national policy on the environment during the Kennedy years was in the office of the Secretary of the Interior, although bills to establish a high-level advisory council on conservation, natural resources, and the environment were introduced into every Congress during the nineteen sixties. Under the Kennedy administration, the nation had moved somewhat indecisively toward a policy for the environment. The policy issue, discussed in Chapter 2, was to become more explicit during the Johnson administration, which followed.

The "New Conservation" became a major theme in Lyndon B. Johnson's campaign for the presidency in 1964. In a message to the Congress on February 8, 1965, President Johnson spoke of the darker side of modern technology, which threatened to blight and diminish the quality of American life. Calling for a redefinition of the meaning of conservation, he declared: "The same society which received the rewards of technology, must as a cooperating whole, take responsibility for control." And he continued:

> "To deal with these problems will require a new conservation. We must not only protect the countryside and save it from destruction, we must restore what has been destroyed and salvage the beauty and charm of our cities. Our conservation must be not just the classic conservation of protection and development, but a creative conservation of restoration and innovation. Its concern is not with nature alone, but with the total relation between man and the world around him. Its object is not just man's welfare, but the dignity of man's spirit."[6]

Concern for ". . . the total relation between man and the world around him" was a far-reaching interpretation of public responsibility. It described a general orientation of government, but it did not define a policy in operational terms. And although the Johnson administration performed with vigor and success on many specific environmental issues, it never made explicit this very general expression of policy.

The White House Conference on Natural Beauty of May 24–25, 1965, marked a new high level of national concern regarding the aesthetic aspects of the environment. But the momentum of public enthusiasm stimulated by the conference was insufficiently sustained by presidential action. President Johnson became increasingly preoccupied with the deepening conflict in Vietnam and with growing civil disorder at home. Although conferences on natural beauty or environmental quality were held in as many as half the states, White House follow-up showed neither direction nor vigor. The "natural beauty movement" as an expression of environment policy soon ran its course. Moreover, in a variety of notorious instances, the President took no action to restrain his own administrative appointees and their subordinates from pursuing policies that flagrantly contradicted his "new conservation" concept, and indeed his personal insistence on obtaining more revenues from leases of federal mineral resources contributed to the disastrous oil pollution of the Santa Barbara Channel.[7] The Johnson administration, notably through the efforts of Secretary of the Interior Stewart L. Udall, had taken a large step forward toward a national policy for the environment. But it had stopped short of the threshold. The locus of environmental policy making shifted to the Congress.

On the matter of general policy formulation, as distinguished from specific decisions, President Johnson may have gone as far as he could go, given the prevailing level of public comprehension and concern. Yet a profusion of legislative proposals and committee action in the Eighty-ninth, Ninetieth, and Ninety-first Congresses indicated growing popular support for the environmental-quality issue; and this evidence appeared to be corroborated by analysis of public opinion. It could be argued that during the latter years of the nineteen sixties the people were more responsive to the idea of a national policy for the environment than was the Congress, and that the Congress was more responsive than the executive branch.

In effect, the Congress backed into the question of a national policy for the environment in the course of attempting to cause the national government to give greater attention and higher priority to ecological values. "Environment," for the first time, appears to have become an explicit object of legislative action in the Ecological Research and Surveys Bill introduced in the Eighty-ninth Congress, First Session, on July 13, 1965, by Senator Gaylord Nelson of Wisconsin. The purpose of the proposed act was ". . . to authorize a comprehensive program of research, studies, and surveys in order to produce an understanding of our natural resources and the environmental forces responsible for their development and well-being and to provide a basis for the future protection, enhancement and proper utilization of the natural environmental systems of the United States." Administration of the ecological research and surveys would have been placed in the Department of the Interior. Although the Nelson bill was not enacted, it was a pivotal piece of legislation. Emphasis had shifted from the earlier Congressional concern with "resources" to a new policy focus—"the environment." In an attempt to respond to public pressure to "do something" about the worsening environmental situation, the leaders in the Congress tried first to give the issue visibility and to provide a basis for environmental policy through ecological fact finding and evaluation. Congressional proposals prior to 1969 did not attempt in more than very general terms to state the substance of the policy to be pursued.

As many as twenty bills relating to environmental policy or administration were introduced into the Ninetieth Congress. Among these, several, following the pattern of the Murray bill in 1959, proposed the establishment of a council of environmental or ecological advisers in the Executive Office of the President, and a periodic report from the President to the nation on the state of the environment. These proposals differed in two important respects from their prototype, the Council of Economic Advisers. First, they did not contain a statement of policy as explicit as that contained in the Employment Act of 1946 establishing the Council. Second, unlike the Employment Act, or the earlier Murray bill, the environmental-quality bills made no special provision for Congressional referral or review. Nothing comparable to the Congressional Joint Committee on the Economic Report was provided in relation to environmental issues. Except for the requirement of a presidential environmental-quality report and the authorization of funds for ecological surveys and research, the environmental-quality bills were more hortatory than action forcing.

The immediate purpose of the greater number of these bills was not immediate enactment, but public discussion. Their sponsors generally viewed them as initial drafts, to be expanded, revised, and refined in the course of public debate following publication and public hearings. During the second session of the Ninetieth Congress, the environmental-quality leadership was prepared to move beyond the initial provisions for ecological research and high-level review and advice and to attempt to formulate more-explicit statements of environmental policy. The first policy statements were primarily expressions of principle, but successive drafts incorporated operational and action-forcing provisions.

On July 17, 1968, a joint colloquium on a National Policy for the Environment was held at the Capitol under the sponsorship of the Senate Committee on Interior and Insular Affairs (Henry M. Jackson, Chairman) and the House of Representatives Committee on Science and Astronautics (George P. Miller, Chairman). Preparatory to this colloquium, both the Senate and House committees published background reports on the issue. The Senate document—"A National Policy for the Environment"—reprinted in the published hearing of the Joint House-Senate Colloquium, stated the essence of a national policy in language appropriate to a joint resolution of the Congress:

> It is the intent of the Congress that the policies, programs, and public laws of the United States be interpreted and administered in a manner protective of the total needs of man in the environment. To this end, the Congress proposes that arrangements be established to make effective the following objectives of national policy for the environment.
> 1. To arrest the deterioration of the environment.
> 2. To restore and revitalize damaged areas of our nation so that they may once again be productive of economic wealth and spiritual satisfaction.
> 3. To find alternatives and procedures which will minimize and prevent future hazards in the use of environment-shaping technologies, old and new.

4. To provide direction and, if necessary, new institutions and new technologies designed to optimize man-environment relationships and to minimize future costs in the management of the environment.

A somewhat more detailed enumeration of national policy objectives was included in the *Congressional White Paper* summarizing the results of the Joint House-Senate Colloquium. But the first move to legislate a statement of national policy for the environment came in the Ninety-first Congress in an amendment to S.1075 (Jackson), entitled the "National Environmental Policy Act of 1969." Title I of this bill moved beyond any previous legislative proposals in providing an explicit and operational statement of environmental-quality objectives. And in so doing, it brought into view a conflict between the executive branch and the Congressional environmental-quality leadership that had been latent since the Murray bill failed to win approval in 1960. At issue have been the respective roles of the President and the Congress in the initiation and interpretation of national policy, and particularly the ability of the Congress to modify through a superordinate national policy for environmental quality the unilateral action of the executive agencies in pursuit of their particular missions.

An amended but substantially intact version of the Jackson bill was signed into law by President Nixon on January 1, 1970. The National Environmental Policy Act of 1969 (PL 91–190) culminated a decade-long effort to declare and confirm the responsibility of the American Government for the management of man's impact upon his environment. Practical analysis of the Act must necessarily await its implementation, but the official announcement of the signing of the bill into law summarized its salient features:

"(1) It declares that it is the policy of the Federal Government to use all practicable means to create and maintain conditions under which man and nature can exist in productive harmony and fulfill the social, economic, and other requirements of present and future generations of Americans.

(2) It establishes within the Executive Office of the President a full-time, three-man Council on Environmental Quality

which will be appointed by the President and subject to Senate confirmation.

(3) It requires the President to submit to Congress annually, beginning July 1, 1970, environmental quality reports. This report will set forth the status of the Nation's various environmental programs and will review the impact of these on the environment and on the conservation, development, and use of our national resources.

(4) The Council on Environmental Quality will have the following major duties: (a) assist and advise the President in the preparation of the annual report; (b) develop and recommend to the President national policies which promote environmental quality; and (c) accumulate necessary data for a continuing analysis of changes or trends in the national environment."[8]

In approving the bill the President spoke of the challenge of the environment not only to America but to other industrialized societies and to the less technologically advanced nations as well. He saw the task in America as larger than that of the federal government, involving the states, the cities and massive efforts of volunteers.[9] "We are most interested in results," the President declared. "The act I have signed gives us an adequate organization and a good statement of direction. We are determined that the decade of the seventies will be known as the time when this country regained a productive harmony between man and nature."[10]

Although the principles involved in the National Environmental Quality Act were more than a decade in gestation, seldom has a specific measure of as great potential significance and implication for policy and power been enacted as swiftly and with as little controversy or debate. Less than six months elapsed between passage of the original bill (S.1075, Jackson) on the "consent calendar" of the Senate and its approval by the President. It is safe to predict, however, that the Act, particularly under the provisions of Title I, will ultimately entail controversy between the powerful and often highly autonomous environment-shaping agencies of the federal government and the Council on Environmental Quality. Title I contains provisions to insure that its idealistic rhetoric will result in realistic action. For the Act requires in every recommendation or report on proposals for legislation or other major federal action detailed statements regarding the environmental impact of what is proposed, and further requires all federal agencies to review their statutory authority, administrative regulations and procedures for consistency with the objectives stated in the Act, and where necessary to propose to the President such measures as may be required to bring their actions into conformity with the Act.

POLITICAL FACTORS IN ENVIRONMENTAL POLICY

Two sets of political circumstances have complicated and slowed the implementation of a national policy for the environment and the establishment of environmental management as a public function. The first of these relate to the politics of the Congress. Rivalries among the members of Congress are both personal and jurisdictional. Environmental quality has heretofore been an issue of mixed popularity and uncertainty. Many members in both houses have sought public identification with the environmental-quality issue. But many others have evidenced caution, being doubtful whether public demand for environmental quality was strong enough to overcome the inertia and self-interested opposition of established institutions. Environmental quality does not fall unequivocally within the jurisdiction of any particular committee of the House or the Senate. Similar proposals have thus been independently considered by a number of different committees. This diversity of sponsorship and review may in the long run prove to be beneficial, but in the short run it could complicate and retard legislative action.

The second set of political circumstances relates to the executive. In the administrative agencies, as in the Congress, prerogatives, jurisdictions, and personal interests are at stake. But rigidities of position are likely to be greater among the mission-directed, administrative agencies; their latitudes for redirection or trade-off are usually less than those available to Congressional committees. Adoption of a new major policy focus, and especially one, such as the environment, that cuts across many long-established organizational lines in the executive branch is certain to be perceived as threatening to many of the agencies. The addition of a new advisory body in the Executive Office of the President would normally be opposed by the older advisory agencies upon whose jurisdiction it would be almost certain to infringe. Nor would the cabinet-level administrators and their bureau chiefs normally favor a high-level council authorized to review, delay, or even indirectly countermand their decisions.

The apparent inhospitality of President Johnson and initially of President Nixon to statutory environmental councils evidently derives from a different set of considerations. Here conclusions beyond the public facts are necessarily conjectural. Instead of the observed behavior of large numbers of Congressmen and administrators over extended periods of time, one must surmise, in the behavior of an American President, the motives, assumptions, and values of a somewhat more than ordinary human individual. A President may support or oppose a particular line of policy for reasons that may never become public knowledge. Speculation as to presidential reasoning may be poorly spent effort. But when the course of major national issues depends upon the presidential state of mind, an attempted reading of the President's mind through the evidence of his actions may be justified, especially among those who do not share the President's views, and hope in some manner to overcome them.

The reasoning that induced President Johnson, in effect, to abandon an increasingly popular environmental-quality policy and to identify himself unequivocally with an unpopular war in Vietnam may be comprehensible only in terms of the complex personality of the man himself. The inordinate cost of the war, and the Congressional insistence upon fiscal economies on the domestic scene, discouraged the launching of any new and expensive national efforts and pushed the government toward ecologically costly efforts to increase its revenues through mineral leases. Although the Johnson administration had moved more decisively than any previous administration to confront the process of environmental deterioration, it did not (perhaps could not) sustain the efforts that it had launched. Budget requests to implement environmental-quality programs fell far below authorized appropriations, which themselves were rarely commensurate with a realistic assessment of costs.

Financial considerations may have been a factor in the action of President Nixon creating by Executive Order on May 29, 1969, an "ex-officio" Environmental Quality Council chaired by the President himself and composed of the Vice-President and six designated cabinet members. The President's Science Adviser, Dr. Lee DuBridge, was named as Executive Secretary of the Council. Skeptics of the President's intentions saw it as an effort to head off legislation pending in the Congress that would have established an independent council on the environment. It might be expected that a statutory council would become a focal point for proposals for costly new environmental programs and would also provide a forum for critical review of the failure of the government to provide adequate funding for programs already authorized. Doubts concerning the Nixon administration's sincerity were not wholly allayed by the interview of the press with the President's Science Adviser following the White House release of the Executive Order. In the course of his prepared statement, Dr. DuBridge observed: "The problem is that everything we do to improve the quality of the environment has an economic cost attached to it"; and again, ". . . the cost of maintaining the quality of our environment is very large and must be weighed in each case against economic benefits." As James L. Sundquist observed in conclusion to a survey of the Johnson efforts, ". . . mastery of the environment through the Federal budget would require sums so enormous as to sternly test the country's dedication to the cause."[11]

These observations on the economic costs of environmental quality were entirely valid, but Dr. DuBridge did not stress with equal emphasis the total costs (including the economic) of failure to cope with the deteriorating environment. He did, however, emphasize the personal interest of the President in environmental quality and his intention to see that ". . . coordinated action is taken to set goals for our society and to take action to meet those goals as rapidly as possible." The Nixon administration nevertheless continued to be more stringent on environmental-quality funds than the Ninety-first

Congress, the Senate appropriating $1 billion for water-pollution control in response to an administration request for $214 million.

There was little in President Nixon's political life prior to his inauguration that suggested an interest in ecological or environmental-quality issues. The environment played a relatively minor part in his campaign in contrast to its major role in Lyndon Johnson's campaign in 1964. However, on October 18, 1968, in a radio-television address, he outlined a twelve-point program for ". . . the task of preserving the American environment and at the same time preserving our high standard of living."[12] And following his election, he appointed a task force on environmental quality chaired by Russell E. Train (President of the Conservation Foundation), who subsequently became Undersecretary of the Interior in the Nixon administration.[13] The recommendations of the task force, as reported in *The New York Times,* did not propose significant innovations in federal law or structure. The principal recommendation was for a special assistant to the President on environmental policy. But the task force appears to have been unequivocal on the high priority that it believed the new administration should give to the environment. It recommended ". . . that environmental management be made a principal objective of the new administration. Environmental quality is a unifying goal that cuts across economic and racial lines, across political and social boundaries. It is a goal that provides a new perspective to many national problems and can give a new direction to public policy. Its value and support come not from the divisions that plague our society but from the common aspirations of all for a life of dignity, health and fulfillment."

Not until four months after his inauguration and in the midst of Congressional action to create statutory machinery for environmental policy did President Nixon implement any part of the task-force report. Under his Executive Order of May 29th, Dr. DuBridge, the President's Science Adviser and Director of the Office of Science and Technology, became, in effect, the President's environmental-quality adviser, with the OST providing staff support. As previously noted, a concern to head off impending Congressional action and to avoid new spending proposals may have been factors influencing White House strategy. But it also seems plausible that the relatively low-priority assessment of the President and his advisers on environmental-policy issues had been changed somewhat by events occurring during his first weeks in office. Press comment seemed to suggest that the Nixon administration had miscalculated the political potency of the environment issue and was belatedly attempting to improve its image. The journal *Engineering News Record* commented: "Bills on environmental quality are proliferating in Congress like mushrooms after a heavy rain."[14] Robert Cahn, Staff Correspondent in Washington for the *Christian Science Monitor*, summarized widespread press reaction to the Executive Order under the headline "U.S. public pressure wins top level anti-pollution priority."[15]

The wave of protest following President Nixon's appointment of Governor Walter Hickel of Alaska as Secretary of the Interior could have easily led to a reappraisal of environmental quality as a political issue. The views of Governor Hickel on the conservation of natural resources and the environment were widely believed to be those of a nineteenth-century frontiersman. Conservation organizations throughout the country opposed the nomination, newspaper comment was generally adverse, and Senate confirmation was delayed until after several days of public hearings before the Committee on Interior and Insular Affairs. The volume and intensity of public reaction was politically impressive and extended far beyond the apprehension that might normally have been expected from conservationists. The administration was "on notice" that the actions of the Department of the Interior on conservation and environmental issues would be under close scrutiny in the Congress and throughout the country.

A test of departmental responsiveness was not long in coming. In late January of 1969, a break in an underwater oil well in the Santa Barbara Channel, off the coast of California, covered thirteen miles of ocean frontage with a thick, black, sticky, penetrating coat of crude oil. Destruction of bird and marine life was extensive, and damage to beaches, boats, and water front installations was enormous. Efforts to arrest the flow of oil were only partially successful, and the blight continued. Not the least of the damage was the loss of pride and confidence among the residents of the Santa Barbara area, whose satisfaction in living in one of the most favored locations on Earth now required a major modification. Secretary Hickel's response to the crisis was prompt and vigorous. But the United States Government could not stop the flow of oil nor easily revoke the licenses to drill in the channel that had been granted during the Johnson administration under the authority of Secretary Udall in the face of warnings of the dangers that in fact ensued.[16]

The American public was becoming sensitized to environmental-quality issues, and unperceptive government agencies doing business as usual suddenly found themselves in deep trouble over matters that formerly could have been considered as merely technical, if not routine, operations. For example, in early May of 1969, the announced intention of the Department of Defense to dump 27,000 tons of surplus, but still deadly, nerve gas and other chemical weapons in the Atlantic Ocean brought a storm of protest in Congress, in the press, and throughout the country. The Pentagon was forced first to suspend and then to revise its plans for disposal, by chemically decomposing some of the gases instead of "cheaply" dumping them at sea. Following a critical report from a panel of the National Academy of Sciences, the Department of the Army agreed to a study of less-hazardous methods of weapons disposal.[17]

In his remarks accompanying the signing of the National Environmental Policy Act of 1969 and in his State of the Union message to the Congress on January 22, 1970, President Nixon placed the redemption of America's ravaged environment among the top priorities of his administration. Commenting editorially in *The New York Times* on the President's apparent reversal of earlier opposition to environmental quality legislation, James Reston described him as a "new convert." Reston declared that ". . . it would probably be a mistake to put the contrast down to political hypocrisy. It is only in the last year that Mr. Nixon, like many other Americans, have come to realize that a population increasing by over two million a year and an indifferent industry expanding even faster are poisoning the atmosphere of the nation and raising vast new political as well as social problems."[18]

Although the question of public willingness to support the costs of environmental-quality programs remains to be answered, the reality of widespread public concern over the state of the environment cannot successfully be denied. But the concern has been most manifest in crisis situations. The high level of public indignation that environmental catastrophe arouses cannot indefinitely be sustained, whereas the activities and behaviors that destroy environmental quality proceed for the most part unremittingly and with powerful economic incentives and assistance. Social concern with the state of the environment cannot have continuing effect unless it is institutionalized. For protection of the environment to be effective, it must be established as a continuing public function—not merely reactive to disaster but anticipatory of possible threats. To become an effective public function, environmental management must obtain the type of institutional and organizational resources to enable it to develop and maintain a broad public constituency. Only in this way can the role of government in environmental quality be sustained in competition with other public needs and functions.

THE STRUCTURE OF ENVIRONMENTAL ADMINISTRATION

The task of environmental administration has emerged without the benefit of institutions designed for its purposes. As new functions of environmental management have become necessary, they have usually been placed in organizational structures intended for other purposes. Where new programs or agencies have been created, they have frequently found their activities restricted or counteracted by actions of other agencies. This has notably been true in matters pertaining to the use of rivers and lakes and their adjoining lands, to coastal lands and tidewaters, to forests and wilderness areas, to wildlife, and to localities of distinctive historical character.

Reorganization of governmental agencies for purposes of environmental management has been incremental. It has sometimes occurred voluntarily within the bureaucratic structure, sometimes in response to public demand. New structures for environmental purposes have thus far primarily reflected the interests of client groups, as in marine science and technology; have been initiated within government to obtain more-effective performance, as in the environmental-science services of the Department of Commerce; or have almost been pushed into existence by the mutually antagonistic and neutralizing pressures of conflicting interest, as in water-resources policy. In all these cases, the purpose and scope of the efforts were sufficiently specific to allay fears elsewhere in the federal bureaucracy and throughout the country of unforeseeable exercises of arbitrary power under an open-ended mandate for environmental management. But the Environmental Science Services Administration, established in 1965, could not avoid at least one admonitory editorial, which called for defining environmental science in very specific terms and indicated "vigorous and sustained opposition to such unlimited expansion" as the editorial writer saw in the expression "environmental science."[19]

The various possible approaches to the structuring of government for environmental management proceed from either of two assumptions: *first,* that the existing structure should be adapted ad hoc to meet issues as they arise; and *second,* that the structure should anticipate the task to be performed. The first position is the more conventional and conservative and is illustrated by most of the organizational changes on behalf of environmental policy made in government thus far. The implications of the second position are harder to define, because the conclusions are dependent upon the perceptions of the task, and these are certain is some measure to vary among advocates of organizational change. But regardless of how the organizational task is approached, certain factors inherent in environmental problems remain to be reckoned with regardless of the structural solutions that may be preferred. And it should also be recognized that positions are taken on administrative organization for reasons unrelated to substantive policy. It is almost axiomatic that advocates of presidential supremacy dislike Congressional initiative, and that executive-agency staff are suspicious of any administrative reorganization plan that is not their own. These biases are never publicly admitted, but can readily be deduced by persons who have learned how to translate the ostensibly high-minded, solemn, and conscientious memoranda of executive agencies on proposed new legislation into their actual political meanings.

The organizational problems of environmental management are systems problems, requiring for their solution coordinative policies affecting a variety of interactions. Characteristically, these problems cut across functional and jurisdictional boundaries established for other purposes. They are problems for all levels of government, including the international. In the world today, environmental problems are most easily dealt with at the national level. This is as true in the federal system of the United States as in unitary governments such as France and Sweden. Only at the national level is it possible to assemble the money, to mobilize the political strength, to obtain the technical and administrative competence, and to maintain the relative objectivity that adequate solutions to environmental problems require.

Although certain aspects of environmental management are distinctly local, there are very few that do not have more general implications. The local level of government is frequently the least satisfactory forum for the consideration of conflicting values in the environment. Politics at the local level tend to become highly personal, and economic interests become intermeshed with friendships, enmities, and a variety of other self-interest motivations, which greatly complicates efforts toward environmental control. As a general proposition (and hence not invariably valid), it may be said that the strength of environmental exploitation is most easily brought to bear on local government, whereas environmental protectionists mobilize most effectively at the national level. Local officials in the United States have tended traditionally to be friendly to economic interests promising to bring taxable assets and payrolls into the community, and to be hostile to non-economic interests, which are perceived as threatening progress, development, jobs, and enhanced land values in the area. It is a sad commentary on the quality of American public life that, in a very large number of local jurisdictions throughout the United States, public officials, on environmental-quality issues, are permitted to engage in anti-public action that is "corrupt" without being actually illegal.

On the national level, the environmental exploiter tends to be more easily isolated from his ostensible economic bene-ficiaries, who are usually locally based. If an environmental issue can be formulated in terms of "national interest," con-servationists and protectionists have a response to the argu-ment that they should mind their own business in their own "back yards"—a common counsel when they attempt to con-serve a shore line or to protect threatened wildlife in com-munities other than the ones in which they are legal residents or property owners. Moreover, national representatives of natural-resource industries (in housing, in agriculture, and in transportation, for example) often tend to be more accom-modating to conflicting views than are businessmen, farmers, managers, and public officials on the home front. They can "afford" to be, for their own immediate economic returns are seldom at stake, and they are also concerned with a fa-vorable national image for their industry or trade association and will seldom admit to being indifferent to ethical considera-tions, as officials of the Chicago Mill and Lumber Company once did when rejecting an appeal from conservationists to refrain from cutting a tract of big timber in Louisiana that was habitat for the nearly extinct ivory-billed woodpecker.[20]

Political circumstances at the level of American state gov-ernment tend to resemble those of localities more than those of the nation. But the states vary greatly in size, in economy, and in level of political sophistication. And they are unavoid-ably dependent upon the national government because of its general fiscal superiority and its jurisdiction over navigable waters, over the greater part of the public lands, and over such environment-affecting public works as interstate high-ways, airports, and irrigation projects. Moreover, many of the states are competitive with one another on economic and en-vironmental issues. National ground rules are essential to pro-vide the guidelines within which the states may act.

The magnitude, complexity, and dynamic character of the environmental challenge preclude the feasibility of simplistic or highly centralized administrative solutions. The need for broadly comprehensive and co-ordinative effort should be evident, but how to shape and devise institutions and procedures that can realistically be expected to achieve these qualities is far from evident. In a world governed through national states, the organization of environmental management at the national level is the determining factor in what can be done at the international and state/local levels of action. Analysis of the international aspects of environmental policy will be deferred for discussion in another volume. The mode of discourse appropriate to the international or global aspects of environmental control does not easily combine with discussion of political and administrative behavior illustrated, as in this volume, by reference primarily to a particular country. In the United States, however, no consideration of environmental policy or administration is complete that does not take account of the involvement of state/local government and of the nongovernmental industrial sector of the economy.

THE NATIONAL LEVEL

The culmination of a decade of agitation, debate, and delay over environmental management as a national function has been a strategy for policy making that has three related aspects. Stated summarily, these are: (1) declaration of a national policy for the environment, (2) establishment of a high-level council for surveillance, review, and reporting on the state of the environment, and (3) reorganization of the executive departments for more effective co-ordination and administration of environmental policy. Legislative proposals to implement each of these objectives were introduced into the Ninety-first Congress.

To Declare a Policy: At least thirty-five bills in the Ninety-first Congress proposed to declare a national policy for the environment—to make explicit the responsibility of the nation for the management of the environment. Senator Edmund Muskie of Maine proposed an Environmental Quality Improvement Act of 1969 (S.2391), which declared a national policy for the environment by reference to seven previously enacted federal statutes. This bill declared that primary responsibility for implementing the policy rested with state and local government, encouraged and supported by the federal government through appropriate regional organizations, and specified a series of ecological factors to which departments and agencies were instructed to give attention. The preamble of the Department of Conservation and Environment Act (S.2312), proposed by Senator Clifford Case of New Jersey, contained a statement of national policy in principle, declaring, ". . . the safety and general welfare of the people require that the environment of the Earth on which we live must be protected." The Conservation Advisers Act of 1969 (H.R.3118), introduced by Representative Henry S. Reuss of Wisconsin, began by declaring (Sec. 2) that it was ". . . the continuing policy and responsibility of the Federal Government . . . to use all practical means . . . for the purpose of creating and maintaining an environment . . . of highest quality." Similar statements of policy preceded the texts of most environmental-quality proposals, as for example, in the bill introduced by Representative John D. Dingell of Michigan (H.R.6750) "To amend the Fish and Wildlife Coordination Act to provide for the establishment of a council on Environmental Quality and for other purposes." In none of these proposals, however, was the policy declaration stated in operational, or action-forcing, terms. However, in contrast to other proposals, Senate Bill 1075, proposed by Senator Henry M. Jackson of Washington and enacted as the National Environmental Policy Act of 1969, treated the establishment of a national policy as a major substantive provision of the legislation.[21]

Title I of S.1075—"Declaration of a National Environmental Policy"—stated that it is the continuing policy and responsibility of the federal government to use all practicable means, consistent with other essential considerations of national policy, to improve and co-ordinate federal plans, functions, programs, and resources "for the protection and improvement of the environment." The distinctive section of the bill (Sec. 102) authorized and directed ". . . that the policies, regulations, and public laws of the United States be interpreted and administered in accordance with the policies set forth . . ." in the Act, and then laid down a series of procedures to insure so far as possible that the Congressional intent would not be ignored or misdirected at the departmental level. These procedures included agency review of existing legislative and administrative provisions for consistency with the Act and, in every recommendation or report on proposals for legislation or other significant action affecting the environment, a certification that the environmental impact of the proposal had been studied and considered with reference to criteria specified in the act.[22] In its August 1 issue, the weekly news magazine *Time* pointed out the power implicit in Title I of the Jackson bill. If the bill became law, *Time* foresaw, its effects might be felt by ". . . every imaginable special interest—airlines, highway builders, mining companies, real estate developers," and it ". . . opens all Federal policies to challenge. . . ."[23] Regardless of the fate of these and other environmental-policy proposals, it seems probable that, in some form, the Congress will ultimately adopt a declaration of policy that will unequivocally establish environmental quality as a responsibility of government and environmental maintenance as a broad social function. The more-significant question, therefore, is not the adoption of a national policy declaration, but whether the policy can be made effective.

An Environmental Council: The establishment of a high-level policy council was the second feature of environmental-quality legislation proposed since 1959 in every session of the Congress. President Nixon, as we have noted, was fully aware of council proposals pending in the Ninety-first Congress when he established by Executive Order the Environmental Quality Council and announced the conversion of the Citizens Advisory Committee on Recreation and Natural Beauty to a fifteen-member Citizens Advisory Committee on Environmental Quality. This action complicated the course of Congressional legislation on this aspect of structure for the implementation of national policy, necessitating revision of a number of statutory proposals before the Congress.

The most important difference between the Nixon Council and the Congressional proposals was the ex-officio, interagency character of the former and the "independent" character of the latter. The interagency type of council is exemplified by the Water Resources Council, the National Security

Council, the Council on Marine Resources and Engineering Development, and the Federal Council on Science and Technology. These and other high-level interagency conciliar bodies have important differences among them. But they share a common function of co-ordination at, or near, the cabinet level. They simultaneously (a) provide for representation of the various agency members' interests in the purposes of the council, (b) exemplify a need for co-ordination and provide evidence (which may or may not be valid) that co-ordination is occurring, and (c) provide a convenient mechanism for asserting the influence of the President without interposing directly in the administration of any specific department or office. The council device thus operates to strengthen presidential government and to transfer (at least temporarily) political pressures on policy matters from the White House or the Capitol to less politically vulnerable bodies. Depending on the wishes of the President, councils could be vigorous and "results-oriented," they could be brokers among conflicting interests, or they could be merely high-level study or stalling groups.

The high-level council appears, at least to some extent, to be a response to the need for augmenting the ability of the presidency to cope with the ever-growing comprehensiveness and complexity of the problems of a technoscientific age. But the presidency is a highly personal office. Whether institutional devices to reinforce the personal role of the President will permit the responsibility of the office to be expanded indefinitely is conjectural. Americans take pride in what they like to describe as the most powerful office on Earth, and only occasionally is doubt seriously expressed that its duties may exceed the capacity of any man to fulfill. The type of council created by the Nixon Executive Order would appear to have the effect of adding new and complex duties to those already required at cabinet level. Moreover, its interagency character would cause it to be suspected of the inconclusiveness, jurisdictional defensiveness, and bureaucratic conservatism that tend to characterize interagency committees. With the President as its chairman, this fear might be less valid, but only if the President assumed the added burden of decision that the functions of the new council would require.[24]

However, upon signing the act (S.1075) establishing a statutory council President Nixon announced his intention to reconstitute his cabinet-level council to avoid duplication of responsibilities.

The statutory environmental councils[25] proposed in the Ninety-first Congress generally consisted of from three to nine members, attached, in most cases, to the Executive Office of the President. Membership would have been from outside the federal establishment, and, in a number of cases, contingent on recognized evidence of competence to consider questions of environmental quality. The functions of these councils would generally have been broader and more explicit than the council established by President Nixon. Conceptually, they appear to have been "lineal descendants" of the high-level natural-resources review board proposed during the deliberations of the Hoover Commission in 1949 and recommended in the report on natural resources by the National Academy of Sciences to President Kennedy in 1962.[26]

In brief, the functions of the statutory councils would have been to survey and monitor the state of the environment, to review proposals and activities impinging upon the environment, and to report its assessments of conditions and trends to the President and (in some bills) to the Congress. Variants of these proposals were numerous. All the council proposals contained provisions for the appointment of staff. Senator Edmund Muskie's bill (S.2391), however, would have established an Office of Environmental Quality to perform the operational research and analysis tasks necessary for the deliberations and reports of whatever high-level council was created. In the establishment of the Nixon Council, it was contemplated that the President's Science Adviser and the Office of Science and Technology, which he headed, would provide primary staff support. Critics of these arrangements noted, however, that the OST, as it then existed, was not equipped to provide the type and volume of assistance that ought to be required. They objected to the assumption implied in the President's action that the task of environmental policy was primarily a scientific or technical function. The testimony of presidential advisers Hornig and DuBridge suggested this limiting assessment of the problem, whereas the critics saw the function of environmental policy making and management as essentially political and evaluative, involving ethical and aesthetic as well as scientific considerations.

Within a year of its establishment, the nature and extent of the responsibility of the statutory Council on Environmental Quality was called into question. Formally and literally the council is responsible only to the President; it is established by statute in the Executive Office of the President and reports only to the President. Yet the extensive range of considerations with which the council must deal and the potentially direct impact of its decisions upon the federal agencies, the states, the economy, and the public generally make its deliberations a matter of wider concern than can be said of most of the other councils advisory to the President. In the drafting of the National Environmental Policy Act, suggestions were made that the council report to the Congress as well as to the President. But to whom in the Congress? A logical concomitant of a council reporting to the Congress would have been a Joint Committee on Environment to receive the council's reports. Such a committee was indeed considered in the Ninety-first Congress, but failed of adoption, possibly because of rivalries among the members over the strategic advantage that leadership on the joint committee might confer in this increasingly active area of politics.

A Department of the Environment? Growing evidence of need for co-ordination among governmental agencies has raised among some observers a presumption of inadequacy in the prevailing structure of government. This inadequacy may be of two kinds. The structure may be intrinsically sound, but lack operational means to meet new problems that transcend organizational boundaries. Co-ordinative mechanisms, interagency councils for example, are then provided to supplement an otherwise adequate administrative structure. But if the basic structure of administration is poorly adapted to its primary task, co-ordinative efforts may be expected to show correspondingly limited effectiveness and may even make an administratively "bad" situation worse. Belief that the federal structure is indeed inadequately adapted to the needs of environmental policy and the co-ordinated treatment of natural-resource issues has induced a third aspect of proposed change—departmental reorganization.

Proposals to create a Department of Conservation of National Resources date back to the Hoover Commission and before.[27] In the Ninety-first Congress, this approach was elaborated in the bill of Senators Case of New Jersey, Moss of Utah, and Gravel of Alaska (S.2312) to establish around the core of the Department of the Interior a new Department of Conservation and the Environment. This measure, like its antecedents, proposed to bring together most of the natural-resource agencies under a common departmental roof. Representative Emilio Q. Daddario of Connecticut, whose Subcommittee on Science, Research and Development of the House Committee on Science and Astronautics had been active in reviewing ecological and environmental issues, also proposed a new department. House of Representatives Bill H.R.12000 would establish a Department of Resources, Environment and Population, bringing into operational relationship the major critical elements in man's effort to manage the ecology of Spaceship Earth. Skeptics of the efficacy of reorganization usually point out that, for a number of good reasons, no major function of government can be wholly integrated under one departmental structure. Advocates of departmental reorganization for environmental policy usually concede this. But they argue that it is not necessary to bring all environment-affecting programs under one administrative roof to have a more effective structure for environmental management than that now prevailing. They remind the skeptics that the structure of the federal agencies that evolved ad hoc during the first two thirds of the twentieth century was most certainly not intended to protect or enhance environmental quality, and in fact explains some of the worst failures of government to cope effectively with environmental problems or even to recognize their existence.

Not the least of the difficulties of departmental reorganization, however, is its ramifying character.[28] It is impossible to reorganize one major function of government without effects upon structure and operations in other areas of administration. Moreover, it is not only the functions of government that are involved in the reorganization of administrative agencies. Also to be considered is the responsiveness and accountability of the agencies. It has been argued that a moderate degree of competitiveness among the agencies in any functional area is likely to stimulate greater responsiveness to public need than would be likely under a thoroughly co-ordinated functional area. The independent high-level council might, however, provide a more certain avenue of access for citizen opinion on environmental-policy issues than interagency competition. And the problem of responsiveness and accountability is not only one of co-ordination versus competition. It is also increasingly a problem of the sheer magnitude of the executive establishment and of the human limitations of the man who is President to fulfill all the demands inherent in that extraordinary office.

It is conceivable that the growing tasks of government may in time force Americans toward a collective rather than monocratic national executive. A modified cabinet form of government might emerge de facto if existing federal administrative agencies were regrouped under six or seven superdepartments for purposes of broad policy guidance and co-ordination. Problems of co-ordination, not only at the presidential summit, but at all levels, tend to force larger units of administrative organization for substantively related purposes. The Department of Defense became the first of the superdepartments because of the overwhelming logic of co-ordinated operations in modern warfare. The protection of the self-renewing capabilities of the environment would be a hardly less logical concept around which to organize a new level of administrative action. But action at the superdepartmental level would be co-ordinative rather than operational. The conventional generic term for these agencies would be "ministries." The expression has never been popular in an America that has liked to think of its public officials as the "hired hands" of the legislatures. But the nation is now far removed from the days when "ministries" suggested freedom-threatening agents of royal prerogative. A designation to distinguish the status and functions of these agencies from the traditional departments of government would be desirable.[29]

The idea of a new configuration of superdepartments, which experienced Washington observers had tended to dismiss as theoretical, suddenly became highly relevant to environmental politics when President Richard M. Nixon in his 1971 State of the Union message to Congress proposed to consolidate seven Cabinet-level domestic departments into four. One of these new agencies was a Department of Natural Resources, a proposition which had been proposed before, notably by a minority of the Natural Resources Task Force of the Hoover Commission on governmental organization. As the name implied, natural resources and not environment was the organizing concept underlying this aspect of the general reorganization plan. In part, this rationale may have been influenced by the decision of the Administration to organize a concerted attack upon environmental pollution through an independent Environmental Protection Agency, and to separate its policing functions from the developmental and managerial tasks of the department. Discussion of this development and further description of the proposed Department of Natural Resources will be deferred until Chapter 10, where administrative implementation of the National Environmental Policy Act of 1969 will be considered.

Whatever modifications may occur in the departmental structure of government, there will also be a necessity for co-ordinated, and even programmed, action cutting across functional lines. Organization for project management, developed notably in the defense and space agencies, brings together, under common purposeful direction, personnel of diverse and complementary skills, some even from without the official structure of government. It seems probable that this form of organization would work better within the structure of a large superdepartment than across the boundaries of mutually independent subdepartments. It may be that the complexities of matrix organization require attitudes toward teamwork, authority, and responsibility that have seldom been found in traditional public administration. But it may also be that the more co-operative and responsible, and less competitive and authoritarian, behaviors that matrix organization requires are the behaviors that societies generally will have to adopt if they are to cope with the problems of a technoscientific age.

BEYOND THE NATIONAL GOVERNMENT

Although government at all levels in America has expanded greatly during the past half century, the concentration of political power and policy decision has been greatest at the national level. Focus for this concentration has been the presidency. If, in fact, there is a limit beyond which it is not feasible to expand presidential responsibility, there must either be a leveling off of expanding government generally, or alternative systems of public administration must be explored. The alternatives involve a redistribution of power among the major federal agencies, a decentralization of power to the states or to intermediary bodies, the creation of new instrumentalities of public action including partnership between government and non-governmental institutions, or some combination among these possibilities. For environmental management, devolution of responsibility to the states alone does not seem to be a practical solution. Except where circumscribed by federal law, the states, at least in theory, are free to act on environmental-policy issues. That their response to environmental problems has usually been slow, conservative, and sometimes negative, does not encourage the belief that they will readily accept initiative for the protection and management of the American environment. They may, however, play important roles in co-operation with national or regional leadership. And there has been effective policy leadership and administrative innovation in individual states. The states are not all alike, and it is conceivable that some of them might decide to demonstrate what state government can do in this difficult area of public policy.

Some have made a beginning. In 1968, California created a State Environmental Quality Council, with largely ex-officio members, to "make a thorough study" of the problems of environmental quality throughout the state and to "review and make recommendations . . . on proper state, regional or local governmental mechanisms, which would formulate broad policies, objectives and criteria for the coordinated protection, management, and improvement of California's natural environment."[30] Across the continent, Governor

Curtis of Maine convened on April 8, 1969, a Task Force on the Maine Environment, to "develop a comprehensive plan for the orderly development of Maine's future." And on May 14, Governor Davis of Vermont, by Executive Order, established a Governor's Commission on Environmental Control, with a charge to develop a comprehensive program of proposed legislation including the establishment of a permanent Commission on Environmental Controls. In the Michigan legislature, a different type of action on behalf of environmental quality was proposed in the "Natural Resource and Environment Protection Act of 1969." This bill authorized suits by public or private plaintiffs against individuals, corporations, or government agencies to stop or prevent impairment or destruction of the natural resources of the state.[31] And so, although handicapped by lack of fiscal resources, it was evident that, given leadership and motivation, the states could play a significant role in environmental management. Significant state action began to gain some momentum after 1970 and a further account of these developments will be found in Chapter 10.

Regional aspects of environmental administration are diverse and complex. An obvious weakness of state government on many environmental issues is the interstate character of the problems. Some interstate environmental problems have been approached through the device of the interstate compact.[32] River basins afford a logical unit for regional co-operation, but only with respect to a limited range of problems. Air-pollution control, environmental health, forest conservation, and agriculture may require very different patterns of regional organization, depending on the purposes that regionalism is intended to serve. Nevertheless, the former National Resources Planning Board considered the problem of regional organization for resources administration and appears to have favored the river basin region, based on the model of the Tennessee Valley Authority.[33] The major difficulty in dealing with regional aspects of government in America results from lack of agreement over what the "regions" are to do. An ecological systems approach to the problem of regional organization might reveal a new and compelling logic that has heretofore evaded analysis.

Regional institutions will no doubt evolve if the logic for them becomes more evident and their utility more persuasive.

Evolution has been occurring also in relationships between government and non-governmental institutions, including especially the institutions of higher education and research, and the science-based industrial sector. This pattern of collaboration may be truly an American innovation. It originated in the Agricultural Extension Program and developed prodigiously and in unforeseen directions in government-industry-university collaboration in the space program and in the development of weapons systems. Whatever misgivings critics may have about the applications of this collaboration and of the effects upon research and higher education, there appears to be little reason to doubt its problem-solving power. Its dangers have been documented, but they do not force the conclusion that so effective a system for the generation and application of knowledge should be abandoned because it is difficult to control. The potentialities of this instrumentality for the performance of public functions deserves the most serious consideration and experimentation. Ways must be found not only to overcome serious technical problems that obstruct current efforts toward environmental-quality goals, but also to manage the heavy fiscal burden of restoring the damage of decades of environmental mismanagement. Methodological break-throughs are needed to obtain quicker, more reliable, and monetarily less costly results than can be presently obtained with conventional approaches in many areas of environmental management. The challenge of environmental deterioration is now as great as, though of a different order from, that confronting a nation at war. Risks to be taken in meeting this challenge might properly be evaluated by this standard of urgency.

At the heart of the environmental issue are implications for change that are disturbing and even threatening to influential sectors of American society. The price of survival in the world of Spaceship Earth may prove to be very different from what the prophets of the more abundant life have led people to expect. Environmental administration has become necessary because, without it, contemporary man cannot prevent the destruction of his life-support base. But to protect and maintain this base (the planetary biosphere), public policies and powers will be required that would have been unthinkable in the simpler past. A highly technoscientific culture must be paid for by a discipline that some sectors of a free-enterprise economy will find it hard to accept. For the worst offenders, whose activities cannot be made consistent with ecological values, an economic death sentence is already being prepared. The dawning of the space age coincides with the twilight of public acquiescence in policies that permitted man freely to exploit and impair the human environment on Earth for political or monetary considerations. If men and governments are moved to timely action by ecological wisdom, life in the future can be more pleasantly environed, and less technologically regimented than it is today. But if, as is more likely, the necessary steps toward arresting environmental decay are belated and inadequate, the ultimate state of a spaceship society will resemble some of the less attractive projections of current science fiction.

SUMMATION

In summary, what is environmental management as a public function? Obviously, it cannot be the management by any single agency of all man's environmental relationships. Not all of the task can be performed by government, nor by any level or subdivision of government. It is a task in which various components of society are engaged in various ways. For the United States, the single most significant participant in the task is the national government, for only it has jurisdiction over the entire continental and adjacent oceanic ecosystem. And only the national government can mobilize the latent resources of all the states and of the educational and industrial sectors, whose deep involvement is essential to coping with the challenge that environmental deterioration now presents.

The initial task of environmental administration is the marshaling and interpretation of facts. It is the survey and surveillance of the ecosystem, and the recording, analysis, and assessment of the meaning of changes within it. In addition, the task entails the development of alternative proposals for maintaining and improving the productive and self-renewing capabilities of the environment. Although the process for protecting and reshaping the environment would be set in motion by environmental-management agencies, the technical procedures for coping with various environment-related matters (e.g., use of pesticides, strip mining, or drainage projects) would not need to be undertaken by such agencies. Their tasks would be to establish the goals, ecological base lines, standards, and review procedures for sound environmental policy, and to develop means for their enforcement.

Environmental administration is primarily the management of men, not of things. It is the activities of men that alter the environments that are the subject matter of its concern—not things in general. Understood in this sense, environmental management as a public function becomes "manageable" as a concept, as an activity of government, and as a responsibility of society generally. Its mission is comprehensive and complex, but hardly more so than many more-familiar areas of public service. If the *idea* seems visionary, impractical, or dangerous, it is because it is viewed from a perspective formed in the past. The accelerating rate of historical change outmodes past assumptions and may render prior wisdom false. Unless the present course of human society is reversed by causes now unforeseen, the ultimate establishment of environmental administration as a major function of society seems inevitable. Man's needs in the future will best be served by persons in the present, who perceiving this eventuality, take measures toward laying a sound foundation for environmental administration now.

ENVIRONMENTAL MANAGEMENT
AS AN ETHICAL SYSTEM

The management of man's relationships with his environment is a practical expression of a system of ethics; it is an application of values, beliefs, and moralities to relationships not only between man and nature, but between man and man. Yet nowhere in human experience do ethical concepts appear to be more confused nor moral issues more often evaded by misconstruction. A new statement of ethics is needed to guide man's conduct in a world in which the conditions of a spaceship prevail. It will not be sufficient to rely solely upon internalized patterns of behavior for assuring ecological good conduct among the transient passengers of Spaceship Earth. Ecologically valid ethics must also be institutionalized in law and in administration, and made operational in relations among men and between man and the rest of the natural world. The ultimate outcome of the changes that are required can be hardly less than a new phase in the development of human society.

Twentieth-century man has been working his way into an environmental predicament with which he is emotionally and philosophically unprepared to cope.[1] Should current dominant trends and attitudes continue, the future can, at best, hold little promise for the quality of life that the more fortunate of civilized men have generally found attractive. For the less fortunate, the near future may be somewhat more attractive, offering hope for more food, clothing, shelter, medical care, and education. Technology can provide greater material abundance at less labor than has ever before been possible. But whatever satisfaction is obtained from these improvements may be of short duration. Technology cannot guarantee its own wise use; it cannot insure that man will in fact be happier, healthier, and safer in the future than in the past. Unless man can relate to his environment with greater foresight than he has shown, the material benefits and securities of the future may resemble those of the hospital ward or the military post. The psychological deprivations threatening the future could prove more difficult to bear than the material hardships to which men have been inured during centuries past.

Failure to develop a workable environmental ethic adds to the probability of a future in which mass frustration becomes the dominant social problem. We can, for example, create a world in which food, housing, and other necessities are available to all—but in which the allotment permitted to each individual is socially determined and in which no one, regardless of personal preference, may obtain more, or less, than his "fair" share. In the world that technology can build, the good things in life may well be free—to each in his turn— and in an amount consistent with other people's freedom to enjoy them. It may even be possible to spare some "useless" area of the Earth for solitude, but bureaucratic procedures would doubtless be necessary to prevent its being overrun by refugees from a wantless society.

This impending "rationalized" environment will follow, if it does, in part from a failure of foresight—which would also be a failure of imagination. Modern man has seldom sensed the danger of a partial perception of the consequences of his action. Faith in the infinite beneficence of technology and the almost infinite adaptability of human beings has led men into acts of difficult, expensive, and socially unrewarding foolishness. Technological extravagances such as supersonic transport, a tunnel under the English Channel, and a second Central American isthmian canal are foolish not because they are logically absurd, but because they are undertaken in preference to less-glamorous tasks that are feasible and are essential to human welfare.[2] The costs of misapplied technology in foreclosed future opportunities can be very high when the ecological basis of life itself is imperiled.

The ethics of man's environmental relationships travel from the philosophically profound to the childishly absurd.

Our ecological crisis no doubt has deep historical and religious roots.[3] It may also result from human vanity, slovenliness, and an urge for excitement. The tasks of ecological protection and maintenance are essentially "housekeeping chores." They are not "fun," and they confer little prestige. Whatever reputation Hercules won by cleansing the Augean stables was due to the enormity of the task rather than to its heroic character. In short, man's traditional sense of values does not help him greatly in maintaining ecologically valid priorities in relation to his environment. At least in the Western world, he has relied for guidance or justification upon an ethic that commands him to subdue "nature"—but does not tell him how or to what end this effort should be directed. The conventional attitudes of modern industrialized man toward his environment have been shaped by circumstances largely irrelevant to his present condition. Having radically altered his situation in relation to his environment, he has not yet reinterpreted the ancient goals and values to fit the new condition.

One consequence of man's failure to develop a generally acceptable and beneficial environmental ethic has been conflict. Competition among men in subduing the Earth and in exercising dominion over it has been one of the grand themes of human history. In this struggle, the Earth, as well as man, has often been the loser—as when irreplaceable natural resources are destroyed through human blindness. And when the Earth loses, so also does man—since from its soil, water, atmosphere, and living creatures, and above all, from their integration into environments, the total man is sustained.

RELATING MAN TO NATURE

Understanding of man's environmental behavior would doubtless be strengthened by more adequate knowledge of his actual perceptions of the natural world, and his concepts of his relation to it. Information on environmental perception has been rapidly growing, but we are still largely dependent upon conjecture and deduction in discerning how men really understand their environmental condition.[4] This knowledge is important to the process of environmental management chiefly as "feedback." Environmental administration is largely the management of men in relation to their environments, and therefore the behavioral tendencies of men and the beliefs that motivate them are of practical relevance to the administrative process. If men are to relate wisely to their environments, it is necessary that they perceive their environments accurately and realistically. In order to guide men's actions in relation to the environment, it would obviously help the administrator to understand the prevailing perceptions of environmental relationships.

An important function of administration in any context is to promote the internalizing of individual patterns of behavior that facilitate goal attainment. For many environmental objectives, the most efficient and effective avenue is through internalized individual behavior. For example, prevention of highway litter or of man-made forest fires is possible only to the extent that voluntary individual behavior corresponds to official public policy. Men are too numerous and relate in too many ways to the environment to make "policing" alone a feasible method of environmental protection. Environmental administration must therefore be concerned with the beliefs and behaviors of people in relation to the environment and, to whatever extent necessary, must encourage and assist the development of realistic and ecologically responsible attitudes.

Proximity to nature does not in itself cause men to understand or to respect the natural environment. Love of nature is seldom strong among those who wring from it a precarious livelihood, or who suffer the miseries of drought, flood, cold, earthquake, or famine. At a time when man lacked the technology to "control" nature, he attempted to placate and persuade its capricious divinities through ritual and sacrifice. But with the advent of science, the illusion of control through religion was replaced by the concept of control through technology. And through scientific technology, man did indeed obtain a far greater measure of control. But in this very success lay the illusion of ultimate and complete control—an assumption unjustified by our knowledge of the natural world, or of the limitations of human capability.

The limited ethic of the Book of Genesis is an understandable consequence of man's uppermost necessity—to survive amidst an implacable natural environment. For centuries, man's attitude toward his environment has been influenced by his need to free himself from what has seemed to him to be its harsh and often unpredictable behavior. Primitive man, in order to become modern man, had in some measure to "subdue" nature. More accurately stated, man has sought to turn nature to his advantage. To do this, two requirements have been imposed upon him by the circumstances of existence. First, he has had to learn from nature in order to gain whatever measure of freedom he has obtained from it or over it. Second, he has had to master himself to the extent necessary to attain the degree of mastery over nature toward which he aspired, and there appears to be a direct correlation between the degree of purposeful mastery attempted and the self-control required.

The historic search for means to secure the basic necessities of life has inevitably shaped the attitudes of men. From each environment, man has sought those things that would serve his felt needs. Thus he has seen in the environment the things he sought—the natural resources for food, clothing, and shelter. But he has been slow to perceive the environment in its entirety as a resource, for he has seldom recognized in the total environment an answer to any specific need. Prior to the technoscientific age, human concern for the total environment was less pertinent to human welfare, for there was little that man could do to readily or irreversibly affect it. Beyond this, the identification of less-obvious but not-less-real psychological necessities has had to await the advent of modern behavioral science—albeit it was long ago said that man does not live by bread alone.

As noted earlier in this volume, two major ways of looking at the world have characterized man's attitude toward his physical environment; the first may be termed *economic,* the second *ecological.* Each outlook has its distinctive ethic; each has deep roots in different aspects of history; each in its own way has been influenced by the growth of science. The economic viewpoint has been dominant and traditional: the food-clothing-shelter view of life. The ecological, while also rooted in the past, is only now beginning to challenge the dominant concept.

The *economic* viewpoint is simple, direct, and obvious. It speaks to man's unavoidable personal needs; it requires no philosophic subtlety or scientific experiment to demonstrate its validity. It has often been associated with the "market" orientation described in Chapter 1, but the two outlooks are in no sense identical. In a world where man's struggle for survival began with the external forces of nature, the economic attitude has served him well. From it has come a guiding element in the ethics of peasant, pioneer, engineer, and industrialist: to make nature serve man's material needs. Under various interpretations, this ethic implies a world created for man to exploit. Material wealth is seen as the natural and proper goal of man's efforts; to this end, mastery over nature becomes a fulfillment of human destiny.

The ecological viewpoint is difficult to describe, because it tends toward greater complexity and because its elements and their origins are diverse. The essential elements may be summarized as ethical, aesthetic, hygienic, and scientific. The combination may appear strange, and the relative importance of the elements in the attitude of any individual may vary greatly. But some combination of these ingredients may be found in most ecological attitudes. Stated as a simplified abstraction, the ecological viewpoint might be described in these terms: Man is a part of his own environment and is in continuous interaction with it; this total environment exists in dynamic equilibrium governed by natural "laws," which cannot be disregarded with impunity and which exemplify the order and reliability of the universe. In this picture, the poet and the mathematician alike may find beauty, and the moralist and the scientist may find reasons for living in accordance with natural "laws." The ethical and aesthetic elements of this viewpoint are as old as the civilizations of India, Greece, and China. The hygienic and scientific aspects are also of ancient origin, but demonstrable knowledge concerning relations between man and nature is largely a product of modern times.

As argued elsewhere in this volume, the economic and ecological approaches toward man/environment relationships are not necessarily antithetical.[5] There are many occasions when, if all relevant factors were considered, each approach might lead toward very similar or compatible outcomes on environmental-policy issues. The absence of this convergence appears to be largely a consequence of the way in which holders of the respective viewpoints choose to interpret man's relations with his environment. Too often, the perspective is arbitrarily partial—the economist omitting from his purview the ecological consequences of human action, and the ecologist ignoring the structure of economic values. There are, in fact, large areas of overlap. It is in these areas that much of the need and substance of an ethics of environmental relationships is to be found.

Too little is presently known regarding the interaction of cultural and psychobiological factors to permit more than conjecture regarding relationships between human personality and attitudes toward the environment. Yet it would be useful to know whether the personality traits summarized in the term "masculinity" represent an inherent disposition toward aggression, domination, and control. And are there ordering and conserving tendencies in femininity that tend to inhibit unnecessary interference with the natural systems of the Earth? It is conceivable, although undemonstrated, that the care and custody of the Earth would fare better to the extent that woman—the natural embodiment of femininity—played an active and direct role in public policy making and administration. With some significant exceptions—such as life on shipboard—good housekeeping has not been viewed as a task appropriate to men. The tasks of environmental conservation and control may be described functionally as ecological housekeeping. The economics of ecological housekeeping could differ significantly from an economics of exploring, building, and trading, and it may be that the substance and emphasis of economic thought in modern industrial society are to be explained more as a consequence of masculine dominance over social values and institutions than by anything allegedly inherent in economic "laws."

If basic personality dispositions are significant factors in environmental attitudes, it is conceivable that the growing "liberation" of women from the tasks of domestic servitude and childbearing may result in profound social consequences. History and traditional humor may prove to be unreliable indicators of the respective influence of the sexes on societies in the future. Feminine influence in a society in which equality of the sexes exists *in fact,* might assume forms and pursue goals quite different from those observed in male-dominated societies. The influence of women in public health, social welfare, and conservation has already been notable, and it would seem highly probable that it will be a greater factor in the spaceship economy of the future.

Meanwhile, social action occurs within a matrix of assumptions and institutions in which the influence of the past is strongly evident. The values and beliefs that have served human needs for millenniums are still pervasive, even though the radical changes in man's relationship to the world of science and technology have made many traditional patterns of thought and behavior useless and even dangerous in today's world. These precepts and concepts exist in the substrata of the mind; they underlie and condition social attitudes. But they are seldom consciously articulated. Intellectually, the secularized and sophisticated modern man accepts the reasoning of the *Origin of Species,* but he often behaves as if he assumed the creation as described in Genesis:

> Be fruitful, and multiply, and replenish the earth, and subdue it: and have dominion . . .

Thus, an ethic common to three world religions justifies the subjugation of nature: man is prior to nature and, like God, is, at least in concept, outside of nature. The ecological viewpoint finds little overt support in Genesis; the economic view seems almost implicit. We cannot be sure of the extent to which Judaic ethics have influenced environmental attitudes in the Islamic and, more importantly, in the Christian worlds. But the felling of druidic oaks by Christian zealots is symbolic of the antipathy of a Christian attitude toward pantheistic nature worship, and of indifference to the natural world. Subjugation of the world to man's dominion was ordained by the God of Genesis. As to the fate of the world—it mattered little. Man's temporal travail on Earth was but preparation for the eternity to come. Nevertheless, the evolution of Christian thought has been advanced by St. Francis, and more lately by Albert Schweitzer, toward a religious ethic consistent with the ecological attitude.

Karl Marx, on the other hand, rejected the religious basis of ethics in what Arnold Toynbee has nevertheless suggested is a form of Judaeo-Christian heresy. Marxism, committed to economic determinism as an explanation of human behavior, has tended to be inhospitable to ecological thinking in relation to natural resources or the human environment. But Marxism, like Christianity, is susceptible of varied interpretations and of accommodation over time to the growth of scientific knowledge.

Growth of religious concern for man's behavior in relation to his environment is becoming evident in overt action. For example, among religious leaders, Dr. Truman B. Douglass, of the United Church of Christ, expressed what appears to be a growing attitude that the desecration of nature is an immoral act, an offense inconsistent with the concept of God as Creator. In a message to the United Church Board of Home Ministries, on October 27, 1965, which was reported by United Press International, he declared that although the Bible teaches that man was appointed to exercise "dominion" over the Earth, this does not mean that he is free to exploit nature ruthlessly for his own immediate desires: "We are to be responsible custodians and stewards of the precious and irreplaceable gifts of the natural order, which are to be used for the good of the whole." "Do we have a right," he asked, "to hand on to our successors a riddled, raped and ravaged planet?"[6] And the more sensitive issue of population policy has been linked (as it should be) to environmental quality in The First National Congress on Optimum Population and Environment, scheduled for June 7–11, 1970, and of which the Episcopal Diocese of Chicago has been a principal sponsor. Thus, if the Judaeo-Christian ethic could once have been read as indifferent to man's misuse of the Earth, it can no longer be maintained that this interpretation is universally accepted by religious leadership. There is a great need and opportunity for religious thought, freed from fetters of

dogma, to assume a role of leadership in extending and re-
fining human ethics to meet the ominous challenges of the
coming era of Spaceship Earth.

NOT PRUDENCE BUT NECESSITY

Even our underdeveloped understanding of man in relation
to his environment reveals the most fundamental and elementary fact about the significance of the relationship: regardless
of how man perceives his environment, he cannot escape
interaction with its complex totality. If man is to relate himself to his environment with wisdom and foresight, he must
understand it as it is—something more than the sum total of
its parts, more than an aggregation of natural resources; itself
a resource—the basic resource of life and all man's hopes.

Who would judge it prudent for an astronaut to manipulate
the controls in his spacecraft without knowledge of the total
system or contrived environment of which they are an integral part? And yet humanity, often in ignorance or optimistic
disregard of its mechanisms, presumes to manipulate the environmental controls of Spaceship Earth with impunity. If
the astronaut is only moderately imprudent, he may possibly
save himself by return to the mother spaceship, Earth. But
if humanity should render its earthly environment inhospitable, where then?

To exist in outer space, man has had to examine the conditions governing his existence on Earth. In contriving an
artificial environment upon which his life depends, he dare
not take any part of his environment for granted, nor can
he safely overlook the interrelating of the parts and their
synchronization in relation to the whole. This whole environment is not merely biophysical in the narrow sense, but must
include, as we have noted, behavioral factors—the social, psychological, and undefined spiritual factors that elude measurement but may nonetheless motivate achievement and sur-
mount adversity. The spaceship—microcosmic man-made
planet—may therefore serve as model and symbol of man's
cosmic predicament and may afford guidance toward a re-
formulation of prudent and ethical conduct.

To see environment as a resource to be understood, conserved, and utilized with regard to the total needs of the total man has become an ethical necessity. This comprehension was not a necessity as long as human numbers were few and technology simple. Primitive man in isolated cases may have destroyed himself through destroying his sustaining environment. But the world was relatively big and empty. There was room for error—even vast and catastrophic error. The human race moved on and found new lands in which to flourish.

Circumstances are now different. Talk of the necessity of interplanetary migration—even in fancy—tips our hand, revealing that we hold a limited number of ecological cards. The environmental resources of the Earth are no longer in any sense boundless. Nor, except in the occasional poetic flights of astronomical fancy, are the endless reaches of the universe open to direct exploration by living man. He is rigorously limited in time and in space. Eternally and absolutely limited by the environment necessary to sustain his life, man's highly touted mastery of nature is a self-deluding myth; not a myth that is really believed—not even a new one. King Canute of Denmark and England is alleged to have staged a notable demonstration of its falsity centuries ago. But it has persisted and has grown with science and technology as a vague, unexamined assumption underlying all too much of our present-day behavior.

Man remains—as ever—at the sufferance of the cosmic order. But today, in a sense more complex and more difficult to comprehend than in the simpler past, man's survival depends upon his ability to safeguard his environment through control of himself. For, through his own effort and ingenuity, he has become the greatest threat to its stability, and thus, indirectly, he threatens his own future.

Arthur C. Clarke, philosopher of the future and writer of prophetic science fiction, has suggested two common-sense rules of ethical relevance for safeguarding the future:

1. Do not attempt the unforeseeable.
2. Do not commit the irrevocable.

He explains that "though these rules have often been broken, in the past it seldom mattered; for the damage was confined to the meddler and his immediate vicinity. This is no longer the case; the consequences of meddling are now global and will soon be astronomical."[7] This counsel is essentially that of prudence, and it corresponds to that contained in the 1965 report of the Committee on Science in the Promotion of Human Welfare of the American Association for the Advancement of Science,[8] and the valuable little book *Science and Survival*, written by the Chairman of the Committee, Barry Commoner.[9]

Observing that "the entire planet can now serve as a scientific laboratory," the report recounted a series of cases in which the new large-scale experiments and technological developments of modern science led to unanticipated and unwanted effects. These unhappy outcomes were chiefly the results of ". . . technological application before the related basic scientific knowledge was sufficiently developed to provide an adequate understanding of the effects of the new technology on nature." The system of scientific inquiry and discourse, which might have avoided these failures, was in no case fully used. The remedy, in the judgment of the committee, was not primarily to promulgate a suitable code of ethics for scientists. Although recognizing the importance of the scientists' personal outlook, the committee concluded, ". . . this viewpoint is largely a reflection of the system of discourse in which the scientist must operate. We believe, therefore," it declared, "that steps to strengthen the integrity of science should be centered, to begin with, on the *system* rather than on its participants."[10]

This reasoning applies with equal force to the management of the environment, which is now massively affected by and through the applications of science-based technology. The integrity of society itself is at stake, and it depends upon more than the integrity of science. But the corruption or misuse of science can destroy not only the integrity of society, but society itself. An ethic powerful enough to control the use of science can be hardly less than an ethical system sufficiently strong and comprehensive to shape the goals and procedures of society.

From the outset of this volume, and notably in Chapter 6, it has been argued that man's behavior in relation to his environment is integral to his total culture. One cannot have a special ethic for conservation and the environment, and another ethic for the rest of life, within a coherent society. It is not necessary that society be coherent or that its tendencies favor moral or intellectual integrity. Nor is it necessary that any society or species survive. The argument for a system of ethics that includes an ethic of environmental management is that such congruence is very probably necessary to the survival of civilized man. One who is indifferent to human survival can afford to be indifferent to human ethics and to the environment; others cannot.

Prudence is a necessary but not sufficient basis for an ethic of man/environment relationships. The ethics and politics of prudence have been criticized as unworthy of noble ends or moral purpose, but in the protective management of the environment, prudence is merely a means.[11] It is neither an end nor an issue. If the survival of civilized man is the objective, then an ethic of conservation and protection is not a matter of mere prudence but of necessity.

There is a strong current of informed opinion in contemporary society that foresees major ecological disaster for the human species before the twentieth century has run its course. For example, anthropologists Irven DeVore and Richard B. Lee believe: "It is still an open question whether man will be able to survive the exceedingly complex and unstable ecological conditions he has created for himself."[12] David Lyle suggests, "The human race has, maybe, thirty-five years left."[13] And ecologist C. S. Holling conjectures a half-life for modern man of perhaps ten years.[14] These misgivings are not widely shared, or at least publicly admitted, among the leaders in government, industry, or technology. There is a pervasive belief in modern society that technoscience will find a way out of impending difficulties. The uncertainties of the dynamic, technoscientific world make any prediction hazardous. The projection of present ecological trends would indicate inevitable disaster, but no one can be sure that these trends will persist, or that their effect may not be altered by new and unforeseen developments. The basis of policy for the future cannot therefore be solely statistical, and it cannot safely be guided merely by doubt or faith regarding man's ability to manage his technoscientific culture. Knowledge of what is in fact happening is an essential concomitant to an operational ethic.

Beyond man's elementary needs, his goals rest upon ethical assumptions—upon what he believes to be "good" and "bad" in life. But it has long been observed that what an individual may perceive as good for *him* may in no sense be good for society.[15] In addition, there are several tests for the truth of goodness. When science is invoked to fulfill human purposes, it is not enough that a thing appear subjectively to be good; its goodness must also be measured by the tests of scientific truth. A valid ethic of man/environment relationships cannot therefore be left solely to individual conscience or to collective opinion. And if one were to name the single greatest cause of the ecological crisis of modern society, it would surely be this: that man has thus far failed to unite science and ethics in a manner adequate to guide, restrain, and control individual and collective behavior in relation to the real world. He has been relying upon the inadequately developed ethical systems of traditional society to guide him in a world transformed by the process of science and technology.

Traditional interpretations of ethics have been failing modern man—and the failure is all too visible in decline of religion, decay of morality, and disrespect for public law. It is not that the age-long ethical experience of man has become invalid; it is that inadequate interpretation and development of these ethics in a changed world has made them appear irrelevant. Rearticulation of ethical systems is perhaps the greatest and most difficult price that modern societies must pay for the opportunity to use scientific knowledge without enormous hazard. No modern society has thus far paid this price, and it is doubtful that, unless all do, any can. No nation can itself save the world from ecological disaster, and in a world divided by predatory political ideologies, unilateral efforts toward ecological sanity involve international risks that national governments cannot lightly incur.

Since the advent of the conservation movement, and in other contexts before that, efforts have been made to internalize a "conservation ethic" in individuals.[16] Whatever success these efforts have had has been far less than that needed to arrest the trend toward ecological disaster. The internalizing of new rules of conduct is essential to the effectiveness of ethics in society, but it cannot be obtained solely through efforts focused upon the values and behavior of individuals. The social context of behavior must also be considered. Ecologically valid ethics cannot be effective until they are internalized in individuals and externalized in social institutions. Only through a system of mutual reinforcement can the individual and collective aspects of ecological morality become a decisive force in modern society.

Efforts toward both objectives are being made, but it is doubtful that the magnitude is anywhere proportionate to the need. Time is running out for modern man to bring his ethics into line with his technoscientific capabilities. This task is not only one of upgrading morality; it is also one of reestablishing contact with reality. Contemporary man appears to have become intoxicated by the sudden efflorescence of his technology and to have convinced himself of his competence and infinite adaptability. In reckless pursuit of technological innovation and economic "development," a large part of modern society has lost touch with a large part of reality. The measure of this disorientation is a measure of social sanity or insanity. A society equipped with unprecedented technoscientific power, and that is even partially insane, is a dangerous society.

If this gloomy assessment of man's present predicament is valid, the question of remedy becomes paramount. It is not necessary to debate the related question of determinism versus freedom of choice in the shaping of man's future. Because the question cannot be resolved, it is rational to proceed on the hypothesis that human destiny may to some extent be planned and directed by human choice. This possibility is widely accepted and is indeed a basic assumption of the modern attitude. The question of remedy for present ethical inadequacy is a question of how and where an adequate operational system of ethics can arise. Many elements of such a system have already been developed through the efforts of conservationists and socially sensitive scientists. Some evidence of a new ethical orientation is appearing in proposals for changes in law and administration, and the growing concern in religion has already been noted. It seems possible that a new, pervasive, and dominant ethic might emerge that would radically alter man's behavior in relation to his environment, although it may require a catastrophe of global proportions to catalyze the latent elements of a new philosophy into a coherent and generally accepted public doctrine.

THE ETHICS OF RESPECT

The epitome of modern man is the American. Historical circumstances have combined to make America the scene of some of the sharpest contrasts in environmental attitudes and some of the bitterest conflicts over environmental values. Paradoxically, it may be that, in America, where nature has perhaps been most ruthlessly exploited and where an environmental ethic has perhaps been least comprehensible to the mass of the people, a concept of the environment might now develop that will unite scientific fact, social outlook, and ethical value. In exploring the basis of an environmental ethic, the American may therefore be taken as representative of modern industrialized man everywhere; his successes and his failures in the management of his environment stand out more sharply than those of other peoples.

The basic element of a system of ethics appropriate to a space age does not differ from that which has always been fundamental to wise relationships between man and nature. Only it is now more urgent. This element is respect for the creative forces that have made the world, the universe, and man. This respect should grow rather than diminish with the advance of knowledge. Neither the idolatry of the nature mystic nor the arrogance of the technocrat is an appropriate response to the reality that man increasingly discovers. Modern man can no more explain the presence of the world and himself in it than could his ancestors at the beginning of historic time. From his limited human perspective, he views the world most wisely and most accurately when he views it with an attitude of wonder. The man to whom the world is truly wondrous is not likely to launch himself blindly toward unforeseeable outcomes, nor willingly to invite irrevocable or irreversible effects.

The ethical challenge implicit in respect for creation in the coming era of Spaceship Earth has been stated with simple precision by Norman Cousins: "The real meaning of the human expedition to the moon, if it is read correctly, is that the conditions required to sustain human life are so rare in the universe as to constitute the greatest achievement of creation. Yet the prime beneficiaries of this bounty are now engaged in converting their habitat into a wasteland not less uncongenial to life than the surface of the moon. The biggest challenge of all, therefore, is to prove that intelligent life can exist on earth."[17]

It was perhaps the most characteristically American of philosophers, Ralph Waldo Emerson, who saw that the ultimate aim of all science was to find a true theory of nature, which must also be a theory of creation.[18] But Emerson understood that an infinitude of nature lay beyond the present reach of science and the human intellect. The world in its most common aspects should not therefore be treated as if it were vulgar. There is a continuum of reality, extending from the most mundane things to the mystery of creation, that man perhaps may never be able to understand. The child and the scientist are thus in one sense equal before this ultimate mystery. "Nature," wrote Emerson, "never became a toy to the wise spirit. The flowers, the animals, the mountains, reflected the wisdom of his best hour, as much as they had delighted the simplicity of his childhood."[19]

An ethic adequate to man's responsibility for his environment need not inculcate reverence for creation, but, at peril of disaster, it must be based upon profound and genuine respect. If there is a moral for man in relation to the environment, it is to resist temptation to treat the familiar with contempt on the assumption that it is nothing more than what one sees. The mundane is no less wonderful because it is accessible to man's comprehension and manipulation. And if there is a second moral for man in relation to his environment, it is that science should never be joined to arrogance. In a world in which the child, the scientist, and primitive man are in equal ignorance of the ultimate cause and meaning of creation, there is still a place for the human sense of wonder. The heavens are no less wonderful because through science some small part of their mystery has become known to man.

The essence of an adequate ethic for man's environmental relationships must surely include a sense of wonder and respect for the familiar.

> "If the stars should appear one night in a thousand years, how would men believe and adore; and preserve for many generations the remembrance of the city of God which had been shown!"[20]

❧ IV ❧
ACTION

There are at least three phases of action relating to the control of man/environment relationships and the protection of man's environmental life-support base. Distinguished by their salient characteristics they are: (1) conceptual, (2) organizational, and (3) operational. The first phase is one of awareness and declared intent, illustrated by the United States National Environmental Policy Act of 1969. The second phase involves the development of appropriate institutional structures and procedures—efforts now under way in many countries. The third phase is direct action, altering or redirecting human behavior. These phases do not often occur in logical sequence, but ultimately they must occur if modern society is to meet the challenge that it has set for itself—to maintain and perfect an advanced technoscientific culture without impairing or impoverishing its environmental life-support base. In the majority of the more advanced countries, phase one has barely been reached and phase two scarcely begun. Only in a few countries and for particular issues has phase three been attempted. Meanwhile, time runs out as the hazards to the environment increase more rapidly than society's efforts to cope with the causal factors. Must a major ecological disaster occur to catalyze latent concern into effective public action? To the fully informed, disaster enough has already been experienced to justify far-reaching reforms in beliefs, institutions, and behaviors. A moral imperative is needed to guide the application of informed judgment. In this context, our efforts should be such as to make ecological catastrophe, if it occurs, an unjust fate—not a fitting consequence of human arrogance or dereliction.

MEETING THE CHALLENGE

During the opening years of the nineteen seventies public concern for the human environment developed with unexpected strength and rapidity. A dichotomy for policy makers was presented by conflicts between historical commitments to economic growth and the new concern for quality of life. In the United States, adoption of the National Environmental Policy Act was followed by implementing federal action and by initiatives, some without precedent, at the state level. In a number of other countries, and especially in Western Europe, concern for the environment led to new laws and public agencies. International action was focused on the 1972 United Nations Conference on the Human Environment, but independent initiatives were also taken, especially by the International Council of Scientific Unions, by the International Union for the Conservation of Nature and Natural Resources, and by various intergovernmental regional organizations. Mobilization of public effort on behalf of the environment had begun, but the difficult tasks of translating intent into tangible results remained to be performed. Most difficult and important of these would be to internalize, within people generally, behavior patterns consistent with the requirements for a renewable environment.

As the United States moved into the decade of the nineteen seventies it became increasingly clear that an indefinite period of tension and conflict could be expected between the nation's historical commitment to unfettered economic growth and the new and growing concern for the quality of life. The assumptions underlying public preferences for economic growth and for environmental quality differed so fundamentally that reconciliation or compromise between opposing views (as, for example, in the construction of a trans-Alaska pipeline) was often impossible.

Changing national priorities and resulting implications for political conflict and frustration were discussed in an excellent report prepared early in 1971 by the Environmental Policy Division of the Congressional Research Service.[1] In an introduction to this report Richard A. Carpenter, Chief of the Environmental Policy Division, cited numerous examples of national ambivalence regarding the uses of the environment—an ambivalence typified by the title of a report prepared by President Nixon's National Goals Research Staff entitled "Toward Balanced Growth: Quantity with Quality."

Perhaps no coherent or consistent set of values could encompass the preferences of America's pluralistic society. In the absence of a generally accepted coherent value structure, the enforcement and administration of the laws "depend on the interpretation of value words such as enhance, practicability, economic feasibility, and equity." Thus, Carpenter concluded his introduction as we concluded the first nine chapters of this book, with observations on "the need for an ethic."[2] Surely one of the major tasks of politics in the remaining years of the twentieth century will be to create a popular doctrine of man in relation to his environment—a doctrine that encompasses both economic and ecological considerations; that is respectful of man's dependence upon the viability of the natural world; and that is workable in the existing world of men.

IMPLEMENTING THE NATIONAL ENVIRONMENTAL POLICY ACT

The course of events following the signing of the National Environmental Policy Act of 1969 should have removed all doubt as to its importance or potential effectiveness. In its first annual report, issued in August of 1970, the Council on Environmental Quality reported eighteen actions in the courts and five major administrative proceedings involving the act, then hardly more than six months in effect.

Following his examination of the act at the request of the Council on Environmental Quality, Dr. John B. Calhoun of the Laboratory of Psychology of the National Institute of

Mental Health found it "one of the most revolutionary bills in the history of this country."[3] This view appears to have been shared by the chairman of the council, Mr. Russell Train, who in speaking of the act said, "It demands no less than a revolution in the way we approach problems and make decisions—an objective to which the Council attaches the highest priority."[4]

In what sense is the act revolutionary? Primarily in its basis in a politics of values in distinction to the traditional Madisonian politics of interests. It is also pathbreaking in its reliance upon science-based information and its problem-solving rather than adversary approach to public issues. It legitimizes public concern with otherwise legal acts of government agencies which, however, impair the quality of the environment. By implication it establishes popular rights against unnecessary damage to a common asset in the environment, a right which has hitherto been effectively restricted by traditional doctrines governing the "standing" of persons before courts of law and administrative agencies. The act has, with respect to the human environment, repealed the cliché that "everybody's business is nobody's business."[5]

On March 5, 1970, following the appointment of the three-member council the President, by Executive Order 11514, supplemented and interpreted the act, providing the council a broad charter for operations. By this same order, the President redesignated the earlier Presidential Environmental Council consisting of the President, the Vice-President, and selected Cabinet members as the Cabinet Committee on Environment. Prior to this action on February 10, 1970, the President, in a message on environment, presented a thirty-seven-point program of specific action, one item of which was his announced intention to establish a National Industrial Pollution Control Council, which he did by Executive Order 11523 on April 9, 1970.

This fifty-five-member council of industrialists was appointed the same day under the chairmanship of Bert S. Cross, Chairman of the Board of Minnesota Mining & Manufacturing Company. The principal functions of the council appeared to be to identify and examine problems of the effects on the environment of industrial practices and the needs of industry for improvements in the quality of the environment and to recommend solutions to those problems. In addition the council provided liaison among members of the business and industrial community on environmental issues.

The principal focus of public and official attention to the act during the first year of its operation was upon the environmental impact statements required under Section 102 of the act. Section 102 requires every federal agency, when recommending legislation or action significantly affecting the environment, to prepare a report evaluating the environmental effect of the agency proposal. This statement together with comments and observations by other agencies affected must be submitted to the Council on Environmental Quality and must also be made public. To obtain meaningful agency compliance with this requirement has been a major task for the council and one not easily accomplished.

In April of 1970 the council issued guidelines to the agencies, but encountered public and congressional criticism over the accessibility of the environmental impact statement to interested persons—which in general meant opponents of the proposed agency action.[6] The question of public availability of the environmental impact statements appears to have been satisfactorily resolved, but the question of meaningful agency compliance remains a task of administration, particularly in view of the limited resources available to the council under the initial appropriation. Funds available to the council were substantially increased by the Environmental Quality Improvement Act of 1970 (Public Law 91-224) enacted as Title II of the Water Quality Improvement Act of 1970.

In the course of implementing Section 102 of the act insufficient attention may have been given to the implications of Section 103. All federal agencies are required to ". . . review their present statutory authority, administrative regulations, and current policies and procedures for the purpose of determining whether there are any deficiencies or inconsistencies therein which prohibit full compliance with the purposes and provisions of this Act, and shall propose to the President not later than July 1, 1971, such measures as may be necessary to bring their authority and policies into conformity with the intent, purposes and procedures set forth in this Act."

Under Section 103, a number of federal programs might literally be required to go out of business (so-called "varmint" control, for example). It is more than likely that some agencies may find nothing to report to the President, but it is also possible that an observant Congress and public may see inconsistencies toward which agency officials have conveniently turned a blind eye.

Meanwhile, the Ninety-first Congress moved to strengthen the legislative basis for environmental improvement by a series of major legislative acts.[7] Among these were the Clean Air Act (1967) amendments of 1969 and 1970 (PL91-137 and PL91-604), described as "one of the most comprehensive and 'tough' environmental actions to pass through Congress"; the Water Quality Control Act of 1970 (PL91-224), tightening controls especially over oil pollution; and the Resource Recovery Act of 1970 (PL91-512), which strengthened and extended the Solid Waste Disposal Act of 1965. The Clean Air Act of 1970 (PL91-604), Title IV, which was described as the Noise Pollution and Abatement Act of 1970, calls for the establishment of an Office of Noise Abatement and Control within the newly created Environmental Protection Agency.

In addition to the antipollution legislation, the Ninety-first Congress passed and the President signed the Environmental Education Act of 1970 (PL91-516), providing financial assistance to environmental education efforts at all levels of schooling, including adult and continuing education and in-service training for teachers, public service personnel, and community business and professional leaders.[8] An Office of Environmental Education was established within the United States Office of Education to administer the provisions of the act, and an advisory committee on environmental education was authorized to consist of twenty-one members with the proviso that no less than three of the members be ecologists and three be students.

EXECUTIVE REORGANIZATION

On July 9, 1970, President Nixon sent to Congress two reorganization plans with implications for environmental policy and administration.[9] Reorganization Plan No. 3 of 1970 created an independent Environmental Protection Agency, entailing the consolidation of ten of the federal government's antipollution efforts into a single organization. The new agency, reporting directly to the President, provided a unified responsible body for clean air and water programs, control of pesticides, radiation monitoring, and authority to conduct studies and research on ecological systems. In his message to the Congress transmitting Reorganization Plan No. 3, the President declared that the time had come to "perceive the environment as a single interrelated system." In approaching the control of environmental pollution the agency would seek to identify the pollutants, to trace them through the entire ecological chain, to observe and record their effects, to determine the total exposure of man and his environment, to examine interactions among the various forms of pollution, and to identify the point at which interdiction of the pollutant would be most appropriate. In defining the relationship between the Council on Environmental Quality and the Environmental Protection Agency, President Nixon declared that the two agencies would work in close harmony, reinforcing each other's mission. "The Council," he said, "focuses on what our broad policies in the environmental field should be; the EPA would focus on setting and enforcing pollution control standards. The two are not competing, but complementary. . . ."[10]

Reorganization Plan No. 4 of 1970 provided for a National Oceanic and Atmospheric Administration to be established within the Department of Commerce, primarily for purposes of scientific research and environmental monitoring and forecasting. Its principal component was the Environmental Science Services Administration, comprising the Weather Bureau, the Coast and Geodetic Survey, the Environmental Data Service, the National Environmental Satellite Center, and ESSA Research Laboratories. Also transferred to the new agency were certain activities from the Bureau of Commercial Fisheries in the Department of the Interior, the Marine Sport Fish Program, also from Interior, the Office of the Sea Grant Program from the National Science Foundation, elements of the U. S. Lake Survey from the Department of the Army, the

National Oceanographic Data Center and the National Oceanographic Instrumentation Center from the Department of the Navy, and the National Data Buoy Project from the Department of Transportation.

On February 5, 1971, President Nixon made available the memoranda of his Advisory Council on Executive Reorganization regarding the establishment of a Department of Natural Resources.[11] The President in his 1971 State of the Union message indicated his intention to submit a reorganization plan to the Congress, thus giving presidential support to a restructuring of the Executive Branch in relation to natural resources and the environment, a proposition, as noted in Chapter 8, that in principle has been advocated over a period of several decades.[12]

The rationale for the new department would be the establishment of a center of responsibility for developing broad, unified natural resource policies for consideration by the President and the Congress, making possible a more rational balance in planning and managing resources in the light of conflicting demands, and encouraging the resolution of most disagreements on resource problems at the department level rather than at the White House or by resorting to often inconclusive interagency co-ordinating mechanisms. The proposed new department would consist of five components: (1) land and recreation, (2) water resources, (3) energy and mineral resources, (4) marine resources and technology, and (5) geophysical science services. Under this reorganization plan the Department of the Interior would be almost entirely absorbed in the new agency. In addition, the Forest Service, the Rural Electrification Administration, and the Soil Conservation Service would be transferred from the Department of Agriculture. In addition, the new department would encompass most of the agencies now included in the National Oceanic and Atmospheric Administration, the civilian energy programs of the Atomic Energy Commission, and the water planning and project evaluation functions of the United States Army Corps of Engineers. As of early 1971 the fate of the proposed Department of Natural Resources appeared to be bound up with the fate of President Nixon's efforts to reorganize the Executive Branch generally and to reduce the num-

ber of Cabinet-level departments, with a more rational group-
ing of agencies and programs within particular departments.

In June of 1970 the Public Land Law Review Commission
reported to the President and the Congress the results of its
six-year study of the federal public domain.[13] In its 137
specific recommendations the commission clearly reflected
the schizoid condition of the American people regarding the
use and protection of the nation's natural resources and environment. The document contained both constructive and
innovative measures regarding administration of the public
domain and the protection of the natural environment, but
it also included provisions intended primarily to serve special
interests in agriculture, grazing, mining, and forestry.

Although the report referred only indirectly to matters of
public concern with privately owned land, it had the unintended effect of stimulating and reinforcing a parallel movement for a national land use policy. Legislation to provide a
national land use policy was introduced into the Second Session of the Ninety-first Congress by Senator Henry M. Jackson
of Washington (S.3354), and extended hearings on this bill
took place during the months of March and April of 1970.[14]
A national land use policy was advocated by the Council on
Environmental Quality in its first annual report of August
1970 and endorsed by President Nixon. Again in a message to
the Congress on the environment on February 8, 1971, President Nixon proposed "legislation to establish a national land
use policy which will encourage the states, in cooperation
with local governments, to plan for and regulate major developments affecting growth and use of critical land areas." Effective land use planning had been the single most important
missing ingredient in the national effort toward environmental
improvement. All indications pointed to its emergence as a
national policy issue. And in view of the long and deeply
ingrained tradition of land speculation in America, the issue
promised to be a highly controversial one.

ACTION AMONG THE STATES[15]

In the 1970 legislative sessions environment for the first
time became a major issue among the American states. A sur-

MEETING THE CHALLENGE 233

vey undertaken by the Council of State Governments indicated widespread attention in the states to the preservation of environmental quality. In at least twenty-nine states significant environmental legislation was proposed or enacted. As has often been the case, some states pioneered while others lagged.

Among the more significant areas of state action were land use regulations. Although the states have residual constitutional authority to control the use of all land, they have historically relinquished these powers to the usually ineffectual administration of local jurisdictions. A movement to reclaim this authority was now developing,[16] as illustrated by the 1970 legislation of the state of Vermont which established a statewide land-use planning and zoning system as a part of more comprehensive environmental protection legislation to be administered by an environmental board of nine members and nine district commissions of three members each, all appointed by the governor. Subdivisions and development projects cannot proceed without a permit from a district commission. The granting of permits is guided by statutory criteria which specify that the project must not cause undue air or water pollution, unreasonable soil erosion, or unreasonable highway congestion; must be in conformance with local, regional, and state land-use plans; must not have an undue adverse effect on the scenic or natural beauty of the area, historic sites, or rare and irreplaceable natural areas; and must not place an unreasonable burden upon the ability of local government to maintain educational and other governmental services.

Similar land-use controls were enacted by the state of Maine, which established an Environmental Improvement Commission to administer controls over the location of real estate developments.

Major administrative reorganizations occurred during 1970–71 in several states, and in some of these a significant concentration of powers occurred under a central environmental agency. The state of Illinois, for example, established an Environmental Protection Agency with responsibility for monitoring the environment, recommending regulations, administering permits, investigating violations, initiating complaints, and prosecuting cases before a five-member governor-appointed Pollution Control Board. To provide practical research assistance to the agency and the board, the Illinois legislature created an Institute for Environmental Quality, an independent agency in the Executive Branch to "investigate practical problems and implement studies and programs relating to the technology and administration of environmental protection."

In the state of New York a new Department of Environmental Conservation was given a broad range of powers not only over pollution control but over land use and resource management including "the protection and management of marine and coastal resources." The department has authority "to foster and promote sound practices for the use of agricultural land, river valleys, open land, and other areas of unique value," and to "encourage industrial, commercial, residential, and community development which provides the best usage of land areas, maximizes environmental benefits and minimizes the effects of less desirable conditions."

Major administrative reorganizations also occurred in New Jersey (Department of Environmental Protection), Oregon (Department of Environmental Quality), and Washington (Department of Ecology). The previously noted Vermont legislation created a new and comprehensive Environmental Conservation Agency. In California the State Environmental Quality Study Council began to emerge as a real force of environmental policy making.

A new development of public and environmental policy occurred in the state of Michigan when the Environmental Protection Act of 1970 was signed on July 27.[17] This act is the nation's first statute giving the citizen an explicit and unencumbered right to sue in court without having to prove that he has suffered direct or special damage or has otherwise established legal standing. Aimed especially at negligent public officials, any citizen, governmental agency, corporation, association, or organization can sue or be sued provided that the purpose of the suit is "the protection of the air, water, and other natural resources, and the public trust therein, from pollution, impairment or destruction." In other legislation, the state of Michigan, in what has been called a "truth-in-pollution" law, required every business discharging wastes other than sanitary sewage into the waters of the state to report at least annually to the Water Resource Commission of the state the nature of its discharges along with an estimate of the annual total number of gallons of waste water discharged.

Another innovation at the state level was provided by Maryland, which through the Maryland Environmental Service established a public utility agency to handle both liquid and solid wastes on a statewide basis. The service may acquire, design, construct, and operate both waste and water treatment plants and solid waste disposal facilities. The state is divided into service regions, and the Maryland Environmental Service must prepare for each region a five-year plan for "the most effective and economical means" of handling waste water and solid wastes. Although the initial draft of the authorizing legislation was weakened to permit a stronger local voice in the approval of service region plans, it nevertheless represented a major advance in the exercising of state responsibility for waste disposal management.

New and amendatory measures were numerous in the 1971 state legislative sessions and it appeared almost certain that environmental policy would remain high on the agenda of state legislative action during the balance of the decade. Similar developments had been occurring in the Canadian provinces.

The concept of a constitutional right to a healthful environment appeared to be making some headway in the states. An amendment was proposed to the Arizona Constitution, and the new Constitution of the state of Illinois, approved by the voters on December 15, 1970, declared (Article XI, Section II) that:

Each person has the right to a healthful environment. Each person may enforce this right against any party, governmental or private, through appropriate legal proceedings subject to reasonable limitation and regulation as the General Assembly may provide by law.[18]

Constitutional provisions in Virginia and Rhode Island also clarified and strengthened their provisions dealing with the conservation and protection of the environment.

INTERNATIONAL DEVELOPMENTS

While the United States has, as of early 1971, begun to act decisively to arrest environmental deterioration, its action has not been unique among industrial nations. Concern with the environment has been manifest in most industrialized states, with major governmental reorganizations occurring in the United Kingdom, Sweden, France, and Canada. This concern has been bounded by neither national boundaries nor political ideologies. In an essay widely circulated throughout the world in the summer of 1968, Russian academician Andrei Dmitrievich Sakharov identified environmental pollution as a global danger to human survival,[19] and in a commencement address at Glassboro State College in New Jersey on June 4, 1968, President Lyndon B. Johnson proposed that the "United States scientists join with the scientists of the Soviet Union and other nations to form an international council on the human environment."[20] In midsummer of 1968, following a proposal from the Ambassador of Sweden, the Economic and Social Council of the United Nations recommended to the General Assembly a convening of the world Conference on the Human Environment. On December 3, 1968, by its Resolution 2398 (XXIII), the General Assembly of the United Nations adopted "without objection" the report of the Economic and Social Council, thereby setting in motion preparatory efforts leading to the Conference on the Human Environment to be held in Stockholm in the summer of 1972.[21] Meanwhile, in September 1968 UNESCO sponsored the Intergovernmental Conference of Experts on the Scientific Basis for Rational Use and Conservation of the Resources of the Biosphere, which, for obvious reasons, has been foreshortened in practical reference to the Biosphere Conference.[22]

The Biosphere Conference, attended by representatives from sixty-seven nations, adopted twenty recommendations of which the twentieth proposed that "a plan for an international and interdisciplinary program on the rational utilization and conservation of the resources of the biosphere be prepared for the good of mankind." This recommendation, accepted by

UNESCO's General Conference at its Fifteenth Session, was developed into an action program of some thirty projects entitled "Man and the Biosphere" (Document 16-C78) and was adopted by the Sixteenth Session of UNESCO's General Conference meeting in October 1970.

Among other evidences of international concern with the worsening state of the environment was the action of the fifteen-nation North Atlantic Treaty Organization, whose Committee on Challenges of Modern Society (CCMS), meeting for the first time in December of 1969, identified problems of the environment as a major global concern and one toward which its concerted efforts would be directed. Also meeting in December of 1969, a committee of experts appointed by the United Nations Association of four Nordic countries recommended adoption of an international declaration of environmental rights.[23] The committee suggested the following propositions to be included in the declaration:

Air, water, soil and other environmental resources belong to mankind, and must be cared for in such a way as to promote the welfare of mankind.

Everyone has the right of living in an environment where human beings can develop in a satisfactory way, both physically and mentally. This right means an environment with clean air, clean soil and access to unspoiled nature, as well as protection against the damages which can accompany the unrestricted exploitation of natural resources.

In order to make the enjoyment of such a right possible, each person must show respect and consideration whenever dealing with environment.

It is the duty of society to guarantee to each individual the right of living in the best possible environment, by acting at international, national, and local levels——

Thus, the Nordic declaration parallels the efforts to establish an environmental bill of rights as an amendment to the Constitution of the United States,[24] and it is a near certainty that numerous drafts of declarations similar in intent if not in language will be presented to the 1972 United Nations Conference.

Meanwhile, however, international action occurred on other

fronts. Under the sponsorship of the Council of Europe, the year of 1970 was declared "European Conservation Year" and a variety of conference publications and other activities were undertaken to heighten popular awareness of the nature of man/environment relationships and of the need for international co-operation on behalf of environmental protection. The UN-sponsored Economic Commission for Europe announced plans for a conference on problems of the environment to be held in Prague, Czechoslovakia, in May of 1971 and the government of Finland announced an international seminar to be held in that country beginning in late June of 1971 on man/environment relationships.

A development with possible major implications for the international scientific community was the establishment, early in 1970, of the Scientific Committee on Problems of the Environment (SCOPE) by the International Council of Scientific Unions. SCOPE was first proposed at the 1968 meeting of ICSU in Paris and was urged particularly by representatives of the International Union of Geodesy and Geophysics and by the International Union of Biological Sciences. An ad hoc committee was appointed to draw up a more detailed proposal, which was reported in late 1969 to the executive committee of ICSU.[25] The first meeting of SCOPE took place in August of 1970 in Madrid and proceeded to organize a Commission on Monitoring which was to devise a unified global environmental monitoring network based upon previous studies by American, Russian, and Swedish scientists, and to recommend a plan to the 1972 United Nations Conference. In addition to its recommendations concerning SCOPE, the ICSU ad hoc committee proposed that there be created an International Center for the Environment (ICE), with a permanent staff and headquarters to undertake long-range research and co-ordinative data collection and analysis relating to the world environment. A similar proposal for a world environment center was introduced into the United States Congress as a Senate Resolution by Senator Warren G. Magnuson of Washington.[26]

These and other developments abroad required governments in the United States and elsewhere to consider what actions they should take in relation not only to the 1972

United Nations Conference but to international environmental issues generally. In the United States, the National Environmental Policy Act declares it a national policy "to promote efforts which will prevent or eliminate damage to the environment and the biosphere" and calls upon all agencies of the federal government to "recognize the world wide and long-range character of environmental problems and where consistent with the foreign policy of the United States, lend appropriate support to initiatives, resolutions, and programs designed to maximize international cooperation in anticipating and preventing a decline in the quality of mankind's world environment." Pursuant to this general policy position and in light of international developments the National Academy of Sciences in the summer of 1970 created a Committee on International Environmental Programs chaired by Dr. Thomas Malone, who also became the secretary of ICSU's SCOPE. A major task of the academy committee was to study proposals for international institutions for environmental control and to assist the Department of State with information and recommendations concerning American policy. Meanwhile, Secretary of State William Rogers appointed Christian Herter, Jr., as a special assistant on environmental affairs and a departmental task force paralleled the work of the academy committee in examining problems, prospects, and plans for international action for environmental protection.

Unofficial efforts to explore international environmental issues were numerous. Among them was the Thirteenth National Conference of the U. S. National Commission for UNESCO, which made "Man and His Environment: A View Toward Survival" the principal focus for its November 1969 meeting in San Francisco. Papers prepared for this conference were subsequently published for general public accessibility.[27] A detailed study of global environmental problems with emphasis on scientific and technical aspects was undertaken by the Massachusetts Institute of Technology beginning in the fall of 1969 and culminating in a month-long seminar at Williamstown, Massachusetts, in the summer of 1970. The resulting Study of Critical Environmental Problems (SCEP) produced a detailed 319-page report entitled *Man's Impact on the Global Environment: Assessment and Recommenda-*

tions for Action.[28] Legal aspects of international environmental policy became a major concern of the American Society of International Law and in early 1971 a panel on international law and global environment was established by the society under the chairmanship of former Secretary of the Interior Stewart Udall.

UNRESOLVED PROBLEMS

Out of the debates, interactions, and conflicts regarding man/environment relationships four major and interrelated issues emerge. Among the large unsolved problems of modern society they will continue to compel the attention of peoples and governments through the remaining years of the twentieth century. They are:

1. Containing population growth
2. Controlling energy utilization
3. Developing a stable and ecologically sound economic order, and
4. Formulating a coherent and credible political-ethical doctrine for human behavior in relation to the natural world.

Action with respect to all of these issues has been undertaken on both national and international levels by governments and through private initiative. If the challenge of these problems has not been met it has at least been recognized.

Population. The long-evaded issue of unlimited population growth in a finite world has at last begun to be faced. United Nations Secretary-General U Thant has identified the population explosion as the primary problem facing the world, and the UN Second Development Decade has accepted birth control as a necessary strategy "so that population will not outrun economic growth." The UN General Assembly has established a trust fund for population activities, and the relationship between population and environment is certain to appear in many parts of the agenda for the 1972 United Nations Conference on the Human Environment.

The December 1969 conference of Nordic experts declared that "present day environmental problems are basically due to the global population explosion, which compels accelerated exploitation of irreplaceable natural resources, often in such a way as to cause extensive pollution of the environment."[29]

In the United States, upon recommendation of President Nixon, the Ninety-first Congress established through enactment of Public Law 91-213 a Commission on Population Growth and the American Future, approved March 16, 1970. The Congress, however, enlarged the conservative agenda proposed by the President, broadening the commission's research mandate to include consideration of "the impact of population growth on environmental pollution and on the depletion of natural resources" and "the various means appropriate to the ethical values and principles of this society by which our Nation can achieve a population level suited for its environmental, natural resources and other needs." Thus, the concept of optimum population was in effect recognized by the Congress of the United States.[30]

Popular awareness of the concept of optimum population in relation to environment was advanced by the meeting of the first Congress on Population and Environment (COPE), meeting in Chicago in June 1970. A Deputy Assistant for Population Affairs was also established during 1970 by administrative action in the Federal Department of Health, Education, and Welfare. Slowly and cautiously the nations and the international community were beginning to face the challenge of population—but only the bare beginnings had been made and the major tasks of action lay ahead.

Energy. During the first years of the 1970s, public leaders in the foremost industrial states became aware of an energy problem of unforeseen dimensions.[31] Discovery of the problem resulted partly from shortages of energy—demands having outrun delivery capacities for electrical current and fossil fuels. Equally compelling, however, was growing public resistance to increasing energy supply at the cost of ecological values and environmental amenities. The siting of electrical generating plants,[32] open pit mining practices,[33] and the ex-

ploitation of oil and natural gas[34] encountered growing and
often effective popular opposition. Beyond these considerations, a hitherto unsuspected problem began to appear in the
capacity of the planetary environment to support indefinitely
the residual effects of ever increasing energy output. The
residual products of energy generation added heat to the
atmosphere and water, affected the chemical composition and
turbidity of air and water, and in the case of oil and nuclear
energy produced lethal waste products for which no ecologically satisfactory methods for control or disposal were evident.
The energy issue brought the advocates of economic growth
and of environmental quality into direct conflict. A need for a
national energy policy and indeed perhaps an international
energy policy became increasingly evident to informed observers.

Economics. Perhaps largely as a consequence of the severe
economic dislocations produced by World Wars I and II and
the worldwide economic depression of the 1930s, the attention of economists during the past half century has been
directed largely toward a special group of economic problems that, in the minds of many people, have become coincident with the science of economics. Problems of monetary
flexibility and unemployment dominated much of the economic thinking of the period and there was a tendency even
among economists to confound the techniques of economic
analysis with the subject matter to which they were being applied. By the 1960s, however, it became increasingly evident
to more perceptive economists, as well as to students of natural systems, that economic thinking and practices in modern
society had much to do with worsening environmental conditions and that a dogma-free economic analysis offered a valuable tool for helping to bring the processes of environmental
deterioration under control.

Pioneering work in the effort to broaden economic thinking,
particularly in relation to environmental problems, was done
by John Kenneth Galbraith,[35] Kenneth E. Boulding,[36] and
Joseph J. Spengler.[37] A direct and widely influential attack
upon conventional economic dogmas was the book *The Cost
of Economic Growth,* by Professor Ezra J. Mishan of the

London School of Economics and Political Science.[38] By the 1970s it had become widely apparent that an economics which did not take account of ecological consequences of economic activity was only a partial economics and therefore inadequate. The work of Allen Kneese and John Krutilla (among others) developed and defined economic analysis in relation to the flow of materials through the economy and the environment;[39] ecologists such as Eugene P. Odum and Kenneth E. F. Watt were making increasingly effective use of economic concepts in their analyses of ecosystems. These developments were significant steps in the harmonization of economic and ecological concepts. They were important not because of any intrinsic merit in the harmonization, but because they were necessary antecedents to a complete and valid understanding of the interactions of man with man-made and natural systems employing substances derived from and returned to the natural environment. But the great task of constructing an ecologically valid economic philosophy for technological man in relation to the environment of "spaceship earth" remained yet to be accomplished.

Ideology. The development of a more valid economic theory leads directly to the last of these four unsolved problems—that of formulating a coherent, believable political-ethical doctrine for guiding public policies of modern societies. No new political doctrine of great power and persuasion has gained general currency in the world since the days of Karl Marx.[40] During the century since Marx, the world has been transformed to a degree without historical precedent. This transformation has led to developments and consequences which Marx could not possibly have foreseen and for which his doctrines could not therefore take account. Similarly, political philosophies formulated in the seventeenth and eighteenth centuries live on in the laws and institutions of late-twentieth-century governments wherein many of the conditions of life differ radically from those existing at the time the philosophies were formulated. It seems strange that the century roughly intervening between the promulgation of the Communist Manifesto and the explosion of the first atomic bomb should have produced no new and creative political philosophy nor one drawing upon the knowledge of man and the world which had been developed during the most notable advance in scientific knowledge in human history.

What is now needed is a coherent set of political-ethical propositions that would, in effect, be what Buckminster Fuller has called "an operating manual for spaceship earth." This is not to say that all that man has historically believed about himself, based on intuitive and empirical knowledge, has no validity. Knowledge is not necessarily obsolete because it is old. But biological and behavioral science have provided many new insights into the nature of the human species and into the problems of individual and social control and self-control. The growth of scientific knowledge presents a continuing potential challenge to human faith and prejudice, and it becomes increasingly difficult to sustain belief in propositions that are demonstrably contrary to the apparent state of affairs as revealed by repeatedly validated scientific evidence. While it would be an exaggeration to say that, as of today, what is believable must be demonstrably true, this generalization is nonetheless becoming increasingly valid for increasing numbers of people—particularly those representing the leadership in government, education, science, and the economy in what has come to be called the scientific superculture of the modern world. Predictions in the realm of social thought are always hazardous, but the essential elements of a political philosophy for the future are lying about, unassembled, awaiting an architect who can bring them together into some coherent and persuasive formulation. It is, therefore, not unreasonable to conjecture that before the twentieth century draws to a close a new powerful and persuasive political doctrine will have emerged in the modern world which may rapidly and profoundly affect the fortunes of governments and political parties—and hopefully will significantly advance the capabilities of modern society to cope with its environmental problems.

PERSONAL COMMITMENT

It is perhaps the absence of a body of political thought adequate to the needs of our times that causes many persons concerned with the worsening environment to ask: "What can we do?" The political folklore of American politics is expressive of values and conditions that prevailed in the days of Thomas Jefferson and Andrew Jackson. The failure of citizen responsibility in the late twentieth century is an institutional as well as a conceptual failure. Problems of the environment are only one set among a vast array of challenges to modern society that cannot be met through recourse to the town meeting methods or county courthouse procedures of the early nineteenth century.

With respect to the specific issues of the environment, there is much evidence to indicate a widespread belief that *all* men are responsible for the protection and preservation of the environment. This proposition was incorporated into the National Environmental Policy Act of 1969, which declares ". . . that each person has a responsibility to contribute to the preservation and enhancement of the environment." Similarly the 1969 Nordic Declaration on the Protection of the Human Environment, after stating the right of each individual to live in a good environment, added that "In order to make the enjoyment of such a right possible, each person must show respect and consideration whenever dealing with environment."

The moral imperative to respect the environment appears to be gaining acceptance but it is not so easily implemented. The individual needs help in order to take effective action on environmental issues; he needs help also to unlearn the beliefs and behaviors that have become destructive as a consequence of demographic and technoeconomic changes in society. Acts which are harmless or are easily reparable when done by few may become damaging to the point of catastrophe when done by many. Thus, an adequate doctrine for man/environment relationships must also be an adequate doctrine for man-to-man relationships. An important part of such a doctrine would be its assistance to people in conceptualizing the outcome of events, and in thinking increasingly in ecological time dimensions so that the relationship between present actions and possible futures would more often influence present choices.

Conventional response to the question "What can I do?" includes the following admonitions: (1) really care, (2) be accurately informed, (3) let your views be known, and (4) reinforce your influence through association with others. If society is seldom moved by the actions of a single individual, it is also true that society cannot and will not act without the concerted actions of many individuals. The latent power of society thus rests in the individual, but that power cannot be actualized unless it is mobilized in some concerted fashion.

The most notable single effort to stimulate popular awareness and to organize for effective action on environmental issues was the Earth Day movement of 1970. Earth Day activities consisted of seminars, conferences, meetings, programs, publications, and demonstrations taking place in literally thousands of places—on college and university campuses and in elementary and secondary schools—and including civic events in a large number of communities across the nation, co-ordinated by a volunteer youth group entitled Environmental Action, and assisted by a number of ecology-conscious congressmen, scientists, and foundations. Activities before and after the official Earth Day, April 22, attracted a great deal of attention in the news media and brought into active involvement large numbers of persons to whom ecology had been little more than an obscure word. One tangible outcome was the stimulation of environmental activist groups on the campuses of American colleges and universities and the publication of guides and handbooks toward environmental action.[41] Earth Day was not merely concerned with environmental issues, however. Its leaders saw the ecological aspect as a critical phase of the larger issue of the quality of life in the modern world. In the words of Denis Hayes, national co-ordinator of Environmental Action, "we feel that Earth Day has failed if it stops at pollution, if it doesn't serve as a catalyst in the values of society."[42]

There are a large number of associations in the United States, and in many other countries as well, organized for the protection and improvement of the human environment. These organizations are sources of information and guidance for individuals not obtainable as readily in other ways. But the organizations depend for their effectiveness upon the membership, the payment of dues, and the voluntary participation of many individuals. Fortunately, the pluralism of North American and West European society provides the individual with a wide range of choice among organizations concerned with conservation and environmental affairs. He may support the organization that most directly represents his orientation of interests. Few individuals have the resources of information, time, and money to appear at the legislative and administrative hearings, the judicial procedures, and the countless conferences, seminars, and study sessions through which public policy is developed. But their support and involvement in citizen organizations can make possible the presence there of people able to represent their views and values effectively.

Nearly every organized effort for the conservation and protection of environmental quality needs large numbers of reliable volunteer workers. The organizations almost never have sufficient money to undertake the tasks they set for themselves and their professional staffs are correspondingly small. The unpaid individual who can give some part of his time and attention to the work of these organizations makes their accomplishments possible. To these organizations and these individuals, the nations owe the greater part of what has as yet been done to safeguard the threatened wildlife, landscapes, and natural resources of the earth.

Beyond this participatory role, the individual as a voter and citizen can work to obtain an institutional framework in the public service that will enable him and others to behave in an ecologically respectable manner. The development of effective waste management systems, of materials' recycling and the elimination of unjustifiable planned obsolescence, and the protection of open space and wildlife call for a degree of civic conscience and social responsibility which few societies have developed or sustained. Individualistic or anarchistic rebellion against the discipline required to sustain the viability of "spaceship earth" is feasible only so long as it does not go beyond mere posturings of self-indulgence by a protected minority, buffered by society from the otherwise fatal consequence of utterly unecological behavior. Irrational and dogmatic views of the human situation may be found at all levels of society and in all cultures, as readily among socialist commissars and corporation tycoons as among campus "radicals." The commitment of individuals to the unavoidably collective task of maintaining the ecological enterprise is essential because the task is not and cannot be the exclusive mission of any class or group of people. A very small number of people can now destroy the world; it will take the collective efforts of nearly all mankind to save it. But to lead this effort a smaller number of persons may play a critical role.

The probability of an early end to the world that man has known is now too great for complacency. The chances for avoiding military or ecological disaster are not known and the best guesses of many informed observers are not encouraging—but for many possible disasters the means for avoidance are known. To this extent there is room for hope. Only as the present acts of men predestine the future does the future appear to be foreordained. What men do now, therefore, determines what they may experience hereafter. Given the apparent choices that men may make, the quality of life in the future will depend upon the personal commitment of persons to the action required today for a better world tomorrow. There can be no assurance that this effort will succeed. The world has become increasingly precarious, and annihilation may be the common fate. But those who work perseveringly and intelligently to avoid man's self-destruction will in their own action, at least, have justified the human experiment. And if, to paraphrase Senancour, annihilation overtakes their efforts, they will have acted to make their failure and their fate unjust.

NOTES

The following notes and citations are provided to assist the reader to follow up on various points of interest touched upon in the text. They also indicate the sources of direct quotations and of evidence for statements that might raise doubt in the minds of some readers. Annotation invariably involves compromise between providing too little and too much information. There is no general rule to guide the author, since what may be too little for one group of readers may be too much for others. I have tried to avoid unnecessary documentation, and have not referenced data easily obtained in an encyclopedia or with the assistance of a competent librarian. Page numbers are the last item in each referenced publication. The abbreviation for "pages" is therefore omitted, except for single-page citations, which are preceded by "p." Volume numbers are given in Roman numerals, except in the case of law journals, where standard form for legal periodicals is followed.

CHAPTER 1

ENVIRONMENT: A NEW FACTOR IN PUBLIC POLICY

1 For analysis of public attitudes and perceptions in relation to environment, see:

Marston Bates, "Environment," *International Encyclopedia of Social Sciences*, V, 1968, 91–93;

Environmental Perception and Behavior, edited by David Lowenthal. Chicago: University of Chicago, Department of Geography (Research Paper No. 10), 1967, vi, 88;

James J. Gibson, *The Perception of the Visual World*. Boston: Houghton Mifflin, 1950, xii, 235, references 231–35;

"Man's Response to the Physical Environment," *The Journal of Social Issues*, XXII (No. 4, October 1966), whole issue, edited by Robert W. Kates and Joachim Wohlwill;

David Lowenthal, "Assumptions Behind the Public Attitudes," in *Environmental Quality in a Growing Economy*, edited by Henry Jarrett. Baltimore: Johns Hopkins Press, 1966, 128–37, and Gilbert F. White, "Formation and Roles of Public Attitudes," ibid., 105–27; Robert C. Lucas, "Wilderness Perception and Use: The Example of the Boundary Waters Canoe Area," 3 *Natural Resources Journal* (January 1964), 394–411. (Note other articles on perception and natural resources in this issue, pp. 377 ff.);

Kevin Lynch, *The Image of the City*. Cambridge, Massachusetts: Technology Press, 1960, 194, bibliography.

2 For a historical account of environmental theories, including a criticism of environmental determinism, see Franklin Thomas, *The Environmental Basis of Society*. New York: Century, 1925, Johnson Reprint Corp., 1965, vii, 336, bibliography; and O. H. K. Spate, "Environmentalism," *International Encyclopedia of Social Sciences*, V, 1968, 93–96. For an example of a far-reaching theory of political development based upon indirect effects of man/environment relationships, see Karl A. Wittfogel, *Oriental Despotism: A Comparative Study of Total Power*. New Haven: Yale University Press, 1957, xix, 556.

3 One of the most clear and eloquent statements of the difference between seeing and understanding the environment may be found in Aldo Leopold's *Sand County Almanac*. New York: Oxford University Press, 1949, 173–77. See also May Theilgaard Watts, *Reading the Landscape: An Adventure in Ecology*. New York: Macmillan, 1957, x, 230.

4 *The New York Times Magazine* (November 14, 1943), p. 4. For a similar viewpoint developed in detail, see Martin Meyerson, "National Character and Urban Development," in *Public Policy: A Yearbook of the Graduate School of Public Administration, Harvard University*, XII (1963), 78–96.

5 Cf. Arthur A. Ekirch, *Man and Nature in America*. New York: Columbia University Press, 1963, p. 231;

Hans Huth, *Nature and the American: Three Centuries of Changing Attitudes*, Berkeley: University of California Press, 1957, xvii, 250.

Also David Lowenthal, "Is Wilderness 'Paradise Enow'?—Images of Nature in America," *Columbia University Forum* (Spring 1964), 34–40.

6 However, some indication of public attitude and priority was provided by a poll taken in January 1969 by the Gallup organization, the American Institute of Public Opinion, for the National Wildlife Federation. See "Gallup Survey on Conservation," *National Wildlife*, VII (April–May 1969), 18–19.

7 Some of these have been analyzed by Gilbert F. White in "The Choice of Use in Resource Management," 1 *Natural Resources*

Journal (March 1961), 23–30. For a discussion of the utility of
operations-research methods to environmental decision making, see
Louis Hamill, "The Process of Making Good Decisions About the
Use of the Environment of Man," 8 *Natural Resources Journal*
(April 1968), 279–301. See also, Daniel H. Henning, "The Politics
of Natural Resources Administration," *The Annals of Regional Science,* II (December 1968), 239–48.

8 Cf. Arthur Maass, "Benefit-Cost Analysis: Its Relevance to Public
Investment Decisions," *Quarterly Journal of Economics,* LXXX
(May 1966), 208–26; and Richard J. Hammond, "Convention and
Limitations in Benefit-Cost Analysis," 6 *Natural Resources Journal*
(April 1966), 195–222.

9 See A. Allan Schmid, "Quality of the Environment and Man: Some
Thoughts on Economic Institutions," *Journal of Soil and Water
Conservation,* XXI (May–June 1966), 89–91.

10 The interrelations of economics and ecology have been perhaps
most frequently noted in the writings of Kenneth Boulding, e.g.,
"The Economics of the Coming Spaceship Earth," in *Environmental Quality in a Growing Economy,* edited by Henry Jarrett. Baltimore: Johns Hopkins Press, 1966, 3–14. Note also papers by Allen
V. Kneese, "Research Goals and Progress Toward Them," ibid.,
69–87, and M. Mason Gaffney, "Welfare Economics and the Environment," ibid., 88–101. For further observations on these interrelationships, see Allen V. Kneese, "Economics and the Quality
of the Environment—Some Empirical Experiences," in *Social Science and the Environment,* edited by Morris E. Garnsey and James
R. Hibbs. Boulder: University of Colorado Press, 1967, 165–93; and
Paul Davidson, "The Valuation of Public Goals," ibid., 125–63.
Economic and ecological orientation are also considered in Chapter 9 of this volume in relation to ethical values. Economic means
may be used to serve ecological as well as economic ends. See, for
example, John V. Krutilla, "An Economic Approach to Coping
with Flood Damage," *Water Resources Research,* II (Second Quarter 1966), 183–90.

11 A major political reason for segmental decision making on environmental matters has been developed by Clyde S. Wingfield in "Power
Structure and Decision-making in City Planning," *Public Administration Review,* XXIV (June 1963), 74–80. An illustration of the
political consequences of our traditional approach to resources policy is developed by Roy Hamilton in "The Senate Select Committee
on National Water Resources: An Ethical and Rational Criticism,"
2 *Natural Resources Journal* (April 1962), 45–54.

12 For example, the influence of regional science. See Walter Isard
et al., *Methods of Regional Analysis—An Introduction to Regional
Science.* Cambridge, Massachusetts, and New York: M.I.T. Press
and John Wiley, 1960, 784. For consideration of functional and
psychological aspects of human organization in relation to geographical space, see Melvin Webber et al., *Explorations into Urban
Structure.* Philadelphia: University of Pennsylvania Press, 1967,

246; and *Urban Life and Forum*, edited by Werner Z. Hirsch. New York: Holt, Rinehart & Winston, 1963, 248.

13 I have developed this point at greater length in "The Urban Environment as an Ecological System," 1 *Indiana Legal Forum* (Spring 1968), 298–309. See also Webber, op. cit.

14 Cf. Henry C. Hart, *Administrative Aspects of River Valley Development*. New York: Asia Publishing House, 1961, 112; and *The International River Basin*, edited by J. D. Chapman. Vancouver: University of British Columbia, 1963, xvi, 53. There is a large and growing literature on the effects of man-made environmental change. More sources of information are cited in the notes relating to Chapter 5.

15 Cf. Daniel R. Mandelker, *Green Belts and Urban Growth—English Town and County Planning in Action*. Madison: University of Wisconsin Press, 1962, 176. For further comment on British environmental planning, see J. B. Cullingworth, *Town and Country Planning in England and Wales*. Toronto: University of Toronto Press, 1964, 301.

16 Cf. William L. Slayton, "The Administrator's Role in Bringing Better Design into City Rebuilding," *Journal of Housing*, XIX (September 14, 1962), 365–68.

17 Cf. Robert Alan Dahl, *Pluralist Democracy in the United States: Conflict and Consent*. Chicago: Rand McNally, 1967, xix, 417.

18 Lynton K. Caldwell, "The Human Environment," *Journal of Higher Education*, XXXVII (March 1966), 149–55; Robert S. Morison, "Education for Environmental Concerns," *Daedalus*, XCVI (Fall 1967), 1210–23; and "The Universities and Environmental Quality —Commitment to Problem Focused Education," a report to The President's Environmental Quality Council by John S. Steinhart and Stacie Cherniak, Washington: Office of Science and Technology, September, 1969, 22.

19 "The Problem Shed as a Unit of Environmental Control," *Archives of Environmental Health*, XVI (January 1968), 124–27. For some practical problems of application, see Harvey Lieber, "Controlling Metropolitan Pollution Through Regional Airsheds: Administrative Requirements and Political Problems," *Journal of the Air Pollution Control Association*, XVIII (February 1968), 86–93.

20 Athelstan Spilhaus, "The Experimental City," *Daedalus*, XCVI (Fall 1967), 1129–41.

21 C. A. Doxiadis, *Ekistics—The Science of Human Settlements*. Southampton, England: Town and Country Planning Summer School, 1959, 25, and *The Science of Ekistics*. Athens, Greece: Doxiadis Associates, 1959, 21.

22 The ecosystem concept is developed in the following selections from a very large literature:

S. Dillon Ripley and Helmut K. Buechner, "Ecosystem Science as a Point of Synthesis," *Daedalus*, XCVI (Fall 1967), 1192–99;

Thomas D. Brock, "The Ecosystem and the Steady State," *Bioscience*, XVII (March 1967), 166–69;

D. A. Maelzer, "Environment, Semantics, and System Theory in Ecology," *Journal of Theoretical Biology*, VIII (May 1964), 395–402;

D. R. Stoddart, "Geography and the Ecological Approach: The Ecosystem as a Geographical Principle and Method," *Geography*, L (July 1965), 242–51;

Harlan Lewis, "Evolutionary Processes in the Ecosystem," *Bioscience*, XIX (March 1969), 223–27;

P. A. Jordan, "Ecology, Conservation, and Human Behavior," *Bioscience*, XVIII (November 1968), 1023–29;

E. P. Odum, "The Strategy of Ecosystem Development," *Science*, CLXIV (April 18, 1969), 262–70.

23 For early instances of use of the spaceship analogy, see: Adlai E. Stevenson, United Nations Economic and Social Council, *Official Records, 39th Session*, 30 June–31 July 1965;

Kenneth E. Boulding, "The Economics of the Coming Spaceship Earth," in *Environmental Quality in a Growing Economy*, supra, Note 1, 3–14; Barbara Ward, *Spaceship Earth*. New York: Columbia University Press, 1966, viii, 152.

24 A range of illustrations from the early nineteen sixties include:
U. S. Public Health Service, *Environmental Planning Guide*, Publication No. 823. Washington, D.C.: Government Printing Office, 1961, note Preface and Introduction;

Kevin Lynch, *The Image of the City*, supra, Note 1;

Philip L. Wagner, *The Human Use of the Earth*. Glencoe, Illinois: Free Press, 1960, 270;

Journal of the American Institute of Architects, XXXV (March 1961), special issue on urban design;

Jane Jacobs, *The Death and Life of Great American Cities*. New York: Random House, 1961, 458;

Jean Gottman, *Megalopolis: The Urbanized Northeastern Seaboard of the United States*. New York: Twentieth Century Fund, 1961, xi, 810; bibliographical references;

August Heckscher, *The Public Happiness*. New York: Atheneum, 1962, 304, Chapters 13–14.

25 This viewpoint has both practical and theoretical justification. Cf. remarks by William L. Slayton relative to "the need for a comprehensive approach to the development and renewal of urban areas" in a talk "Toward a Comprehensive Urban Policy: National Interest" at the Annual Conference, American Institute of Planners, Detroit, Michigan, November 29, 1961. Lancelot Law Whyte, considering comprehensiveness of approach from the viewpoint of science, remarks, "There are some who consider the possibility of complete knowledge, even within limited fields, as so absurd or so distasteful as to lead them to resist any attempt to prepare for a comprehensive synthesis. This attitude may have its advantages for the individual who adopts it, but it is alien to the spirit of science," in *The Unitary Principle in Physics and Biology*. New York: Holt, 1949, 18–19.

26 Human preferences in relation to climate and landscape may be influenced by hereditary factors, both genetic and cultural. Our knowledge of the actual mix of factors influencing preferences is as yet very meager. Factors other than environmental preferences now seem to determine where most people live.

27 Cf. Norman Wengert, "Resource Development and the Public Interest; A Challenge for Research," 1 *Natural Resources Journal* (November 1961), 207–23.

28 This opinion seems consistent with a conclusion reached by some students of natural-resources administration that better policy guidance is a concomitant, if not a necessary antecedent, of more effective administrative co-ordination. Cf. Irving K. Fox and Lyle E. Craine, "Organizational Arrangements for Water Development," 2 *Natural Resources Journal* (April 1962), 31 ff., especially pages 34 and 39. But the development of policy and organization are inseparable because, as Vincent Ostrom puts it in "The Water Economy and Its Organization," 2 *Natural Resources Journal* (April 1962), 72, "Since the patterns of organization have a fundamental influence on the developments of perspectives, values and ideas regarding resource politics and patterns of resource development, any question of comprehensive planning must necessarily involve comparable questions about design of organizational arrangements."

29 Sunday, January 4, 1970, p. D6.

CHAPTER 2

QUALITY OF THE ENVIRONMENT AS A SOCIAL ISSUE

1 John Dewey, *The Public and Its Problems*. New York: Henry Holt, 1927, vi, 224.

2 For further discussion of this theme, see "Man's Response to the Physical Environment," *The Journal of Social Issues*, XXII (October 1966), edited by Robert W. Kates and Joachim F. Wohlwill, whole issue; also Gardner Murphy, "Testing the Limits of Man," in *Social Implications of Man in Space*, ibid., XVII (No. 2, 1961), 5–14. Note also "Conclusions" of Robert F. Lamson in "The Future of Man's Environment," *The Science Teacher*, XXXVI (No. 1, January 1969), 25–30.

3 For example, see Clarence J. Glacken, *Traces on the Rhodian Shore: Nature and Culture in Western Thought from Ancient Times to the End of the Eighteenth Century.* Berkeley: University of California Press, 1967, xxviii, 763, bibliography;

Philip C. Ritterbush, "Environment and Historical Paradox," in *General Systems; Yearbook of the Society for General Systems Research*, XII (1968), 107–14;

Lynn White, Jr., "The Historical Roots of Our Ecological Crisis," *Science*, CLV (March 10, 1967), 1203–7;

Richard L. Means, "Why Worry About Nature?" *Saturday Review*, L (December 2, 1967), 13–15.

4   Robert Strausz-Hupé, *Geopolitics: The Struggle for Space and Power*. New York: G. P. Putnam's Sons, 1942, xii, 274. The author emphasizes the theories of the German geographer Friedrich Ratzel on the social and political significance of space; note especially pages 27–36. See also Andrew Gyorgy, *Geopolitics, The New German Science*, University of California Publications in International Relations, III (No. 3). Berkeley: University of California Press, 1944, 141–303.

5   For example, by Morley Roberts in *Bio-politics: An Essay in the Physiology, Pathology, and Politics of the Social and Somatic Organism*. London: Dent, 1938, 240; by Durward L. Allen in *Our Wildlife Legacy*. New York: Funk and Wagnalls, 1954, Chap. 13; by J. P. Miller in "The New Science," New York *Herald-Tribune* (September 2, 1963), p. 1; and by Lynton K. Caldwell in "Biopolitics: Science, Ethics and Public Policy," *Yale Review*, LIV (October 1964), 1–16.

6   For example, by Harold and Margaret Sprout in *The Ecological Perspective on Human Affairs with Special Reference to International Politics*. Princeton, New Jersey: Princeton University Press, 1965, 236; and Fred W. Riggs, *The Ecology of Public Administration*. New York: Asia Publishing House, 1961, 152. See also articles on "Society and Ecology" in *American Behavioral Scientist*, XI (July–August 1968), edited by Robert Strausz-Hupé, whole issue.

7   "The Political Science of Science," *The American Political Science Review*, L (December 1956), 961–79.

8   Among cases in point are successful opposition to a Pacific Gas and Electric nuclear power plant on Bodega Bay, California, and to the Bureau of Reclamation's proposed dams in the Grand Canyon of the Colorado in 1964; reversal of the plans of the Department of the Army to dump 27,000 tons of surplus poison gas in the Atlantic Ocean; revision of the Army Corps of Engineers Kentucky Red River Gorge project, and relocation of a jet airport planned for the Florida Everglades in 1969. Cf. "Environmental Quality as a Major Public Issue of Legislative Importance," *Legislative Analysis No. 1*, Washington: Public Health Service, Consumer Protection and Environmental Health Service, November 6, 1969, esp. pp. 1–5.

9   Recently edited by David Lowenthal. Cambridge, Massachusetts: Harvard University Press, 1965, 472.

10 Cf. Hunter A. Dupree, *Science in the Federal Government: A History of Politics and Activities to 1940*. Cambridge, Massachusetts: Harvard University Press, 1957, 460.

11 For detailed accounts, see Samuel P. Hays, *Conservation and the Gospel of Efficiency—The Progressive Conservation Movement 1890–1920*. Cambridge, Massachusetts: Harvard University Press, 1959, 297, bibliography;
    Elmo R. Richardson, *The Politics of Conservation: Crusades and*

Controversies 1897–1913. Berkeley: University of California Press, 1962, ix, 207, bibliography;

Richard M. Highsmith, J. Granville Jensen, and Robert D. Rudd, *Conservation in the United States.* Chicago: Rand McNally, 1962, 322;

Frank E. Smith, *The Politics of Conservation.* New York: Pantheon Books, 1966, 338;

Norman Wengert, *Natural Resources and the Political Struggle.* New York: Doubleday, 1955, p. 71;

Ernest A. Englebert, "Political Parties and Natural Resources Policies: An Historical Evaluation, 1790–1950," 1 *Natural Resources Journal* (November 1961), 224–26;

Roland C. Clement, "Meaning of Conservation," *Audubon Magazine,* LXVII (July–August 1965), 218–19;

Michael Frome, "The Politics of Conservation," *Holiday,* XLI (February 1967), 79, 100 ff.;

R. L. Gordon, "Conservation and the Theory of Exhaustible Resources," *Canadian Journal of Economics and Political Science,* XXXII (August 1966), 319–26;

John V. Krutilla, "Conservation Reconsidered," *American Economic Review,* LVII (September 1967), 777–86;

George R. Hall, "Conservation as a Public Policy Goal," *Yale Review,* LI (Spring 1962), 400–13;

George Macinko, "Conservation Trends and the Future American Environment," *The Biologist,* L (Nos. 1–2, January 1968), 1–19.

12 *Encyclopedia of Associations,* 5th edition (Vol. I, National Organizations of the United States), Detroit, Michigan: Gale Research Company, 1968.

13 Published by members of the faculty in the Department of Economics and School of Business, University of Kansas, 1955, 103–4.

14 "The Conference Call: Message of the President of the United States to the Congress, February 8, 1965," in *Beauty for America: Proceedings of the White House Conference on Natural Beauty, May 24–25, 1965.* Washington: U. S. Government Printing Office, 1965, 1–2.

15 Richard L. Means, "The New Conservation," *Natural History,* LXXVIII (August–September 1969), 16–25. David Lowenthal observes, "A new religion is in the making," in *Columbia University Forum* (Spring 1964), p. 34.

16 "The Changing Scope of Environmental Health," *W.H.O. Chronicle,* XX (March 1968), 95–99. See also articles in *Archives of Environmental Health* and the *American Journal of Public Health.* For general background, see John J. Hanlon, *Principles of Public Health Administration,* 4th ed. St. Louis, Missouri; Mosby, 1964, 719; and Joseph A. Salvato, *Environmental Sanitation.* New York: John Wiley, 1958, xii, 660.

17 James H. Cassedy, *Charles V. Chapin and the Public Health*

Movement. Cambridge, Massachusetts: Harvard University Press, 1962, 44–45.

18   Controversies over public health attitudes on water pollution and testing are discussed by Cynthia Brodine and George C. Berg, "Water Crisis—The Rochester Area," *Scientist and Citizen*, IX (March 1967), 41–49; Thomas A. Fink, "The Law and the Water," ibid., 50–54; and John M. Hewings, *Water Quality and the Hazard to Health: Placarding Public Beaches*. Toronto, Ontario: University of Toronto, Department of Geography, Natural Hazard Research, Working Paper No. 31, 1968, p. 66.

19   George Rosen, "Human Health, Community Life, and the Rediscovery of the Environment," *American Journal of Public Health*, LIV, Part II (Supplement to January 1964), 1–6.

20   American Medical Association, *Proceedings of the AMA Congress on Environmental Health Problems*, May 1–2, 1964, p. 108;

   Proceedings—2nd AMA Congress on Environmental Health Problems, April 26–27, 1965, p. 118;

   Proceedings—3rd AMA Congress on Environmental Health Problems, April 4–5, 1966, p. 122;

   Proceedings—4th AMA Congress on Environmental Health Problems, April 24–26, 1967, published in *Archives of Environmental Health*, XVI (January 1968), whole issue;

   AMA Congress on Environmental Health—Fifth Annual Session, April 29–30, 1968, *Archives of Environmental Health*, XVII (February 1969), whole issue;

   The 6th *AMA Congress on Environmental Health* was held April 28–29, 1969.

21   *American Journal of Public Health and the Nation's Health*, LIV (Supplement to January 1964), whole of Part II.

22   *Mayo Clinic Proceedings*, XL (January 1965), whole issue.

23   *Man in Equilibrium with His Environment*, October 13, 1965; *Conserving Man's Environmental Resources*, February 25, 1966; *Resources, Economics and a Quality Environment*, May 2–3, 1966; *Political Processes in Environmental Management*, June 24, 1966; and *The Dynamic Spectrum: Man, Health and Environment* (final project report), October 1966.

24   Cf. Ezra J. Mishan, *The Costs of Economic Growth*. New York: Frederick A. Praeger, 1967, xxi, 190.

25   Vol. CCXXXV (June 23, 1962), p. 8.

26   "American Directions: A Forecast," *Harper's Magazine*, CCXXX (February 1965), 39–45.

27   Ibid.

28   Vol. CCXIX (January 1967), 52–54.

29   Mr. Rockefeller had, however, held a number of non-political positions in the government, including chairman of the Outdoor Recreation Resources Review Commission, and the Citizens Advisory Committee on Outdoor Recreation and Natural Beauty.

30   *Beauty for America: Proceedings of the White House Conference on Natural Beauty*, supra, p. 679.

31 For an editorial comment on Lyndon Johnson's strange inconsistency on environmental-quality issues, see "Destroyers: Conflicting Policies of the Johnson Administration," *New Republic*, CLIV (June 25, 1966), 5–6.

32 A conclusion also reached by James L. Sundquist in *Politics and Policy: The Eisenhower, Kennedy, and Johnson Years*. Washington: The Brookings Institution, 1968, 322–81. Nevertheless, Lyndon Johnson's contribution to the environmental-quality movement was very great. On January 12, 1969, *The New York Times* commented editorially: "Of outstanding importance has been the administration's leadership in protecting natural resources and striving to keep the environment livable," p. 12E.

33 "The Education of Wally Hickel," *Time* (August 1, 1969); see *The New York Times* issues of January 1–15, especially January 12, p. 69, for comment on the deluge of mail to the Congress protesting the Hickel nomination.

34 Papers prepared for the first of these conferences have been published as *Environment for Man: The Next Fifty Years*, edited by William R. Ewald, Jr. Bloomington, Indiana: Indiana University Press, 1967, ix, 308; also by the same editor and publisher, *Environment and Change: The Next Fifty Years*, 1968, xvi, 397, and *Environment and Policy: The Next Fifty Years*, 1968, xiv, 459.

35 See Long Island community newspapers, e.g., *Great Neck Record*, June 19, 1969, "Our Environment Is Their Concern," and July 3, 1969, "Politics and Politicians."

36 "Environmental Defense Fund," *The National Observer* (April 22, 1968);
     See also comment by Richard L. Means in "The New Conservation," op. cit., p. 24.

37 Headquarters of the Conservation Law Society of America is in San Francisco, California. As an example of its work, see Robert W. Jasperson, "Grand Canyon and the Law," in François Leydet, *Time and the River Flowing: Grand Canyon*. San Francisco: The Sierra Club, 1964.

38 "Environmental Quality as a Major Public Issue of Legislative Importance," *Legislative Analysis No. 1*, Washington: Public Health Service, Consumer Protection and Environmental Health Service, November 6, 1969, p. 1.

CHAPTER 3

ENVIRONMENTAL QUALITY: AN INTEGRATIVE CONCEPT

1 Readers interested in the process of policy formation as studied by political scientists may find the following references useful:
     The Policy Sciences: Recent Developments in Scope and Method, edited by Harold D. Lasswell and Daniel Lerner. Stanford, California: Stanford University Press, 1951, p. 344;

Carl S. Friedrich, "Policy—A Science?" in *Public Policy, A Year-book of the Graduate School of Public Administration, Harvard University*, IV (1953), 267–81;

Raymond A. Bauer and Kenneth S. Gergen, *The Study of Policy Formation*. New York: The Free Press, 1968, xxii, 392, and *Public Policies and Their Politics: An Introduction to the Techniques of Government Control*, edited by Randall B. Ripley. New York: W. W. Norton, 1966, xviii, 174 (includes list of further suggested readings).

2   To Samuel Kercheval, July 22, 1816, *The Works of Thomas Jefferson*, Paul Leicester Ford, ed. (12 vols., Federal ed.). New York: G. P. Putnam's Sons, 1904–5, Vol. XII, p. 9.

3   To Governor H. D. Tiffin, February 2, 1807, *The Writings of Thomas Jefferson* (9 vols., H. A. Washington, ed.). Washington: Taylor and Maury, 1853–54, Vol. V, p. 38.

4   *Holism and Evolution*. New York: Macmillan, 1926; reprinted 1961 by Viking Press, xvii, 362.

5   For analyses of the limitations of rationality in relation to comprehensive and long-range planning, see Herbert A. Simon, "Theories of Decision-Making in Economics and Behavioral Sciences," *The American Economic Review*, XLIX (June 1959), 253–83; Charles E. Lindblom, "The Science of Muddling Through," *Public Administration Review*, XIX (Spring 1959), 79–88; and Yehezkel Dror, "Muddling Through—'Science or Inertia?'" ibid., XXVI (September 1964), 153–57. Also pertinent are chapters by John Friedmann and Zygmunt Bauman in *Action Under Planning: The Guidance of Economic Development*, edited by Bertram M. Gross. New York: McGraw-Hill, 1967;

For the role of decision making in the planning process, see David Braybrooke and Charles E. Lindblom, *A Strategy of Decision: Policy Evaluation as a Social Process*. New York: Free Press of Glencoe, 1963, ix, 268.

6   Tendencies toward "built-in" error are analyzed by Theodore Morgan in "The Theory of Error in Centrally-Directed Economic Systems," *Quarterly Journal of Economics*, LXXVIII (August 1964), 394–419.

7   There is a very large literature describing the scope and substance of ecology. For the general reader, the following writings may be useful:

F. Fraser Darling, "Conservation and Ecological Theory," in *British Ecological Society Jubilee Symposium*, edited by A. Macfadyen and P. J. Newbould (a supplement to the *Journal of Ecology*, LII) (March 1963). Oxford, England: Blackwell Scientific Publications, 1964, and "The Unity of Ecology," *Advancement of Science*, XX (November 1963), 297–306;

See also the journal *Bioscience*, Special Issue on Ecology (July 1964), 9–72; noting particularly E. P. Odum, "The New Ecology," XIV (July 1964), 14–16; and see P. A. Jordan, "Ecology, Conservation and Human Behavior," XVIII (November 1968), 1023–

29. In addition, see, among a large number of books, Peter H. Klopfer, *Behavioral Aspects of Ecology*. Englewood Cliffs, New Jersey: Prentice-Hall, 1962, p. 166; and E. P. Odum in collaboration with H. T. Odum, *Fundamentals of Ecology*, 2d ed. Philadelphia: Saunders, 1959, p. 546.

8   For the synthesizing role of ecology, see Stanley A. Cain, "Can Ecology Provide the Basis for Synthesis Among the Social Sciences?" in *Social Sciences and the Environment*, edited by Morris E. Garnsey and James R. Hibbs. Boulder, Colorado: University of Colorado Press, 1967, 27–52;

S. Dillon Ripley and Helmut K. Buechner, "Ecosystem Science as a Point of Synthesis," *Daedalus*, XCVI (Fall 1967), 1192–99; and Paul B. Sears, "Human Ecology: A Problem in Synthesis," *Science*, CXX (December 10, 1954), 959–63.

9   Relationships between ecology and geography are discussed in the following articles:

Robert W. Kates, "Geography: The Case for the Specialized Government in a Science of Environment," in *Social Sciences and the Environment*, supra, 53–76;

D. R. Stoddart, "Geography and the Ecological Approach," *Geography*, L (July 1965), 242–51;

Robert S. Platt, "Environmentalism versus Geography," *The American Journal of Sociology*, LIII (March 1948), 351–58;

George F. Carter, "Ecology, Geography, Ethnobotany," *Scientific Monthly*, LXX (February 1950), 73–80.

10 See Thomas D. Brock, "The Ecosystem in the Steady State," *Bioscience*, XVII (March 1967), 166–69. For a discussion of societal homeostasis and a list of pertinent references, see Lynton K. Caldwell, "Health and Homeostasis as Social Concepts: An Exploratory Essay," in "Diversity and Stability in Ecological Systems," *Brookhaven Symposia in Biology No. 22*. Upton, New York: Brookhaven National Laboratory, 1969, 206–23.

11 *General Systems: Yearbook of the Society for General Systems Research*. Published since 1956 under the editorship of L. von Bertalanffy, A. Rapoport, and also more recently of Richard L. Meier, this yearbook is a major source of information on multidisciplinary studies in the characteristics and properties of systems.

12 J. H. Woodger, *Biology and Language: An Introduction to Methodology in the Biological Sciences including Medicine* (The Farner Lecturer, 1949–50). Cambridge: Cambridge University Press, 1952, pp. 183 ff., 357, Postscript.

13 For further examination of the planetary basis for life, see: George Evelyn Hutchinson, "The Biosphere or Volume in Which Organisms Actually Live," in *The Ecological Theater and the Evolutionary Play*. New Haven: Yale University Press, 1965, 1–26; Harlow Shapley, "The Probable Environment of Other Planets," in *The Biology of Space Travel*, edited by N. N. Pirie. London: Institute of Biology, 1961, 107–16; Gilbert V. Levin, "Significance and Status of Exobiology," *Bioscience*, XV (January 1965), 17–30;

and *Extraterrestrial Life: An Anthology and Bibliography*, compiled by Elie A. Shneour and Eric A. Ottesen. Washington: National Academy of Sciences-National Research Council, 1966, vii, 478 (supplementary to *Biology and the Exploration of Mars*, NAS-NRC Publication 1296). In a more popular vein, see Stedom House, 1964, p. 242.

14 See Carl O. Sauer, "The Agency of Man on the Earth," in *Man's Role in Changing the Face of the Earth*, supra, 49–69. Milpa culture is described on pages 56–57. Also relevant is R. L. Sherlock, "The Influence of Man as an Agent in Geographical Change," *Geographical Journal*, LXI (April 1923), 258–73.

15 See Paul B. Sears, "The Inexorable Problem of Space," *Science*, CXXVII (January 3, 1958), 9–16.

16 Cf. David Lyle, "The Human Race Has, Maybe, Thirty-Five Years Left," *Esquire*, LXVIII (September 1967), pp. 116 ff.;
    See also Aldous Huxley, *The Politics of Ecology: The Question of Survival*. Santa Barbara, California: Center for the Study of Democratic Institutions, 1963, p. 7.

17 F. Fraser Darling, "The Danger of Simplified Ecosystems," *Transactions of the New York Academy of Science*, XXII (April 1960), 408–18.

18 For discussion of outer-space life-support systems, see Orr E. Reynolds, "Space Bio Sciences," *AIBS Bulletin*, XII (October 1962), 49–51;
    Charles H. Roadman and Frank B. Varis, "Life Support for Manned Space Flight," ibid., 53–55;
    Charles G. Wilber, "Exploration in Space," ibid., XIV (August 1964), 30–34, and *Physiological Problems in Space Exploration*, edited by James D. Hardy. Springfield, Illinois: Charles C. Thomas, 1964, 344.

19 This point is stressed and developed by Earl Finbar Murphy in *Governing Nature*. Chicago: Quadrangle Books, 1967, p. 333. Note especially Chapter 3, "The Costs of Working Against Nature."

20 United Nations Economic and Social Council, *Official Records, 39th Session*, 30 June–31 July 1965, p. 90, paragraph 42.

21 *Spaceship Earth*. New York: Columbia University Press, 1966, viii, 152.

22 "The Economics of the Coming Spaceship Earth," in *Environmental Quality in a Growing Economy*, supra, 3–14.

23 *Natural History*, LXXIX (January, 1970), 22 ff.

24 Ibid., 22.

25 "The Effects of Space Exploration on Man's Condition and Stature," in *The Future of Religions*, edited by Jerald C. Brauer. New York: Harper & Row, 1966, p. 45. See also "Social Implications of Man in Space," *The Journal of Social Issues*, XVII (No. 2, 1961), edited by Herbert E. Krugman and Donald N. Michael, whole issue.

26 "The Heron and the Astronaut," *Life*, LXVI (February 28, 1969), p. 26.

CHAPTER 4

PROTECTING THE ECOLOGICAL BASIS OF HUMAN LIFE

1 For a projection of trends and probabilities in man's resource needs, see: National Academy of Sciences-National Research Council, Committee on Natural Resources, *Natural Resources: A Summary Report to the President of the United States,* Publication No. 1000 and special reports 1000 A–G. Washington: National Academy of Sciences-National Research Council, 1962; and Hans H. Landsberg, Leonard L. Fischman, and Joseph L. Fisher, *Resources in America's Future: Patterns of Requirements and Availabilities, 1960–2000.* Baltimore: Johns Hopkins Press, 1963, p. 1017. For an optimistic assessment of resource substitutes, see Thomas B. Nolan, "Use and Renewal of Natural Resources," *Science,* CXXVIII (September 5, 1958), 631–36.

2 George Macinko, "Saturation: A Problem Evaded in Planning Land Use," *Science,* CXLIX (July 30, 1965), 516–21.

3 Cf. Robert Ardrey, *The Territorial Imperative: A Personal Inquiry into the Animal Origins of Property and Nations.* New York: Atheneum, 1966, xii, 390.

4 Cf. Konrad Lorenz, *On Aggression,* translated by Marjorie Kerr Wilson. New York: Harcourt, Brace & World, 1966, p. 306;
    Nikolaas Tinbergen, *Social Behavior in Animals.* New York: John Wiley, 1953, p. 150, and "On War and Peace in Animals and Man," *Science,* CLX (June 28, 1963), 1411–18;
    Peter H. Klopfer, *Behavioral Aspects of Ecology.* Englewood Cliffs, New Jersey: Prentice-Hall, 1962, p. 166;
    Edward T. Hall, *The Hidden Dimension.* Garden City, New York: Doubleday, 1966, xii, 201.

5 Cf. Robin Fox, "A Prospect for Human Ethology: A Challenging Comparison of Human and Animal Cultures," *Canadian Scientist,* II (March 1968), 19–22 (note references). See also comparisons drawn by V. C. Wynne Edwards in *Animal Dispersion in Relation to Social Behavior.* London: Oliver and Boyd, 1962, xi, 653; and studies undertaken at the Hudson Institute concerning human behavior under severe environmental stress, e.g. Jean M. Ingersoll, *Historical Examples of Ecological Disaster—Famine in Russia, 1921–22.* Harmon on Hudson, New York, December 1965, 1–51.

6 Evident and possible man-made hazards are described by Lewis Herber in *Our Synthetic Environment.* New York: Alfred A. Knopf, 1962, p. 285.
    The delayed and indirect effects of biologically active agents are discussed by René Dubos in *Man Adapting.* New Haven: Yale University Press, 1965, 220–25.

7 For evidence, see: Wesley Marx, *The Frail Ocean.* New York:

Coward-McCann, 1967; and Ray Hebert, "The Fragile Desert," *Cry California,* I (Fall 1966), 15–20. See also various discussions in *Future Environments of North America,* edited by F. Fraser Darling and John P. Milton. Garden City, New York: Natural History Press, 1966, xv, 767. Note especially articles by Durward L. Allen, J. Ross Mackay, and Gilbert F. White.

8 For particulars of this indictment, see: Fairfield Osborn, *Our Plundered Planet.* Boston: Little, Brown & Co., 1948, xiv, 217, and *The Limits of the Earth,* ibid., 1953, 238; William Vogt, *Road to Survival.* New York: W. Sloane Associates, 1948, p. 335.

9 Lynton K. Caldwell, "Problems of Applied Ecology: Perceptions, Institutions, Methods, and Operational Tools," *Bioscience,* XVI (August 1966), 524–27.

10 Lawrence B. Slobodkin discusses conceptual problems of the ecology of man and analyzes relationships between the societal (political) level and technological or ecological (operational) level of discourse in "Aspects of the Future of Ecology," *Bioscience,* XVIII (January 1968), 16–23.

11 Cf. Lawrence J. Henderson, *The Fitness of the Environment: An Inquiry into the Biological Significance of the Properties of Matter.* New York: Macmillan, 1913, reprinted by Beacon Press, 1958, with introduction by George Wald, 317. See, further, Harold F. Blum, *Time's Arrow and Evolution,* 2d rev. ed. New York: Harper & Bros., 1962, 220 and index.

12 Much of the evidence concerning range of tolerances has been gathered in the course of studies of adaptation. For a compendium of data, see *Handbook of Physiology: Adaptation to the Environment,* edited by D. B. Dill et al. Washington: American Physiological Society, 1964, ix, 1056. Note also Eugene Schreider, "Physiological Anthropology and Climatic Variations," in *Environmental Physiology and Psychology in Arid Conditions: Reviews of Research.* Paris: UNESCO, 1963, 37–73.

13 See Frank M. Stead, *Managing Man's Environment in the San Francisco Bay Area.* Berkeley: University of California, Institute of Governmental Studies, 1963, p. 49; and James E. Vance, *Geography and Urban Evolution in the San Francisco Bay Area.* Ibid., 1964, 89. For a description of problems of protecting the Bay from commercial destruction, see "A Body of Water, Not Real Estate," *The Nature Conservancy News,* XXIX (Summer 1969), p. 7; and Gil Bailey, "1969—The Year We Save, or Lose, San Francisco Bay," *Cry California,* IV (Winter 1968/69), 13–17; also Roger Almsted, "Angel Island," ibid., 27–29.

14 See *Restoring the Quality of Our Environment: Report of the Environmental Pollution Panel of the President's Science Advisory Committee.* Washington: The White House, 1965; note especially Appendix 43, "Benchmark Surveillance." The technical literature on monitoring and control is now very large. Probably the best general coverage is provided by the reports of the House of

Representatives Subcommittee on Science, Research, and Development, and the National Academy of Sciences, in 1966. See reports listed in this chapter under the heading "Congressional Documents." Quantitative techniques for determining the monitoring standards are more advanced than is generally realized. See Robert B. Platt and John F. Griffiths, *Environmental Measurement and Interpretation*. New York: Reinhold, 1964, xii, 235; and Kenneth E. F. Watt, *Ecology and Resource Management*. New York: McGraw-Hill, 1968, xii, 450.

See also issues of the journal *Environmental Science and Technology*, 1967–.

15 See, for example, Jane Jacobs, *The Death and Life of Great American Cities*. New York: Random House, 1961, index entries under "Safety"; see also Robert E. Faris and Dunham H. Warren, *Mental Disorders in Urban Areas: An Ecological Study of Schizophrenia and Other Psychoses*. Chicago: University of Chicago Press, 1939, xxxviii, 270.

16 Note, for example, discussions in *Ecology of Health*, edited by E. H. L. Corwin. New York: Commonwealth Fund, 1949; Murray C. Brown, "Environment and Health," *Chicago Medicine*, LXXI (June 22, 1968), 515–20; and the series of papers presented in the symposium of the Geological Society of America on "Environmental Geochemistry in Relation to Human Health and Disease," at the December 1968 meeting of the American Association for the Advancement of Science. For a historical account of disease/environment relationships, see Henry E. Sigerist, *Civilization and Disease*. Ithaca, New York: Cornell University Press, 1943, xii, 254, reprinted by the University of Chicago Press, 1962.

17 Cf. René Dubos, *The Mirage of Health: Utopias, Progress, and Biological Change*. New York: Doubleday, 1961, 235.

18 New York: Norton, 1932, revised 1939.

19 I have discussed some of these theories and the concept of social stability in "Health and Homeostasis as Social Concepts: An Exploratory Essay," *Brookhaven Symposia in Biology, No. 22*, op. cit., 206–23.

20 *Science*, CLXII (December 13, 1968), 1243–48.

21 See "Information Programs About Environmental Contamination," *Science*, CXLIV (May 8, 1964), p. 616; note also the San Francisco *Chronicle* (December 2, 1968), p. 5.

22 "Scientist and Citizen: St. Louis Group Broadens Educational Role," *Science*, CLVII (August 25, 1967), 903–5.

23 Following is a list of some of the major documents on environmental-policy issues published by the United States Government during the six-year period May 1963 through May 1969:

Executive Reports

1963: *The Use of Pesticides*. Report of the Life Sciences Panel, President's Science Advisory Committee (May 15).

1965: *Beauty for America.* Proceedings of the White House Conference on Natural Beauty, Washington, D.C. (May 24–25).

1965: *Restoring the Quality of Our Environment: Report of the Environmental Pollution Panel of the President's Science Advisory Committee* (Tukey Report, November).

1965: *Weather Modification and Climate Control.* Report of the Special Commission on Weather Modification, National Science Foundation (December).

1966: *Waste Management and Control.* A report to the Federal Council for Science and Technology by the Committee on Pollution, National Academy of Sciences-National Research Council (Publication 1400).

1967: *A Strategy for a Livable Environment.* Report of Department of Health, Education and Welfare Task Force on Environmental Health and Related Problems (Linton Report, June).

1968: *From Sea to Shining Sea.* A report on the American Environment. Report of the President's Council on Recreation and Natural Beauty (October).

Congressional Documents

1963: *Interagency Coordination in Environmental Hazards (Pesticides).* Hearings before the Subcommittee on Reorganization and International Organizations of the Committee on Government Operations, United States Senate, 88th Cong., 1st Sess. (May, June, July, August, October). In seven parts with five appendices.

1963: *Air Pollution Control.* Hearings before a Special Subcommittee on Air and Water Pollution of the Committee on Public Works, United States Senate, 88th Cong., 1st Sess. (September). Hearings on air pollution have been held by this subcommittee in 1964, 1965, 1966, 1967, and 1968. Hearings on the Air Quality Act of 1967 were held before the Committee on Interstate and Foreign Commerce, House of Representatives (August 1967).

1966: *Weather Modification.* Hearings before the Committee on Commerce, United States Senate, 89th Cong., 1st and 2d Sess., Parts I and II (November 1965, February, March, April, 1966). See also *Weather Modification and Control.* A report prepared at the request of Hon. Warren G. Magnuson, Chairman, for the use of the Committee on Commerce, United States Senate, by the Legislative Reference Service, the Library of Congress (April 1967).

1966: *Ecological Research and Surveys.* Hearings before the Committee on Interior and Insular Affairs, United States Senate, 89th Cong., 2d Sess. (April 27).

1966: *Environmental Pollution. A Challenge to Science and Technology.* Report of the Subcommittee on Science and Astronautics, House of Representatives, 89th Cong., 2d Sess. (October).

1966: *The Adequacy of Technology for Pollution Abatement*. A report of the Research Management Advisory Panel, through the Subcommittee on Science, Research and Development, to the Committee on Science and Astronautics, U. S. House of Representatives, 89th Cong., 2d Sess. (July 11); and *Hearings before the Subcommittee on Science, Research and Development of the Committee on Science and Astronautics*, U. S. House of Representatives, 89th Cong., 2d Sess., Vols. I and II (July and September).

1967: *Establish a Select Senate Committee on Technology and the Human Environment*. Hearings before the Subcommittee on Inter-governmental Relations, Senate Committee on Government Operations (March–April).

1968: *Environmental Quality*. Hearings before the Subcommittee on Science, Research and Development of the Committee on Science and Astronautics, U. S. House of Representatives, 90th Cong., 2d Sess. (January, February, March).

1968: *Managing the Environment*. Report to the Subcommittee on Science, Research and Development to the Committee on Science and Astronautics, 90th Cong., 2d Sess. (June 17).

1968: *A National Policy for the Environment*. Special Report to the Committee on Interior and Insular Affairs. United States Senate, 90th Cong., 2d Sess. (July 11).

1968: *Joint House-Senate Colloquium to Discuss a National Policy for the Environment*. Hearing before the Committee on Interior and Insular Affairs, United States Senate, and the Committee on Science and Astronautics, U. S. House of Representatives, 90th Cong., 2d Sess. (July 17). See also summary of colloquium and commentary in *Congressional White Paper on a National Policy for the Environment*. Submitted to the United States Congress under the auspices of the Committee on Interior and Insular Affairs, United States Senate, and the Committee on Science and Astronautics, U. S. House of Representatives, 90th Cong., 2d Sess. (October).

1969: *National Environmental Policy*. Hearing before the Committee on Interior and Insular Affairs, United States Senate, 91st Cong., 1st Sess. (April 16).

1969: *Environmental Quality*. Hearing before the Subcommittee on Fisheries and Wildlife Conservation of the Committee on Merchant Marine and Fisheries, U. S. House of Representatives, 91st Cong., 1st Sess. (May).

24 See H. J. Res. 54, House of Representatives, 91st Cong., 1st Sess. January 3, 1969 ("Joint Resolution Proposing an Amendment to the Constitution of the United States relating to the conservation of natural resources and the natural beauty of the United States"). "Section 1. The right of the people to clean air, pure water, free-

dom from excessive and unnecessary noise, and the natural, scenic, historic, and aesthetic qualities of their environment shall not be abridged." For a reasoned argument on behalf of such rights, see Douglas L. Brooks, "Man's Right to a Clean Environment," *Proceedings of the Thirty-Fourth North American Wildlife and Natural Resources Conference,* 1969. See also S. J. Res. 169, Senate, 91st Cong., 2d Sess. January 19, 1970 (Nelson).

25 See pamphlet *This Is IUCN.* Morges, Switzerland: International Union for the Conservation of Nature and Natural Resources, August 1969, pages unnumbered.

26 *Intergovernmental Conference of Experts on the Scientific Basis for Rational Use and Conservation of the Resources of the Biosphere. UNESCO House. Paris, 4–13 September 1968—Final Report.* Paris: UNESCO, SC/MD/9, January 1969, 35 + annexes.

27 *Resolution 2398* (XXIII). Adopted "without objection" at the 1733d Plenary Session. See also Economic and Social Council Resolution 1346 (XLV) of 30 July 1968 on the question of convening an international conference on the problems of human environment.

28 United Nations Economic and Social Council, *Problems of the Human Environment: Report of the Secretary-General.* New York: United Nations E 14667 (Economic and Social Council, Fortyseventh Session, agenda item 10, May 26, 1969).

29 *The Web of Life.* New York: Devin-Adair, 1953, vii, 144.

CHAPTER 5

ADAPTING NATURAL ENVIRONMENTS TO HUMAN NEEDS

1 *Mankind Evolving: The Evolution of the Human Species.* New Haven: Yale University Press, 1962, p. 89.

And Bruce L. Welch writes, "The animal is never in any two environments (or population densities) the same; its resistance to disease and its physiological and behavioral potentials are changed. It and its environment are functionally inseparable," in *Psychophysiological Response to the Mean Level of Environmental Stimulation: A Theory of Environmental Integration.* Williamsburg, Virginia: College of William and Mary, Laboratory of Population Ecology, 1965, p. 84, reprinted from *Symposium on Medical Aspect of Stress in the Military Climate.* Washington: Walter Reed Army Medical Center, 1965.

2 See *Handbook of Physiology, Section 4, Adaptation to the Environment,* edited by D. B. Dill et al. Washington: American Physiological Society, 1964, ix, 1056. Note especially article by Chauncey D. Leake, "Perspectives of adaptation: historical backgrounds," 1–9.

3 Cf. Demitri B. Shimkin, "Adaptive Strategies: A Basic Problem in

Human Ecology," in *Three Papers on Human Ecology*. Oakland, California: Mills College Assembly Series 1965–1966, 37–52.

4   "The Ecosystem as a Conceptual Tool in the Management of Natural Resources," in *Natural Resources: Quality and Quantity: Papers presented before a faculty seminar at the University of California, Berkeley, 1961–1965*, edited by S. V. Ciriacy-Wantrup and James L. Parsons. Berkeley: University of California Press, 1967, 139–61, quotation from p. 140.

5   "The Ecosystem—A Unifying Concept for the Management of Natural Areas in the National Park System," in *Rocky Mountain-High Plains Parks and Recreation Journal*, III (No. 2, 1968). See also Lynton K. Caldwell, "An Ecosystems Approach to Public Land Policy," in *Proceedings of the 10th Annual Western Resources Conference*. Fort Collins, Colorado: Colorado State University, July 1968. See also articles in *American Behavioral Scientist*, XI (July–August 1968).

6   For problems posed by the conflict between traditional values and changing needs, see Frederick Sargent II and Demitri B. Shimkin, "Biology, Society, and Culture in Human Ecology," *Bioscience*, XV (August 1965), 512–16.

7   Cf. Kurt Lewin, *Principles of Topological Psychology*. New York: McGraw-Hill, 1936, xv, 231; and *Field Theory in Social Science: Selected Theoretical Papers*, edited by Dorwin Cartwright. New York: Harper, 1951, xx, 346. See also the more recent work of Roger G. Barker, *Ecological Psychology: Concepts and Methods of Studying the Environment of Human Behavior*. Stanford, California: Stanford University Press, 1968, p. 242.

8   *The Lonely Crowd, A Study of the Changing American Character*. Garden City, New York: Doubleday, 1953, 359. See also Martha Wolfenstein, "The Emergence of Fun Morality," in *The Journal of Social Issues*, VII (No. 4, 1951), p. 15.

9   Cf. Arnold W. Green, *Recreation, Leisure, and Politics*. New York: McGraw-Hill, 1964. For various aspects of public policy concerning outdoor recreation and the environment, see the following publications: *Outdoor Recreation for America: A Report to the President and to the Congress by the Outdoor Recreation Resources Review Commission*. Washington: U. S. Government Printing Office, 1962, xiii, 246; *Study Report Twenty-two Trends in American Living and Outdoor Recreation*, ibid., xiii, 257; Marion Clawson, "The Crisis in Outdoor Recreation," *American Forests*, LXV (March 1959), 22 ff., and (April 1959), 28 ff. See also Ashley L. Schiff, "Outdoor Recreation Values in the Public Decision Process," 6 *Natural Resources Journal* (October 1966), 542–59.

10 For further discussion, see my essay "Problems of Policy and Administration," in *The Careless Technology*, edited by John P. Milton and Taghi Farvar. New York: Natural History Press, 1971.

11 Cf. John Skow, "When the Great Developer Became Extinct," *The Saturday Evening Post*, CXXXIX (October 8, 1966), p. 29.

12 See Benjamin Horace Hubbard, *A History of Public Land Policies.*
    New York: Macmillan, 1942, reprinted in 1965 by the University
    of Wisconsin Press, with foreword by Paul W. Gates, xxvii, 579.

13 Peter Blake, *God's Own Junkyard,* 1st ed. New York: Holt, Rine-
    hart & Winston, 1964, p. 8.

14 "Wasteland," in *More in Anger.* Philadelphia: J. B. Lippincott,
    1958, p. 41.

15 "Bethlehem Strips 1,000 Dunes Acres: Company Spurns Pleas by
    Indiana Conservationists," *The New York Times* (April 14, 1963);
    and "Demolishing the Dunes." LaPorte (Indiana) *Herald-Argus*
    (April 18, 1963), p. 6. The industrialization of the Indiana Dunes
    represents an ecologically costly and economically unnecessary
    misuse of a unique environment. For accounts of the underlying
    issues, see: William Peeples, "The Indiana Dunes and Pressure
    Politics," *The Atlantic,* CCXI (February 1963), 84–88;
        Frederick Sicher, "An Indiana Dunes National Lakeshore," *Na-
    tional Parks Magazine,* XXXVIII (July 1964), 4–7, 15; and Harold
    M. Mayer, "Politics and Land Use: The Indiana Shoreline of Lake
    Michigan," *Annals of the Association of American Geography,*
    LIV (December 1964), 508–23. It was to prevent price escalation
    and spiteful impairment of the environment that the device of a
    "legislative taking" was used in the act establishing the Redwoods
    National Park bill.

16 The scientist and science-fiction writer Fred Hoyle has written a
    morality tale of an environmental "Rake's Progress" in the short
    story "Welcome to Slippage City." The finale to the story is not
    necessarily relevant to the description of how men turn good envi-
    ronments into bad, but readers will have no difficulty whatever in
    identifying the city. *Element 79.* New York: New American Li-
    brary, 1968, 50–62.

17 "Possibly the trickiest word of all is 'needs,' " writes Garrett
    Hardin. For a clear-minded exposure of the "need" fallacy, see
    "Finding Lemonade in Santa Barbara's Oil." *Saturday Review,* LII
    (May 10, 1969), 18–21.

18 For an analysis of some problems of reconciling and relating
    market and non-market decisions on uses of the environment, see
    A. Allan Schmid, "Quality of the Environment and Man: Some
    Thoughts on Economic Institutions," *Journal of Soil and Water
    Conservation,* XXI (May–June 1966), 89–91. The cause of the
    cleavage between market and non-market decisions is partly in-
    stitutional. In 1959, political scientist Coleman Woodbury wrote:
    "The metropolitan outlook is grave—not because its problems are
    impregnable, but because our poor preparation for dealing with
    them is found on so many fronts—in basic understanding of the
    problems themselves, in governmental and private institutional
    means for deciding on policies and pressing forward with them, and
    in public appreciation of the scale and seriousness of the issues."
    Science, CXXIX (June 12, 1959), p. 1590.

19 The Pennsylvania Station in New York City and the train con-

course of the Union Station in Chicago are among the more no-
torious cases. See also Philip Johnson, "Why We Want Our Cities
Ugly," in *The Fitness of Man's Environment, Smithsonian Annual,*
II. Washington: Smithsonian Institution, 1968, esp. p. 158. See also
Nathaniel Alexander Owings, *The American Aesthetic.* New York:
Harper & Row, 1969, p. 198.

20 Cf. A. A. Berle, Jr., "What GNP Doesn't Tell Us," *Saturday Review,* LI (August 31, 1968), 10–12, 40; and Stuart Chase, "Can
We Stay Prosperous?" ibid., L (February 11, 1967), 20–22.

21 For a summary of scientific opinion on the genetic basis of personality and the influence of adaptation, see W. W. Howells, "Universality and Variation in Human Nature," in *Current Anthropology,*
edited by William L. Thomas, Jr. Chicago: University of Chicago
Press, 1955, 227–36 (note references).

CHAPTER 6

SHAPING THE ENVIRONMENTS OF CIVILIZED SOCIETIES

1 "Stanzas from the Grande Chartreuse" (lines 85–86), *The Poetical
Works of Matthew Arnold,* edited by C. B. Tinker and H. F. Lowry.
London: Oxford University Press, 1950, p. 302.

2 For a cautious analysis, see David Braybrooke and Charles E. Lindblom, *A Strategy of Decision: Policy Evaluation as a Social Process.* New York: Free Press of Glencoe, 1963, ix, 268.

3 Theodosius Dobzhansky writes, "The interrelations between the
biological and cultural components of human evolution may be
brought out perhaps most clearly if we consider that they serve the
same basic function—adaptation to and control of man's environments," in *Mankind Evolving.* New Haven: Yale University Press,
1962, p. 20.

4 This holistic and evolutionary approach to human history is most
clearly exemplified by Pierre Teilhard de Chardin in *The Phenomenon of Man,* English translation by Bernard Wall. New York:
Harper & Row, 1959, p. 318. Although the data supporting this
viewpoint represent substantial support in scientific theory, Teilhard's thesis also has a strongly metaphysical character, which,
however, makes it neither less nor more consistent with ultimate
reality.

5 Cf. Jacques Ellul, *The Technological Society,* translated from the
French by John Wilkinson. New York: Alfred A. Knopf, 1964,
xxxvi, 449.

6 See comments by John McHale in "Toward the Future," *Design
Quarterly,* LXXII, Minneapolis, Minnesota: Walker Art Center,
1968; and Isaac Asimov, "After Apollo, a Colony on the Moon?"
Science Digest, LXII (September 1967), 44–48.

7 In the long run, the wearing down of the continents and stream

siltation occur regardless of human agency. Cf. discussions of the Meander and Mississippi flood plains in Richard L. Russell, *River Plains and Sea Coasts*. Berkeley: University of California Press, 1967, pp. 55 ff. For a popular account of Greek ports in Asia Minor, see Kathleen Freeman, *Greek City-States*. New York: Norton, 1950, vii, 274.

8   "The Polipollutionists," *The Atlantic*, CCXIX (January 1967), p. 52.

9   "The Villains Are Greed, Indifference—and You," *Life*, LIX (December 24, 1965), p. 96.

10 Kevin Lynch reports findings that large areas of American cities are so devoid of distinctiveness that their residents find it difficult to describe them, in *Image of the City*. Cambridge, Massachusetts: Technology Press, 1960, p. 194. See also comments by Anselm L. Strauss in *Images of the American City*. New York: Free Press of Glencoe, 1961, xiv, 306.

11 *Saturday Review*, LII (April 5, 1969), 67–69. See also Robert Sommer's book *Personal Space: The Behavioral Basis of Design*. Englewood Cliffs, New Jersey: Prentice-Hall, 1969, xi, 177.

12 For example, the Disney Enterprises complex in Mineral King Valley, California, to accommodate 15,000 visitors per day during the summer months. See *Sierra Club Bulletin*, LIII (September 1968), pp. 5 ff.; and the Disney World amusement park near Orlando, Florida. See also Wesley Pruden, Jr., "They're Looking for Ways to Spend Money," *The National Observer* (August 18, 1969), pp. 1 ff.

13 As of the date of publication of this book, no comprehensive study of environmental education in colleges and universities was generally available. A limited study, unpublished, was made by Dr. Spencer Havlick, of the University of Michigan, for the Conservation Foundation (1968). For a general discussion of the opportunities and problems, see Lynton K. Caldwell, "The Human Environment: A Growing Challenge to Higher Education," *Journal of Higher Education*, XXXVII (March 1966), 149–55; and Robert S. Morison, "Education for Environmental Concerns," *Daedalus*, XCVI (Fall 1967), 1210–23. A. D. Trottenberg believes that one source of failure to develop better environments is inadequate education for perceptual awareness: "Colleges Graduate Visual Illiterates," *Saturday Review*, XLIX (February 19, 1966), 73, 103–4. "What better goal for humanistic education," he asks, "than the creation of a truly humane environment?" (p. 104). For a realistic analysis of the difficulties in developing environmental studies in the universities see *The Universities and Environmental Quality—Commitment to Problem Focused Education: A Report to the President's Environmental Quality Council*. By John S. Steinhart and Stacie Cherniack, Washington: Office of Science and Technology, September, 1969, p. 22.

14 There is a very large literature on the study of nature and the teaching of conservation. Probably the best general source of cur-

rent data is the *Bulletin on Conservation Education,* issued periodically by the Conservation Foundation, 1250 Connecticut Avenue, Washington, D.C. 20036.

15 In *Seven Come Affinity,* edited by Groff Conklin. New York: Fawcett, 1966. The pertinent discussion occurs on pages 281–84.

16 Cf. Stewart L. Udall, *1976: Agenda for Tomorrow.* New York: Harcourt, Brace & World, 1968, xv, 173, especially Chapter 4, "The Growth Gospel: Some Reflections on Jefferson."

17 For example, a blue-ribbon Committee on SST-Sonic Boom of the National Academy of Sciences expressed optimism that in the future it may be possible to design and build a commercial SST that will ". . . generate a boom of acceptable characteristics. . . ." The committee declared its confidence that ". . . American ingenuity can resolve the technical problems." *Report on Human Response to the Sonic Boom* (June 1968), 12 pp. The report details problems for which solutions will be needed if SST sonic boom is to avoid the arousal of political complications. But it does not suggest that American ingenuity might find ways of dispensing with SST in favor of socially more-useful efforts to improve public transportation.

18 See provisions specifying "rights" to a safe and healthful environment in connection with legislation introduced into the Ninety-first Congress: e.g. H. J. Res. 54, January 3, 1969 (Ottinger) Joint Resolution Proposing an Amendment to the Constitution, and S.1075, July 9, 1969 (Jackson) *National Environmental Policy Act of 1969.* A proposed amendment to the Constitution declaring environmental rights in principle was introduced into the Ninety-first Congress by Senator Gaylord Nelson (S. J. Res. 169, January 19, 1970).

19 *The Two Cultures and the Scientific Revolution.* New York: Cambridge University Press, 1959, p. 107.

20 Among the criticisms of the fractionalized and linear patterns of modern culture are Herbert Marcuse, *One-Dimensional Man.* Boston: Beacon Press, 1964, xvii, 260; Joseph R. Royce, *Encapsulated Man.* Princeton, New Jersey: Van Nostrand, 1964, xi, 206; and Donald N. Michael, *The Unprepared Society: Planning for a Precarious Future.* New York: Basic Books, 1968, xiv, 132.

CHAPTER 7

ENVIRONMENTAL MANAGEMENT AS APPLIED SCIENCE

1 Cf. Don K. Price, *The Scientific Estate.* Cambridge, Massachusetts: Harvard University Press, 1965, ix, 323, and *Science and Government: Their Dynamic Relation in American Democracy.* New York: New York University Press, 1954, ix, 203.

See also Alexander A. Vucinich, *Science in Russian Culture—*

A History to 1860. Stanford, California: Stanford University Press, 1963, xv, 463.

2 Cf. Ralph Lapp, *The New Priesthood*. New York: Harper & Row, 1965, 244; see also Spencer Klaw, *The New Brahmins: Scientific Life in America*. New York: Morrow, 1968, p. 315.

3 For interactions of science, technology, and social institutions, see: Benjamin A. Cornelius, *Science, Technology, and Human Values*. Columbia, Missouri: University of Missouri Press, 1965, v, 296; Carl F. Stover, ed., *The Technological Order*. Detroit: Wayne State University Press, 1963, 280; and Aaron W. Warner, ed., *The Impact of Science on Technology*. New York: Columbia University Press, 1965, p. 231.

4 Jacques Ellul comes close to doing this. But it is not clear that his deterministic treatment of technology as a social force is in fact metaphysical. See *The Technological Society,* translated from the French by John Wilkinson. New York: Alfred A. Knopf, 1964, xxxvi, 449 (French original published in 1954 as *La Technique*). Note also issues of the journal *Technology and Culture*, 1959–.

5 John Kenneth Galbraith, *The New Industrial State*. Boston: Houghton Mifflin, 1967, xiv, 427.

Note also Harold P. Green et al., "Technology Assessment and the Law," 36 *George Washington Law Review* (July 1968), whole issue.

6 There are, of course, numerous laws and regulations governing specific aspects of use of the environment. Generally available sources are articles in the *Natural Resources Journal* and the *Natural Resources Lawyer* and in the following casebooks:

Frank J. Trelease, Harold S. Bloomenthal, and Joseph R. Geraud, *Cases and Materials on Natural Resources*. St. Paul: West, 1965, xxv, 1131; George Lefcoe, *Land Development Law, Cases and Materials*. Indianapolis: Bobbs-Merrill, 1966, xlix, 1681;

Daniel R. Mandelker, *Managing Our Urban Environment, Cases, Text and Problems*. Indianapolis: Bobbs-Merrill, 1966, xliv, 1003; J. H. Beuscher, *Water Rights*. Madison: College Printing and Typing Company, 1967, 434 and index;

Joseph L. Sax, *Water Law, Planning and Policy: Cases and Materials*. Indianapolis: Bobbs-Merrill, 1968, xxxii, 520;

Curtis J. Berger, *Landownership and Use*. Boston: Little, Brown & Company, 1968, xxii, 1055;

Charles M. Haar, *Land-Use Planning. A Casebook on the Use, Misuse and Re-Use of Urban Land*. Boston: Little, Brown & Company, 1959, xxxv, 790;

Charles M. Haar, ed., *Law and Land: Anglo American Planning Practice*. Cambridge, Massachusetts: Harvard University Press and M.I.T. Press, 1964, xviii, 290.

For a general article on the legal approach to environmental problems, see Ronald Beazley, "Conservation Decision Making: A Rationalization," 7 *Natural Resources Journal* (July 1967), 345–60. A good systematic treatment may be found in Earl Finbar Murphy, *Governing Nature*. Chicago: Quadrangle, 1967, p. 333. See also papers prepared for a conference on law and the environment sponsored by the Conservation Foundation in September 1969.

7   Note discussions in *The Electric Utility Industry and the Environment: A Report to the Citizens Advisory Committee on Recreation and Natural Beauty by the Electric Utility Industry Task Force on Environment*. Washington: 1968, p. 105.

8   Cf. Barry Commoner, "Nature Unbalanced: How Man Interferes with the Nitrogen Cycle," *Scientist and Citizen*, X (January–February 1968), 9–19; Joseph D. Salvia, "Milk and Pesticides," ibid. (August 1968), 143–53; Kevin Shea, "Cotton and Chemicals," ibid. (November 1968), 209–19. Note also the *Scientist and Citizen*, VII, Pesticide Series, No. 1 (April 1965) and No. 2 (July 1965).

    Scientific technology has been applied to agriculture in international development programs with results that have too often been ecologically disastrous. For a series of documented cases of these ecological mistakes, see John P. Milton and M. Taghi Farvar, *The Careless Technology*. New York: Natural History Press, in press. See also portions of this volume printed as a special supplement to *Natural History*, LXXVIII (February 1969), "The Unforeseen International Ecological Boomerang."

9   The fatuous and uneconomical practice of "vermin" campaigns and bounties still persists over wide areas of the United States, although its generally harmful effects have long been pointed out by well-informed critics; e.g. by Edward Graham in *Natural Principles of Land Use*. New York: Oxford, 1944, 219–21.

10 Many of these environmental management practices are discussed at length by Raymond F. Dasmann in *Environmental Conservation*, 2d ed. New York: John Wiley, 1968, xiii, 375.

11 Raymond Vernon, *The Myth and Reality of Our Urban Problems*. Cambridge, Massachusetts: Harvard University Press, 1962, vii, 90. For discussions of successes and difficulties in urban engineering, see *Proceedings of the First Conference on Environmental Engineering & Metropolitan Planning*. Evanston, Illinois: Northwestern University, 1962, xiv, 265.

12 See "Argonne Universities Association Conference on Universities, National Laboratories and Man's Environment," Chicago, Illinois, July 27–29, 1969, Oak Ridge, Tennessee; U. S. Atomic Energy Commission, Division of Technical Information, 1969, viii, 167.

13 National Academy of Sciences-National Research Council, report in press, but see NAS-NRC Reports, *Resources and Man*. San Francisco: W. H. Freeman, 1969, vi, 259, and *Institutions for Effective Management of the Environment*. Washington: January, 1970, viii, 62.

14 See *Environmental Quality*. Hearings before the Subcommittee on Science, Research, and Development of the Committee on Science and Astronautics U. S. House of Representatives, 90th Congress, 2nd Session, March 12, 1968. Note especially pp. 330–34, "A Na-

tional Institute of Ecology: Synopsis of Plans of the Ecological Society of America."

15 See "Benchwork Surveillance, Appendix Y3," in *Restoring the Quality of Our Environment, Report of the Pollution Panel, President's Science Advisory Committee*. Washington: The White House, 1965, 103–10.

16 For a survey of environmental surveillance capabilities see U. S. Department of Commerce, *ESSA Science and Engineering*. Washington: Environmental Science Services Administration, April, 1968, p. 150. On the specific topic of remote sensing see proceedings of the symposia on remote sensing of the environment published beginning March 1962 by the Institute of Science and Technology, the University of Michigan; and issues of the journal *Remote Sensing of the Environment: An Interdisciplinary Quarterly*, Vol. I, No. 1 (March 1969). See also James P. Latham, *Remote Sensing Papers at the AAAS: Impact and Implications*. Boca Raton, Florida: Florida Atlantic University, Department of Geography, Technical Report No. 2, June 1967. See also R. Keith Arnold, "Remote Sensing in Agriculture, Forestry, and Geography," paper delivered at the 1968 meeting of the American Association for the Advancement of Science, Dallas, Texas; and Edward Risley, "Remote Sensors for Regional Study: Some Policy Considerations," paper delivered at the 1967 Meeting of the American Association for the Advancement of Science, New York.

17 National Aeronautics and Space Administration, *NASA Facts* (B-2-64), 8. See also World Meteorological Organization, *The Role of Meteorological Satellites in the World Weather Watch*, World Weather Watch Planning Report No. 18. Geneva, Switzerland: Secretariat of the World Meteorological Organization, 1967, ix; 38; and John Gabriel Navarra, *Wide World Weather*. Garden City, New York: Doubleday, 1968, p. 206. For a comprehensive survey of satellite technology see William R. Corliss, *Scientific Satellites*. Washington: National Aeronautics and Space Administration, 1967, vii, 822.

18 NAVSPASUR—*U. S. Naval Space Surveillance System*. Dahlgren, Virginia: U. S. Naval Weapons Laboratory, undated.

19 J. Ingersoll, *Historical Examples of Ecological Disaster*, HI-242-RR/A 2-3. Harmon on Hudson, New York: Hudson Institute, 1963, and ibid. (II), HI-303-RR/A 1-2, 1964. See also in this series Robert G. Ayres, *Special Aspects of Environment Resulting from Various Kinds of Nuclear Wars*, Part III, HI-388-RR. November 30, 1964, Chapter IV, "On Ecological Catastrophe."

20 See *The Careless Technology*, supra, and by the same editors a symposium, "The Unforeseen International Ecological Boomerang," in *Natural History*, LXXVIII (February 1969), 42–72.

21 Jean M. Linsdale, *The Frances Simes Hastings Natural History Reservation, 1937–1947*. University of California, Museum of Vertebrate Zoology, 1947, 23 (no subsequent report published but original goals and programs remain the same). See also George C. Wood-

well, "The Ecological Effects of Radiation," *Scientific American,* CCVII (June 1963), 40–49 (reports work on an experimental area at Brookhaven National Laboratory).

22 Navarra, op. cit.; and J. C. Thompson, *The Potential Economic and Associated Values of the World Weather Watch,* World Weather Watch Planning Report No. 4. Geneva, Switzerland: Secretariat of the World Meteorological Organization, 1966, xi, 35, bibliography.

23 See B. P. Uvarov, "Efforts to Control Locusts in Africa Described," *Science,* CXXX (December 4, 1959), 1564–65; Stanley Baron, "No frontier in the fight against the desert locust," *Ceres,* I (September– October 1968), 32–42; Peter H. Haskell, "Ecological Problems in the Control of International Pests," in *The Careless Technology,* supra.

24 *Earthquakes,* Washington: Environmental Science Services Administration, 1969, p. 14.

25 *Ecology and the Industrial Society* (British Ecological Society Symposium Number Five), edited by Gordon T. Goodman, R. W. Edwards, and J. M. Lambert. New York: John Wiley, 1965, viii, 395.

26 Comprehensive surveys of the application of science and technology to a wide range of environmental problems are available in *ESSA Science and Engineering,* op. cit., note 16; *Science and the Environment,* Vol. I of Panel Reports of the Commission on Marine Science, Engineering and Resources. Washington: U. S. Government Print. Off., 1969; and also current issues of the journal *Environmental Science and Technology.*

CHAPTER 8

ENVIRONMENTAL MANAGEMENT AS A PUBLIC FUNCTION

1 There is a very large literature on weather modification and control, including extensive Congressional hearings before the U. S. Senate Committee on Commerce, 89th Cong., 1st and 2d Sess., and two reports published by the National Science Foundation (1965–66).

    For selected comment on the political, legal, and scientific complications, see the following items:

    U. R. Derrick Sewell, ed., *Human Dimensions of Weather Modification.* Chicago: University of Chicago, Department of Geography (Research Paper No. 105), 1966, xii, 423;

    Robert G. Fleagle, ed., *Weather Modification: Science and Public Policy.* Seattle: University of Washington Press, 1968;

    Howard J. Taubenfeld, ed., *Weather Modification and the Law.* Dobbs Ferry, New York: Oceana, 1968;

    Frederick Sargent II, "A Dangerous Game: Taming the Weather,"

   Bulletin of the American Meteorological Society, XLVII (July 1967), 452–58;

   Gordon S. F. MacDonald, "Science and Politics of Rainmaking," *Bulletin of the Atomic Scientists*, XXIV (October 1968), 8–14;

   James N. Corbridge, Jr., and Raphael J. Moses, "Weather Modification: Law and Administration," 8 *Natural Resources Journal* (April 1968), 207–35.

2   "Recommendation 14, Science and Resource Policy," *Intergovernmental Conference of Experts on the Scientific Basis for Rational Use and Conservation of the Resources of the Biosphere. UNESCO House, Paris 4–13 September 1968. Final Report*. Paris: UNESCO SC/MD/9, 6 January 1969, 28–29.

3   New York: Holt, Rinehart & Winston, 1963, xiii, 224.

4   February 23, 1961.

5   A conclusion also apparently reached by James L. Sundquist, who wrote, "The major contribution of John F. Kennedy to national thinking about the outdoor environment was, perhaps, an open mind about the budget." *Politics and Policy: The Eisenhower, Kennedy, and Johnson Years*. Washington: Brookings Institution, 1968, p. 345.

6   See "The Conference Call: (Message from the President of the United States to the Congress, February 8, 1965)," in *Beauty for America: Proceedings of the White House Conference on National Beauty. May 24–25, 1965*. Washington, U. S. Govt. Print. Off., 1–2.

7   The President's policy was reiterated in exchanges between the Bureau of the Budget and the Department of the Interior during the period immediately preceding the leasing.

8   *Weekly Compilation of Presidential Documents*. Monday, January 5, 1970, p. 12.

9   Ibid.

10   Ibid., p. 11.

11   Sundquist, James L., *Politics and Policy*, supra, p. 380.

12   For the text of Richard Nixon's remarks, see: *National Environmental Policy: Hearing Before the Committee on Interior and Insular Affairs*. United States Senate, 91st Cong., 1st Sess. (April 16, 1969), 105–8.

13   The task force report was not published, and statements regarding its recommendations are either based on copies circulated in the Executive Office of the President or from the article under the by-line of Peter Kihss in *The New York Times*, January 14, 1969, "Nixon Task Force Urges Creation of Top-Level Environmental Affairs Post," p. 27.

14   "Legislation on Environment Becomes Gut Issue," Vol. CLXXXIII (July 10, 1969), 18–19.

15   June 4, 1969, p. 13.

16   For further comment on the Department of the Interior and the Santa Barbara oil disaster, see the following listings from the New

York Times Index for 1969: *Water Pollution, California Coast Incident.* February 1–15, p. 92, 16–28, p. 86; March 1–15, p. 93, 16–31, p. 109; April 1–15, p. 91, 16–30, p. 96; May 1–15, p. 95, 16–31, p. 100; July 1–15, p. 91. See also *Time,* XCIII (February 14, 1969), 23–25; and *The Wall Street Journal,* LXXXI (August 27, 1969), 1 and 10.

17 Cf. *Science,* CLXV (July 4, 1969), p. 45.

18 *The New York Times,* CXIX (January 4, 1970), p. 12.

19 *Science,* CLII (April 29, 1966), p. 595.

20 *Audubon Magazine,* XLVI (January–February 1944), 55–56.

21 S.1075 passed the Senate on July 16, 1969, on the "consent calendar," which bypasses floor debate, thus making it the first of the environmental-quality bills to receive action on the floor of the Congress.

22 For background on the genesis of Title I of S.1075 as amended, see *National Environmental Policy: Hearing Before the Committee on Interior and Insular Affairs,* United States Senate, 91st Cong., 1st Sess. (April 16, 1969), especially pp. 115–22.

23 In this issue (August 1, 1969), *Time* introduced a new permanent section: "Environment." In an editorial "letter from the publisher," James R. Shepley announced the newsweekly's intention ". . . to clarify and explore man's long-ignored physical dependence on the biosphere . . ." Comment on the Jackson bill appeared on page 42.

24 Note comment by Luther J. Carter, "Environmental Quality: Nixon's New Council Raises Doubts," *Science,* CLXV (July 4, 1969), 44–46. As of two months after its designation, the Council had held only one meeting, virtually without press coverage or significant public notice.

25 It is hardly feasible to analyze or even to list all environmental-quality bills introduced into the Ninety-first Congress. Many were essentially duplicates of others. Among those proposing a high-level statutory council were the following:

Senate

S.1075 (Jackson) Three-member board of environmental-quality advisers. Passed Senate July 10, 1969.

S.237 (McGovern) Three-member council on environmental quality.

S.1085 (Nelson) Five-member council on environmental quality.

House of Representatives

H.R.25, 6750 (Dingell) Three-member council on environmental quality.

H.R.12549 (Dingell) Five-member council (Revision of H.R.6750).

H.R.3329 (Tunney) Nine-member council of ecological advisers.

H.R.7016 (Moss) Five-member national council on the environment.

Other bills include H.R.6955 (Corman), H.R.7923 (Howard), H.R.8806 (Podell), H.R.8588 (Ashley), H.R.11937 (Foley), H.R.11942 (Griffiths), etc. For a more complete listing, see *Environmental Quality: Selected Bills and Resolutions,* compiled by Mauree W. Ayton.

The Library of Congress, Legislative Reference Service, Science Policy Research Division, June 20, 1969, 8.

26 Commission on Organization of the executive branch of the government, *Reorganization of the Department of the Interior,* 1949, 53–80; and Committee on National Resources, *Renewable Resources* (Report prepared by Paul Weiss). Washington: National Academy of Sciences-National Research Council, Publication 1000A, 1962, p. 33.

27 Summarized in "Administration Possibilities for Environmental Control," in *Future Environments of North America,* edited by F. Fraser Darling and John P. Milton. New York: Natural History Press, 1966, pp. 661 ff.

28 The complex problems of administrative organization are discussed by Stephen K. Bailey in "Managing the Federal Government," *Agenda for the Nation.* Washington: Brookings Institution, 1968, 301–21.

29 Cf. Arnold Brecht, "Organization of Government Departments" (Three Topics in Comparative Administration), in *Public Policy, A Yearbook of the Graduate School of Public Administration, Harvard University,* II (1941), 292–98;

See also Lynton K. Caldwell, "Restructuring for Coordinative Action" (A Symposium, Environmental Policy: New Directions in Federal Action), *Public Administration Review,* XXVII (July–August 1968), 301–3.

30 Senate Bill 710, signed by Governor Ronald Reagan on August 21, 1968.

31 See memorandum prepared by the Michigan Committee for Environmental Information, P.O. Box 2281, Grand Rapids, Michigan.

32 For background, see: Lynton K. Caldwell, "Interstate Cooperation in River Basin Development," *Iowa Law Review,* XXXII (January 1947), 232–43; Frederick L. Zimmerman and Mitchell Wendell, *The Interstate Compact Since 1925.* Chicago: Council of State Governments, 1951, xi, 132. For more recent interstate efforts on environment-related issues, see Edward J. Cleary, *The Orsanco Story: Water Quality Management in the Ohio Valley Under Interstate Compact.* Baltimore: Johns Hopkins Press, 1967, xvi, 335.

33 See account of the NRPB in John D. Millett, *The Process and Organization of Government Planning.* New York: Columbia University Press, 1947, xi, 187. See also Charles E. Merriam, "The National Resources Planning Board," *American Political Science Review,* XXXVIII (December 1944), 1075–88.

CHAPTER 9

ENVIRONMENTAL MANAGEMENT AS AN ETHICAL SYSTEM

1 Cf. Donald N. Michael, *The Unprepared Society: Planning for a Precarious Future.* New York: Basic Books, 1968, xiv, 132. The John Dewey Society Lecture No. 10.

2 Cf. Willy Ley, *Engineers' Dreams.* New York: Viking, 1954, p. 239.

3 Cf. Lynn White, Jr., "The Historical Roots of Our Ecological Crisis," *Science,* CLV (March 10, 1967), 1203–7; and for a contrasting interpretation, Richard A. Baer, Jr., "Land Misuse: A Theological Concern," *The Christian Century,* LXXXIII (October 12, 1966), 1239–41. See also Yi-Fu-Tuan, "Attitudes Toward Environment: Themes and Approaches," in *Environmental Perception and Behavior,* edited by David Lowenthal. Chicago: University of Chicago, Department of Geography (Research Paper No. 109), 1967, 4–17. For accounts of changing human concepts of the environment, see Clarence J. Glacken, "Changing Ideas of the Habitable World," in *Man's Role in Changing the Face of the Earth,* edited by William L. Thomas, Jr. Chicago: University of Chicago Press, 1956, 70–92, and *Traces on the Rhodian Shore; Nature and Culture in Western Thought from Ancient Times to the End of the Eighteenth Century.* Berkeley: University of California Press, 1967, xxviii, 763, extensive bibliography 715–48. See also Henry C. Hart, "The Natural Environment in Indian Tradition," in *Public Policy: A Yearbook of the Graduate School of Public Administration, Harvard University,* XII (1963), 41–77.

4 See Note 1, Chapter 1 for references on human attitudes and perceptions.

5 Notably in Chapter 1.

6 *Report of the Executive Vice President to the Corporate Members —United Church Board for Home Ministries,* Fourteenth Biennial Meeting (Detroit, Michigan: October 27, 1965), 4–5.

7 "The Meddlers," in *Voices from the Sky.* New York: Pyramid Books, 1967, p. 162.

8 "The Integrity of Science," *American Scientist,* LIII (June 1965), 174–98.

9 New York: Viking Press, 1966, p. 150.

10 "The Integrity of Science," supra.

11 Cf. the criticism of the ethics of societal homeostasis by Patrick Romanell in "Does Biology Afford a Sufficient Basis for Ethics?" in *Scientific Monthly,* LXXXI (September 1955), 138–46. In an attack upon the concept of population control, Jean Daluces, writing in *Combat* under the headline "Le malthusianisme, voilà l'ennemi," declared, ". . . le malthusianisme est une maladie typiquement francaise: la politique de 'prudence' . . ." (April 1950), p. 4. But the growing threat of demographic and environmental disaster

in the years since the early nineteen fifties may make "prudence" a more attractive quality.

12 *Time* (July 25, 1969), p. 55.

13 *Esquire*, LXVIII (September 1967), pp. 116 ff.

14 "Stability in Ecological and Social Systems," *Brookhaven Symposia in Biology No. 22.* Upton, New York: Brookhaven National Laboratory, 1969, 128–41.

15 See Garrett Hardin, "The Tragedy of the Commons," *Science,* CLXII (December 13, 1968), 1243–48.

16 See, for example, Stewart L. Udall, "Notes on a Land Ethic for Tomorrow," in *The Quiet Crisis.* New York: Holt, Rinehart & Winston, 1963, Chapter XIV.

17 "The Search for Intelligent Life," *Saturday Review,* LII (August 9, 1969), 20.

18 "Nature," in *The Romantic Triumph: American Literature from 1830 to 1860,* edited by Tremaine McDowell. New York: Macmillan, 1933, p. 122.

19 Ibid., p. 123.

20 Ibid.

CHAPTER 10

MEETING THE CHALLENGE

1 U. S. Congress, *Congress and the Nation's Environment—Environmental Affairs of the 91st Congress.* Prepared by the Environmental Policy Division Congressional Research Service, Library of Congress, at the request of Henry M. Jackson, Chairman, Committee on Interior and Insular Affairs, United States Senate, Ninety-second Congress, First Session, February 10, 1971, 22. This excellent summation covers not only legislation enacted and considered during the Ninety-first Congress, but extensive description of administrative activities as well.

2 Ibid., p. 5.

3 Personal Communication. The report is entitled *Man of the Environment.* URBSDOC No. 161, 21 May 1970, 44. (For Administrative Use and Scientific Review Only) March 23, 1970.

4 Cited by John B. Calhoun, op. cit., 3–4.

5 James H. Clingham, "NEPA: Birth and Infancy," *Catholic University Law Review,* 20 (Fall 1970), 184–95; Eva H. Hanks and John L. Hanks, "An Environmental Bill of Rights: the Citizen Suit and the National Environmental Policy Act of 1969," *Rutgers Law Review,* 24 (Winter 1970), 230–72; Victor J. Yannacone, Jr., "National Environmental Policy Act of 1969," *Environmental Law I* (Spring 1970); Joseph L. Sax, *Defending the Environment: A Strategy for Citizen Action.* New York: Alfred A. Knopf, 1971. To clarify and further strengthen the right of citizens for judicial relief against activities damaging the environment Senator George

McGovern introduced into the Ninety-first Congress, Second Session, the Environmental Protection Act of 1970, S.3575. See hearings before the Subcommittee on Energy, Natural Resources, and the Environment of the Committee on Commerce. United States Senate, Ninety-first Congress, Second Session, May 12, 14, July 1, 10, 1970—Serial 91–80, 160.

See also *Congress and the Nation's Environment*, 43–53; and continuing issues of the *Environmental Reporter*, 1970 (Bureau of National Affairs); the *Environmental Law Reporter*, 1970; and the *Environmental Law Digest* (Environmental Law Institute).

6 "U.S. Said to Delay Ecology Reports," *The New York Times* (November 14, 1970), 23; and "U.S. Environment Law Attacked," *The New York Times* (November 14, 1970), 53.

7 *Congress and the Nation's Environment*, 283. See also *Conservation Foundation Letter: A Report on Environmental Issues* (December 1970) for a summation of antipollution legislation in the Ninety-first Congress.

8 *Congress and the Nation's Environment*, 54–61.

9 *Weekly Compilation of Presidential Documents*, Monday, July 13, 1970, 908–21.

10 Ibid., p. 912.

11 *Memoranda for the President of the United States: Establishment of a Department of Natural Resources; Organization for Economic and Social Programs*. Submitted by the President's Advisory Council on Executive Organization, February 5, 1971.

12 See Chapter 8, notes 26, 27, and 28. Also *The New York Times* (January 24, 1961), 1, 46.

13 *One-Third of the Nation's Land: A Report to the President and to the Congress by the Public Land Law Review Commission*. Washington, D.C.: June 1970, 342. See also *What's Ahead for Our Public Lands? A Summary Review of the Activities and Final Report of the Public Land Law Review Commission*. Compiled for the Natural Resources Council of America by Hamilton K. Pyles. Washington, D.C.: Natural Resources Council of America, 1970, 342.

14 *National Land Use Policy*. Hearings before the Committee on Interior and Insular Affairs, United States Senate, Ninety-first Congress, Second Session, on S.3354 to amend the Water Resource Planning Act (79 STAT. 244) to provide for a national land use policy. March 24, April 28 and 29, 1970, 414.

15 Among the general sources of information regarding recent state action are the following: *Environmental Quality and State Government*, Lexington, Kentucky: The Council of State Governments, December 1970, 53; "States Show Widespread Interest in Environmental Quality," *Council of State Governments Special Report*, March 16, 1970, 6, mimeo; "The States, Playing a Crucial Role in Environmental Management, Try a Variety of Innovations in 1970," *Conservation Foundation Letter: A Report on Environmental Issues*, November 1970, 12.

16 *Conservation Foundation Letter*, November 1970. See also "U.S. Seeks State Reins on Zoning," Washington *Star* (February 9, 1971); and Richard H. Slavin, "Toward a State Land-Use Policy," *State Government*, XLIV (Winter 1971), 2–11.

17 *Congress and the Nation's Environment*, 48–49.

18 Ibid.

19 *Time* (August 2, 1968), 26–27.

20 *Weekly Compilation of Presidential Documents*, Monday, June 10, 1968, 906.

21 United Nations Economic and Social Council, *Problems of the Human Environment: Report of the Secretary General.* New York: United Nations, E-4667, 26 May 1969, 39 plus annexes. Also Chapter 4, note 27.

22 See Chapter 4, note 26.

23 *The Human Environment—A Proposed International Declaration.* The United Nations Associations of Denmark, Finland, Norway, and Sweden. Stockholm, 1969, 16.

24 See Chapter 4, note 24.

25 International Council of Scientific Unions, *Report of the Ad Hoc of ICSU on Problems of the Human Environment*, 1939, 30, mimeo.

26 Congressional Record, CXVI (April 23, 1970), S.6068–70; (April 27, 1970), S.6219–21; (May 6, 1970), S.6708–12.

27 *No Deposit—No Return: Man and His Environment: A View Toward Survival.* Edited by Huey D. Johnson. Reading, Massachusetts, Menlo Park, California: Addison-Wesley, 1970, 351.

28 Cambridge, Massachusetts: MIT Press, 1970, 319.

29 Op. cit., p. 4.

30 *Congress and the Nation's Environment*, 203–13.

31 United States Congress, *A Review of Energy Issues in the 91st Congress.* Prepared by the Environmental Policy Division, Congressional Research Service, Library of Congress at the request of Henry M. Jackson, Chairman, Committee on Interior and Insular Affairs, United States Senate, January 29, 1971, 38. See also "Behind the Energy Crisis," *Resources*, No. 36, Resources for the Future (January 1971), 1–4.

32 *Electric Power and the Environment.* A report sponsored by the Energy Policy Staff, Office of Science and Technology: Washington, D.C.: Executive Office of the President, August 1970, 1971.

33 *Surface Mining and Our Environment; A Special Report to the Nation.* Washington, D.C.: United States Department of the Interior, 1967, 124.

34 There is a very large literature on the impact of oil exploitation on the environment. Unfortunately, for the purpose of this volume, it is not easily referenced, as the greater part of it appears in newspapers and as relatively short articles in journals. A major issue of oil vs. environment developed as a consequence of the discovery of oil on the Arctic coast of Alaska. The issues involved were the subject matter of the Twentieth Alaska Science Conference held on the campus of the University of Alaska August 24–27, 1969.

For a summation of the discussions and papers at the conference see *Change in Alaska: People, Petroleum, and Politics*. Edited by George W. Rogers. College Alaska: University of Alaska Press; Seattle, Washington: University of Washington Press, 1970, 213. See also "Russian Roulette in the Arctic," *The Wilderness Society*, Washington, D.C., February 17, 1971, for a summary of the trans-Alaska pipeline issue.

35 *The Affluent Society*. Boston: Houghton Mifflin, 1958, p. 368.

36 *A Reconstruction of Economics*. New York: Wiley, 1950, pp. xii, 311.

37 "Population Threatens Prosperity," *Harvard Business Review* (January–February 1956), xxxiv.

38 New York: Praeger, 1967, p. 190. See also Mishan's "A Survey of Welfare Economics, 1939–59," in *Surveys of Economic Theory I*, prepared for the American Economic Association and the Royal Economic Society. London: Macmillan; New York: St. Martin's Press, 1965, pp. 212–13. In relation to economic theory generally see K. William Kapp, "Environmental Disruption and Social Costs: A Challenge to Economics, *Kykloe—Internationale Zeitschrift für Sozialwissenschaften*, XXIII (4, 1970), 833–48.

39 Note especially Allen V. Kneese, Robert U. Ayres, and Ralph d'Arge, *Economics and the Environment*. Washington, D.C.: Johns Hopkins Press for Resources for the Future, 1971, p. 132.

40 The rise of Italian Fascism and German National Socialism are not exceptions to this generalization. These ideologies were expressions of exaggerated nationalism and as such had little persuasive influence beyond the countries of their origins.

41 For example, *Ecotactics: The Sierra Club Handbook for Environmental Activists*. Edited by John G. Mitchell with Constance L. Stallings and with an introduction by Ralph Nader. New York: Pocket Books, April 1970, p. 288; and *The Environmental Handbook Prepared for the First National Environmental Teach-In, April 22, 1970*. Edited by Garrett DeBell. New York: Ballantine Books, p. 367.

42 *Newsweek*, LXXV (April 13, 1970), 25–26.

APPENDIX A

Public Law 91-190 91st Congress, S.1075
January 1, 1970

AN ACT

83 STAT. 852

To establish a national policy for the environment, to provide for the establishment of a Council on Environmental Quality, and for other purposes.

Be it enacted by the Senate and House of Representatives of the United States of America in Congress assembled, That this Act may be cited as the "National Environmental Policy Act of 1969".

National
Environmental
Policy Act of
1969.

PURPOSE

SEC. 2. The purposes of this Act are: To declare a national policy which will encourage productive and enjoyable harmony between man and his environment; to promote efforts which will prevent or eliminate damage to the environment and biosphere and stimulate the health and welfare of man; to enrich the understanding of the ecological systems and natural resources important to the Nation; and to establish a Council on Environmental Quality.

TITLE I

DECLARATION OF NATIONAL ENVIRONMENTAL POLICY

SEC. 101. (a) The Congress, recognizing the profound impact of man's activity on the interrelations of all components of the natural environment, particularly the pro-

Policies and
goals.

found influences of population growth, high-density urbanization, industrial expansion, resource exploitation, and new and expanding technological advances and recognizing further the critical importance of restoring and maintaining environmental quality to the overall welfare and development of man, declares that it is the continuing policy of the Federal Government, in cooperation with State and local governments, and other concerned public and private organizations, to use all practicable means and measures, including financial and technical assistance, in a manner calculated to foster and promote the general welfare, to create and maintain conditions under which man and nature can exist in productive harmony, and fulfill the social, economic, and other requirements of present and future generations of Americans.

(b) In order to carry out the policy set forth in this Act, it is the continuing responsibility of the Federal Government to use all practicable means, consistent with other essential considerations of national policy, to improve and coordinate Federal plans, functions, programs, and resources to the end that the Nation may—

(1) fulfill the responsibilities of each generation as trustee of the environment for succeeding generations;

(2) assure for all Americans safe, healthful, productive, and esthetically and culturally pleasing surroundings;

(3) attain the widest range of beneficial uses of the environment without degradation, risk to health or safety, or other undesirable and unintended consequences;

(4) preserve important historic, cultural, and natural aspects of our national heritage, and maintain, wherever possible, an environment which supports diversity and variety of individual choice;

(5) achieve a balance between population and resource use which will permit high standards of living and a wide sharing of life's amenities; and

(6) enhance the quality of renewable resources and approach the maximum attainable recycling of depletable resources.

(c) The Congress recognizes that each person should enjoy a healthful environment and that each person has a responsibility to contribute to the preservation and enhancement of the environment.

Administration.

SEC. 102. The Congress authorizes and directs that, to the fullest extent possible: (1) the policies, regulations, and public laws of the United States shall be interpreted and administered in accordance with the poli-

cies set forth in this Act, and (2) all agencies of the
Federal Government shall—

(A) utilize a systematic, interdisciplinary approach
which will insure the integrated use of the natural
and social sciences and the environmental design arts
in planning and in decisionmaking which may have
an impact on man's environment;

(B) identify and develop methods and procedures,
in consultation with the Council on Environmental
Quality established by title II of this Act, which will
insure that presently unquantified environmental
amenities and values may be given appropriate consideration in decisionmaking along with economic and
technical considerations;

(C) include in every recommendation or report on
proposals for legislation and other major Federal actions significantly affecting the quality of the human
environment, a detailed statement by the responsible
official on—

(i) the environmental impact of the proposed
action,

(ii) any adverse environmental effects which
cannot be avoided should the proposal be implemented,

(iii) alternatives to the proposed action,

(iv) the relationship between local short-term
uses of man's environment and the maintenance and
enhancement of long-term productivity, and

(v) any irreversible and irretrievable commitments of resources which would be involved in the
proposed action should it be implemented.

Prior to making any detailed statement, the responsible Federal official shall consult with and obtain the
comments of any Federal agency which has jurisdiction by law or special expertise with respect to any
environmental impact involved. Copies of such statement and the comments and views of the appropriate
Federal, State, and local agencies, which are authorized to develop and enforce environmental standards,
shall be made available to the President, the Council
on Environmental Quality and to the public as provided by section 552 of title 5, United States Code,
and shall accompany the proposal through the existing agency review processes;

Copies of
statements,
etc.; avail-
ability.

81 Stat. 54.

(D) study, develop, and describe appropriate alternatives to recommended courses of action in any proposal which involves unresolved conflicts concerning
alternative uses of available resources;

(E) recognize the worldwide and long-range character of environmental problems and, where consistent with the foreign policy of the United States, lend appropriate support to initiatives, resolutions, and programs designed to maximize international cooperation in anticipating and preventing a decline in the quality of mankind's world environment;

(F) make available to States, counties, municipalities, institutions, and individuals, advice and information useful in restoring, maintaining, and enhancing the quality of the environment;

(G) initiate and utilize ecological information in the planning and development of resource-oriented projects; and

(H) assist the Council on Environmental Quality established by title II of this Act.

Review.   SEC. 103. All agencies of the Federal Government shall review their present statutory authority, administrative regulations, and current policies and procedures for the purpose of determining whether there are any deficiencies or inconsistencies therein which prohibit full compliance with the purposes and provisions of this Act and shall propose to the President not later than July 1, 1971, such measures as may be necessary to bring their authority and policies into conformity with the intent, purposes, and procedures set forth in this Act.

SEC. 104. Nothing in Section 102 or 103 shall in any way affect the specific statutory obligations of any Federal agency (1) to comply with criteria or standards of environmental quality, (2) to coordinate or consult with any other Federal or State agency, or (3) to act, or refrain from acting contingent upon the recommendations or certification of any other Federal or State agency.

SEC. 105. The policies and goals set forth in this Act are supplementary to those set forth in existing authorizations of Federal agencies.

TITLE II

COUNCIL ON ENVIRONMENTAL QUALITY

Report to Congress.   SEC. 201. The President shall transmit to the Congress annually beginning July 1, 1970, an Environmental Quality Report (hereinafter referred to as the "report") which shall set forth (1) the status and condition of the major natural, manmade, or altered environmental classes of the Nation, including, but not limited to, the air, the aquatic, including marine, estuarine, and fresh

water, and the terrestrial environment, including, but not
limited to, the forest, dryland, wetland, range, urban,
suburban, and rural environment; (2) current and foreseeable trends in the quality, management and utilization of such environments and the effects of those trends
on the social, economic, and other requirements of the
Nation; (3) the adequacy of available natural resources
for fulfilling human and economic requirements of the
Nation in the light of expected population pressures;
(4) a review of the programs and activities (including
regulatory activities) of the Federal Government, the
State and local governments, and nongovernmental entities or individuals, with particular reference to their
effect on the environment and on the conservation, development and utilization of natural resources; and (5)
a program for remedying the deficiencies of existing programs and activities, together with recommendations for
legislation.

SEC. 202. There is created in the Executive Office of
the President a Council on Environmental Quality
(hereinafter referred to as the "Council"). The Council
shall be composed of three members who shall be appointed by the President to serve at his pleasure, by and
with the advice and consent of the Senate. The President shall designate one of the members of the Council
to serve as Chairman. Each member shall be a person
who, as a result of his training, experience, and attain-
ments, is exceptionally well qualified to analyze and interpret environmental trends and information of all
kinds; to appraise programs and activities of the Federal
Government in the light of the policy set forth in title I
of this Act; to be conscious of and responsive to the
scientific, economic, social, esthetic, and cultural needs
and interests of the Nation; and to formulate and recommend national policies to promote the improvement
of the quality of the environment. *(Council on Environmental Quality.)*

SEC. 203. The Council may employ such officers and
employees as may be necessary to carry out its functions
under this Act. In addition, the Council may employ
and fix the compensation of such experts and consult-
ants as may be necessary for the carrying out of its
functions under this Act, in accordance with section
3109 of title 5, United States Code (but without regard
to the last sentence thereof). *(80 Stat. 416. Duties and functions.)*

SEC. 204. It shall be the duty and function of the
Council—

(1) to assist and advise the President in the preparation of the Environmental Quality Report required
by section 201;

(2) to gather timely and authoritative information concerning the conditions and trends in the quality of the environment both current and prospective, to analyze and interpret such information for the purpose of determining whether such conditions and trends are interfering, or are likely to interfere, with the achievement of the policy set forth in title I of this Act, and to compile and submit to the President studies relating to such conditions and trends;

(3) to review and appraise the various programs and activities of the Federal Government in the light of the policy set forth in title I of this Act for the purpose of determining the extent to which such programs and activities are contributing to the achievement of such policy, and to make recommendations to the President with respect thereto;

(4) to develop and recommend to the President national policies to foster and promote the improvement of environmental quality to meet the conservation, social, economic, health, and other requirements and goals of the Nation;

(5) to conduct investigations, studies, surveys, research, and analyses relating to ecological systems and environmental quality;

(6) to document and define changes in the natural environment, including the plant and animal systems, and to accumulate necessary data and other information for a continuing analysis of these changes or trends and an interpretation of their underlying causes;

(7) to report at least once each year to the President on the state and condition of the environment; and

(8) to make and furnish such studies, reports thereon, and recommendations with respect to matters of policy and legislation as the President may request.

SEC. 205. In exercising its powers, functions, and duties under this Act, the Council shall—

(1) consult with the Citizens' Advisory Committee on Environmental Quality established by Executive Order numbered 11472, dated May 29, 1969, and with such representatives of science, industry, agriculture, labor, conservation organizations, State and local governments and other groups, as it deems advisable; and

34 F. R. 8693.

(2) utilize, to the fullest extent possible, the services, facilities, and information (including statistical information) of public and private agencies and organizations, and individuals, in order that duplication of effort and expense may be avoided, thus assuring that

the Council's activities will not unnecessarily overlap or conflict with similar activities authorized by law and performed by established agencies.

SEC. 206. Members of the Council shall serve full time and the Chairman of the Council shall be compensated at the rate provided for Level II of the Executive Schedule Pay Rates (5 U.S.C. 5313). The other members of the Council shall be compensated at the rate provided for Level IV or the Executive Schedule Pay Rates (5 U.S.C. 5315). *Tenure and compensation. 80 Stat. 460, 461.*

SEC. 207. There are authorized to be appropriated to carry out the provisions of this Act not to exceed $300,-000 for fiscal year 1970, $700,000 for fiscal year 1971, and $1,000,000 for each fiscal year thereafter. *81 Stat. 638. Appropriations.*

Approved January 1, 1970.

LEGISLATIVE HISTORY:

HOUSE REPORTS: No. 91-378, 91-378, pt. 2, accompanying H. R. 12549 (Comm. on Merchant Marine & Fisheries) and 91-765 (Comm. of Conference).

SENATE REPORT No. 91-296 (Comm. on Interior & Insular Affairs).

CONGRESSIONAL RECORD, Vol. 115 (1969):

July   10: Considered and passed Senate.

Sept. 23: Considered and passed House, amended, in lieu of H. R. 12549.

Oct.   8: Senate disagreed to House amendments; agreed to conference.

Dec. 20: Senate agreed to conference report.

Dec. 22: House agreed to conference report.

APPENDIX B

United Nations General Assembly Resolution 2398 (XXIII)[1] on

THE PROBLEMS OF HUMAN ENVIRONMENT

The General Assembly,

Noting that the relationship between man and his environment is undergoing profound changes in the wake of modern scientific and technological developments,

Aware that these developments, while offering unprecedented opportunities to change and shape the environment of man to meet his needs and aspirations, also involve grave dangers if not properly controlled,

Noting, in particular, the continuing and accelerating impairment of the quality of the human environment caused by such factors as air and water pollution, erosion and other forms of soil deterioration, waste, noise and secondary effects of biocides, which are accentuated by rapidly increasing population and accelerating urbanization,

Concerned with the consequent effects on the condition of man, his physical, mental and social well-being, his dignity and his enjoyment of basic human rights, in developing as well as developed countries,

Convinced that increased attention to problems of the human environment is essential for sound economic and social development,

Expressing the strong hope that the developing countries will, through appropriate international co-operation, derive particular benefit from the mobilization of knowledge and experience about the problems of human environment, enabling them, *inter alia,* to forestall the occurrence of many such problems,

Having considered Economic and Social Council resolution 1346 (XLV) of 30 July 1968 on the question of convening an international conference on the problems of human environment,

Bearing in mind the important work on some problems of the human environment at present being undertaken by organizations in the United Nations system, in particular the United Nations (including the Economic Commission for Europe), the International Labour Organisation, the Food and Agriculture Organization of the United Nations, the United Nations Educational, Scientific and Cultural Organization, the World

Health Organization, the World Meteorological Organization, the Inter-governmental Maritime Consultative Organization, the International Atomic Energy Agency, as referred to in the report of the Secretary-General on activities of United Nations organizations and programmes relevant to the human environment.[2]

Aware of the important work being done on problems of the human environment by Governments as well as by inter-governmental organizations such as the Organization of African Unity and non-governmental organizations such as the International Union for the Conservation of Nature and Natural Resources, the International Council of Scientific Unions and the International Biological Programme,

Bearing in mind the recommendations of the Intergovernmental Conference of Experts on the Scientific Basis for Rational Use and Conservation of the Resources of the Biosphere,[3] convened by the United Nations Educational, Scientific and Cultural Organization, with the participation of the United Nations, the Food and Agriculture Organization of the United Nations and the World Health Organization,

Convinced of the need for intensified action at the national, regional and international level in order to limit and, where possible, to eliminate the impairment of the human environment and in order to protect and improve the natural surroundings in the interest of man,

Desiring to encourage further work in this field and to give it a common outlook and direction,

Believing it desirable to provide a framework for comprehensive consideration within the United Nations of the problems of human environment in order to focus the attention of Governments and public opinion on the importance and urgency of this question and also to identify those aspects of it that can only, or best, be solved through international co-operation and agreement,

1. *Decides,* in furtherance of the objectives set out above, to convene in 1972 a United Nations Conference on Human Environment;

2. *Requests* the Secretary-General, in consultation with the Advisory Committee on the Application of Science and Technology to Development, to submit to the General Assembly at its twenty-fourth session, through the Economic and Social Council at its forty-seventh session, a report concerning:

(a) The nature, scope and progress of work at present being done in the field of the human environment;

(b) The main problems facing developed and developing countries in this area, which might with particular advantage be considered at such a conference, including the possibilities for increased international co-operation in this area, especially as they relate to economic and social development, in particular of the developing countries;

(c) Possible methods of preparing for the Conference and the time necessary for such preparations;

(d) A possible time and place for the Conference;

(e) The range of financial implications for the United Nations of the holding of the Conference;

3. *Further requests* the Secretary-General, in preparing the report, to

consult with Governments of States Members of the United Nations and members of the specialized agencies and of the International Atomic Energy Agency and with appropriate organizations of the United Nations system, and to draw on contributions from appropriate inter-governmental and non-governmental organizations.

(1) Adopted, "without objection" at the 1733rd Plenary Meeting, 3 December 1968.
(2) E/4553.
(3) A/7291, annex.

LIST OF SPONSORS OF THE RESOLUTION:

Afghanistan, Algeria, Argentina, Australia, Austria, Cameroon, Canada, Chile, Colombia, Congo (Brazzaville), Denmark, Ecuador, El Salvador, Ethiopia, Finland, Guatemala, Iceland, India, Indonesia, Iran, Ireland, Italy, Ivory Coast, Jamaica, Kenya, Kuwait, Libya, Madagascar, Malta, Mexico, Morocco, Nepal, Nigeria, Norway, Pakistan, Panama, Philippines, Romania, Rwanda, Senegal, Sierra Leone, Singapore, Somalia, Sudan, Sweden, Syria, Thailand, Turkey, United Kingdom of Great Britain and Northern Ireland, United Republic of Tanzania, United States of America, Uruguay, Venezuela, Yugoslavia and Zambia.

INDEX